WEBSTER'S
Best of
Crossword
Challenge

Selected by the Editors of Merriam-Webster

**FEDERAL
STREET
PRESS**

A Division of Merriam-Webster, Inc.
Springfield, Massachusetts

ISBN: 1–892859–51–3

Printed in Canada

WEBSTER'S
Best of
Crossword
Challenge
PART 1

Solutions appear after
Puzzle 144 at the end of Part 1.

ACROSS

1. Verne hero
5. Reunion attendee
9. Parsley or celery
14. Whistling swan
15. Gambling game
16. Abnaki's state
17. Heavy burden (from a Coleridge poem)
19. Dark neurosis
20. Rum drink
21. Sighs of delight
23. Lean (upon)
24. Peru native
26. Political exiles
28. Identical
32. Toast topper
33. Butler's prop
34. Political alliances
36. Hebrew hill
39. *Köln* cooler
40. Oafish athlete (from a 1930s comic strip)
42. Own, to Burns
43. Favorite
44. Lunch time, for some: abbr.
45. Army meal
46. Sentry yell
48. Gourmets
51. French-farce setting
54. Laugh sounds
55. Ardent
56. Lower
58. Aleut boot
62. Heart chambers

64. Lovely locale (from a James Hilton novel)
66. Approaches
67. International currency
68. A Stuart monarch
69. Grate flakes
70. Quarrel
71. Small wild duck

DOWN

1. Ale head
2. Stew pot
3. East Asian desert
4. Please
5. Copt's continent
6. Thai tongue
7. Stellar bear
8. General Dayan
9. Actress Thurman
10. Run
11. Invasive, controlling force (from a George Orwell novel)
12. Result
13. Riga natives
18. Neutral hues
22. Artist's apron
25. Stroll along
27. Role for Ingrid
28. Stoop section
29. N.Y. tribe
30. Final campaign (from an Edwin O'Connor novel)

31. Run off with
35. Energy
37. Affluence
38. Fewer
40. Equine game
41. Playful
45. Marsh rodent
47. Regard highly
49. Uh-uh
50. Train sound
51. Swahili title
52. Actor Warren
53. Derby blooms
57. Beat soundly
59. Border
60. Arm bone
61. Critic Pauline
63. Pack animal
65. Sky altar

ACROSS

1. Melodramatic outburst
5. Short-term office worker
9. Málaga Mrs.
12. Hashanah header
13. Arctic abode, sometimes
14. One of LBJ's dogs
15. Do a magic trick, with 44-Across
17. Period of historical importance
18. Express affection
19. Insect wing link
21. Bowed
24. Exodus figure
25. Do a magic trick, with 33-Across
28. Cannes season
29. Ait, in Aix
30. Pts. for Montana
33. See 25-Across
38. Small, lofty spar
39. Pensive poetic product
40. Alan Ladd classic
41. European capital
43. Lobster trap
44. See 15-Across
49. Do the human thing
50. Stellar she-bear
51. Hence, to Caesar
52. Greek letter
53. Sweet fruit
54. Owner's paper

DOWN

1. Overcoat feature
2. Mauna trailer
3. Grill, in a way
4. Jerusalem dough
5. Signs of muscle fatigue
6. Self-ish parts?
7. MMCII halved
8. Region in India
9. "___ Goldmine (I Got the Shaft)," '82 Jerry Reed hit
10. Summer TV offering
11. Name in a Saroyan title
16. Verdi heroine
20. Swiss canton
21. Do a Little job
22. Routine place to get stuck
23. Elizabeth Taylor role
24. Aid's felonious partner
26. Hilarious person
27. TV alien
31. Statesman Hammarskjöld
32. Porky's pad
34. Coffee dispenser
35. Too busy to return calls
36. Beatles hit film
37. Raced to the JP
38. Like certain stories
40. *Graf* ___, notable ship
41. Greek peak
42. German coal region
45. Anger
46. Before, to Browning
47. Vital statistic
48. Rocker Stewart

LET IT RAIN

ACROSS

1. The basics
5. Proper's partner
9. Form finish
12. Drawbridge locale
13. Hollywood's Barrett
14. Penpoint
15. Middling
16. ___-friendly (easy to understand)
17. "Get it?"
18. Chief who played Tonto
21. Little piggy
22. A grand, slangily
23. Raucous disagreement
26. Land unit
28. Play the peeping Tom
31. Lena Horne classic
35. Shredded
36. Do wrong
37. Earl Grey, for example
38. Smidgens
41. Strut the boards
43. Torrential downpours
48. Somebody
49. Gimlet flavoring
50. Unlucky number, to Nero
52. Sponsors' words
53. She does impressions
54. States further
55. ___ Lobos, *La Bamba* group
56. Old English letters
57. Look as though

DOWN

1. Mornings: abbr.
2. Misplay a grounder
3. Alternative to plastic
4. Portly
5. Bluenose characteristic
6. Romantic present
7. Unmoving
8. *Little Women* family name
9. Not pursued
10. Stead
11. Retired for the night
19. Writer Chomsky
20. Joe Orton comedy
23. Alphabetical trio
24. Western Amerind
25. Mum
27. Lady lamb
29. Spike or Harper
30. Baseball stat: abbr.
32. Old Spanish silver coin
33. Chalkboard accessories
34. St. Louis sight
39. Corporate regulation
40. Pilfer on the sly
42. The Stars' state
43. Point for Pele
44. Dismantle
45. Response to Gantry
46. Fairground feature
47. Flank
51. Doctrinal suffix

ACROSS

1. It's next to Tenn.
4. Prefix with buck
8. Small merganser
12. Polka chaser
13. Dinghy needs
14. Prefix with vision
15. Rice athlete
16. Voyage for Picard
17. Not working
18. The Garden, for example
20. Like prunes
21. Thorns in your side
23. Heir's bank account
25. Urban planning spaces
26. Continent
27. Cote matriarch
30. Prefix with cycle
31. Diminutive
32. Tape type
33. Common Market: abbr.
34. Golf unit
35. Sine here?
36. In the open
38. Wall Street unit
39. Fastened, in a way
41. Compare (to)
43. Kerrigan maneuver
44. Rani day wear?
45. Nosh
48. Extremely pleased
49. Similar
50. Get on in years
51. Mailed
52. Minus
53. Nice negative

DOWN

1. Botheration; brouhaha
2. Sound from the barn
3. Charleston's waterfront
4. Minute dust specks
5. Make money
6. Sight on a trip to Bountiful
7. Seek info
8. Swizzles
9. Levant's waterfront
10. Supermodel Macpherson
11. Lawn blight
19. Matter for Mason
20. In a paired fashion
21. Sinatra's eye color
22. The tops
24. Get under one's skin
26. Love, in Castile
28. Fence in a stream
29. Advantage
31. Cast off, as hair
35. First word of many titles
37. African grassland
38. Peltry
39. Retards in motion
40. Car part
42. Rainbow goddess
44. Mineo of *Exodus*
46. In the olden days
47. Three score and ___ (Biblical age)

ACTION FIGURES

ACROSS

1. One fruit that sounds like two
5. IQ, et al.
10. Shade trees
14. Farm unit
15. Memorabilia storage spot
16. Glimpses
17. Former "SNL" cast member
19. Revival meeting setting
20. Boxing wins
21. Supplements (with "out")
22. Jacket variety
24. Have it or hit it
25. Manuscript encl.
26. Wipe the slate
28. Face art
32. Distantly
33. Leslie Caron movie
34. Take the bus
35. Bed with slats
36. Jargon
37. Sign of the future
38. Small plateau
39. Dionysian revel
40. Main role
41. May birthstones
43. Joins, in a way
45. Troubles
46. Meat paste
47. Laurel's bigger half
49. *Othello* role
50. ___ *Boot*
53. George Takei role
54. WKRP's Big Guy player
57. Gets gray
58. Decorate
59. "...baked in ___"
60. Intertwine
61. Trait carriers
62. Sax, e.g.

DOWN

1. Prepare for a trip
2. Reverberate
3. War god
4. Gun (the engine)
5. Fishing gear
6. Singer Merman
7. WQXR and KLSX, e.g.
8. Frank McCourt book
9. Play plot
10. Florida on "Good Times"
11. Ogle
12. Waiter's card
13. JFK speedster
18. Affirmative votes
23. NYC zone
24. "Flamingo Road" star
25. Soaking wet
26. Mr. Zimbalist, Jr.
27. Salary boost
28. Engine knocks
29. Targeted
30. Notions
31. Take care of
32. Zenith
33. Encircles
36. Dillydally
42. Lend a hand
43. Prairie schooners
44. Collar style
46. Army priest
47. Gigantic
48. Pub brews
49. Tired-blood remedy
50. Hoodwink
51. Simone's pal
52. Went like mad
53. He played it again
55. Pindar poem
56. Pickle package

ACROSS

1. Wet-weather wear, for short
5. Existed
8. Ex-commissioner Vincent
11. Alice's cat
12. Pub pour
13. Caviar
14. A high top covers this
15. Discharge, slangily
16. Switch positions
17. Dawdle
20. Broke a fast
21. Blemish
22. Sternly?
25. Heathrow posting: abbr.
27. John Glenn's home
31. Dawdle
35. Actress Moreno
36. Paul Newman flick
37. La Brea substance
38. Brazil port
41. Stephen of screen fame
43. Dawdle
49. New England cape
50. Ancient
51. Doughnut's shape
52. Oklahoma crude
53. Author ___ Yutang
54. Delete
55. Cheer for Limón
56. Header for lion
57. Red-ink entry

DOWN

1. Create currency
2. "Lonely Boy" singer
3. Variety of lily
4. Protection from the elements
5. Baylor's location
6. Tocsin
7. Austrian actress Berger
8. Sent by
9. Tops
10. Positive response
11. Nuremberg article
18. Salty Greek cheese
19. Golf club
22. Tax time: abbr.
23. Pt. of "TGIF"
24. Preschool attendee
26. Eruption residue
28. Toque, for example
29. Call ___ day
30. Poetic preposition
32. Deck item
33. Stadium green
34. Conceived of; imagined
39. Revered statues
40. North of Virginia
42. Worship greatly
43. Thwart
44. Not useful
45. Novelist Ferber
46. Mousy
47. One of the seven deadly sins
48. Canton finish
49. Pigeon's comment

ACROSS

1. Bar bills
5. Campus figure
9. He's despicable
12. Jeans wash
13. Blue rock, for short
15. Cure start
16. Tennis great
18. HRE ruler
19. Little Edward
20. *Desire Under the Elms* character
21. Bacon strip
23. Kiln
24. Like an ill shade
25. Moistens (meat)
28. Lincoln coin
29. Pilfer
32. To have, in Aix
33. Actress Sonia
34. Tokyo Rose's real first name
35. Vile acts
36. As —— (generally)
37. "...in apprehension how like ——!"
38. Indian rule
39. Quite plump
40. Stroll
41. Pest header
42. Coin plant
43. Kindergartner's tool
44. Plays doctor
46. Hamelin pests
47. *Tristram Shandy* author
49. Hoofer Kelly
50. Rainbow
53. Desire
54. Golf great
57. Nastase of court fame
58. A Muse
59. Craft for Columbus
60. "Gosh!"
61. Lots
62. —— about, approximately

DOWN

1. Social grace
2. Workout woe
3. Pacer coach
4. Star Wars initials
5. Naval Academy freshmen
6. Poe talker
7. Unprotected
8. Pine
9. Gymnastics great
10. Kitty food?
11. Noted designer
14. Wacky
15. Greatest number
17. Cut forcefully
22. Film pooch
23. Elevator name
24. American portrait painter
25. Iraqi port
26. Bird-related
27. Skating great
28. Audacity
30. Convex molding
31. Famous spa
33. British machine guns
36. Texas city
37. *Amo, ——, amat*
39. Muscat's location
40. Soviet cooperative
43. Valley between cliffs
45. Deco artist
46. Not verso
47. Hearty gulp
48. Yarn
49. No-see-um
50. Neat as ——
51. Current Attorney General
52. Autocrat
55. Sky altar
56. Lennon's love

ACROSS

1. Balloon filler
4. Kyrgyzstan range
8. International agreement
12. Tool for Bunyan
13. "I wasn't ___ yesterday"
14. A Guthrie
15. Corded material
16. Yellow-flowered plant
18. Held responsible
20. Pay pluses
21. Bolger or Bradbury
22. Measures for Maleeva
23. Notable periods
25. Rome celebrity
26. Caspian, for example
29. Clumsy person
32. Industrious insect
33. Trucker's cargo
34. Singles
35. Swabbies' implements
36. "Maude" star
37. Group of dancers
40. Sewed, in a way
43. Stomach bug?
45. Comic actor Olsen
46. Medicinal plant
47. Word with "blue" or "born"
48. Chest bone
49. Critic Rex
50. Fabric measurement
51. Formed a lap

DOWN

1. Raiment
2. Twist for Torvill
3. Go different ways
4. Beatles' ___ *Road*
5. Clamorous
6. Humorist Buchwald
7. Fearless
8. City in France or Texas
9. Circle segments
10. Hint for Holmes
11. Dreidels, for example
17. Consumed
19. Sloop feature
22. Some convertibles
23. Wane
24. Actress McClanahan
25. Possessions
26. Washington biggies
27. Byron's "before"
28. Beast of burden
30. Flee to Gretna Green
31. *Anything* ___
35. Softened à la Satchmo
36. Howled
37. Skier's transport
38. This can be golden
39. Western Indian
40. Make hazy
41. Essayist Lamb, in print
42. Red-ink notation
44. Brindisi brother

ACROSS

1. Heckle
5. Auctioneer's word
9. Bloodhound's trail
14. Santa Barbara neighbor
15. Impressionist
16. 1969 Hitchcock film
17. Mandarin orange variety
19. Get up
20. Toolbox item
22. Tiny Tim's instrument
23. Diminutive suffix
24. Like a search party's target
28. Watch part
31. Small combo
35. ___ razor (rule of simplest causes)
38. Actual
40. Wright wing
41. Manhattan daily
44. Perfect score
45. Celt or Scot
46. Eager bride's response
47. Hydrox rival
49. Eli's school
51. Draft animals
52. Pince-___
54. Knicks grp.
57. Old door-to-door vendor
65. Sherlock actor
66. Locomotive
67. Actress Dunne
68. Leave at the altar
69. Singer Seeger
70. Sophia of film
71. Capone's foe
72. "What ___ for Love"

DOWN

1. Campus grp.
2. Almost closed
3. Grey of westerns
4. Turns sharply
5. Mr. Spock's father
6. Offers one's ideas
7. Fast time
8. Sketched
9. Author Germaine de ___
10. Trumpet kin
11. *Iliad*, e.g.
12. Ogden of verse
13. Lao-___
18. Old Paris coin
21. Asian appetizer
24. Bingo's kin
25. Earth tone
26. Film part
27. Work hides
29. Bridge monster
30. Profit ender
32. Alter a recording
33. ___-France
34. Actor Moroni
36. Ryan or Tilly
37. *Ghost* star
39. British inc.
42. Affirmative vote
43. C
48. Using one's modem
50. Signs up
53. Ms. DeGeneres
55. Bats one low
56. Cigar fall-off
57. Card game
58. Hacker
59. Harmensz van ___ (Rembrandt)
60. Soft cheese
61. Arizona tribe
62. TV equine
63. Italian city
64. Exigency
65. Puppeteer Baird

ACROSS

1. Marian, for example
5. Petition
8. Alan or Robert
12. Bane of teenagers
13. McLean's was American
14. Monsoon weather
15. Eagle for Jerome?
17. Arabian Sea gulf
18. Notched, as leaves
19. Make a misstep
21. Common contraction
23. Dance step
24. Amin, et al.
29. Short swim
32. It sees right through you
33. Altar words
34. Julia Child's handiwork
35. James Herriot, for one
36. Cousteau's compatriots
38. Skater Babilonia
40. So. state
41. As an alternative
45. Manipulating
49. Ms. McEntire
50. Rabbit for Rob?
52. Rev. Roberts
53. Abbr. on some markdowns
54. Trials and tribulations
55. Quaver, e.g.
56. Irving or Grant
57. Love trailer

DOWN

1. Fashion
2. Perfect server
3. Japanese girdle box
4. Ratio of mass to volume
5. Big galoot
6. Hopkins and Guinness
7. Dean Cain's role
8. Fragrance
9. Mother of Charles?
10. Part of a watch
11. Novelist Tyler
16. Bristle
20. Boosts
22. ___ *Crazy*, Wilder film
24. MXXX halved
25. Dander
26. Cudgel for Carrie?
27. Horatian creation
28. Author Jaffe
30. Harry's successor
31. Livestock enclosure
34. Framework of an Escort, e.g.
36. Giant's word
37. Case breaker, with luck
39. Dickens title opening
41. Pressing need?
42. Pianist Peter from New York
43. *Inter* chaser
44. Campus quarters
46. With one's feet up
47. Vincent Lopez's theme song
48. Knightly exploit
51. Twisted

CERULEAN CINEMA

ACROSS

1. Animal in the Chinese zodiac
6. Door post
10. Hullabaloo
13. Colt Hall-of-Fame QB
15. Airline to Tel Aviv
16. Illumination unit
17. She turned heads – to stone!
18. Place, to Plautus
19. Tina's ex
20. Steve Martin flick
23. Hefty portion
26. Leash kin
27. Scurries
28. Recklessly determined
30. April sign
31. Alpine aria
32. Cockeyed
34. Petite gulp
37. Compass point
38. Call the game
40. Mrs. McKinley
41. Mrs. Hoover
42. Campaigned
43. Use energetically
45. PC symbols
47. Egg: prefix
48. Coptic land
50. Withered
52. Lawrence Durrell book
53. Meager
54. Dietrich film
57. Rower's need
58. Volcano egress
59. In harmony
63. René's pal
64. Threat word
65. Swirled
66. Bad grade
67. Ticked (off)
68. Looks for

DOWN

1. Ho's partner
2. The loneliest number
3. Purge
4. Falter
5. The Big ___, Quaid flick
6. Followers of St. Ignatius
7. Weaver sci-fi thriller
8. H.S. subject
9. Elvis flick
10. Animated
11. Noblemen
12. Yoked beasts
14. Sword, in Kent
21. Delaware tribesman
22. Zero in
23. More timid
24. The Queen of Mean
25. Pilgrim John
29. MacLachlan/Rossellini film
30. In livid color?
33. Beatrix Potter's Tom ___
34. Ski terrain
35. Ancient Asian region
36. Korean city
39. 1,011, to Tiberius
44. Kindred
46. Clash
47. Coronation prop
49. The ___, Netherlands
50. Disgrace
51. Spooky
52. Perfume, in a way
54. Warty one
55. Ubangi feeder
56. Heels
60. Draw
61. Response to a mouse
62. Tooth saver: abbr.

ACROSS

1. Old Glory, for one
5. Remainders receptacle
8. ___-d'oeuvre (masterpiece)
12. Lhasa monk
13. Map abbr.
14. Chi Chi's target
15. Bacall Broadway vehicle
17. First name in mysteries
18. Mr. Carney
19. Code variety
20. Healthy vacation spot
23. Core
26. Produce a brood
28. Craftsman
32. Australian mine find
33. A Gabor
34. *And Then There Were ___*
35. Cure-all
37. Marble
38. Ahab's prop
40. Soft glove leather
41. Hang loosely
44. A Tilly
46. Rare Himalayan sight
47. Consent
52. Dark, to Dickinson
53. Damp
54. Jacob's third son
55. Warbled
56. Minstrel's poem
57. Profound

DOWN

1. Bush's state: abbr.
2. Drink like a dog
3. Electrical unit
4. Festive
5. Having no consciousness
6. 'Tis
7. Wedding-announcement word
8. Shouting praise
9. Gabriel's instrument
10. Actress Raines
11. Sense
16. Foot feature
19. Nonhuman companion
20. Prepare for Christmas
21. Hemingway's nickname
22. ___ impasse (deadlocked)
24. Nimitz's kind of base
25. La-la lead-in
27. Giving a hand
29. Saturate thoroughly
30. Opponent
31. Penurious condition
33. Med. test
36. Mediocre mark
37. Teen follower
39. Like Mulligan's "Nest"
41. Tints
42. McEntire of country
43. Huge amount
45. Hedge against inflation
47. Saddlemaker's tool
48. Pod veggie
49. Flying formation
50. Blvd.
51. Insolent response

ACROSS

1. Eliot's Marner
6. Scorch
10. Peace Nobelist Walesa
14. Love feast
15. Actor's quest
16. Melville opus
17. Philosopher Kierkegaard
18. Sugar suffixes
19. Limo riders
20. 1939 Ford classic
22. Other
23. Talk to the helm
24. Green-lighted
26. Blockage
30. ___ *This Earth,* sci-fi flick
32. Have ___ in one's bonnet
33. Wild duck
35. Frequently
39. Godzilla, e.g.
41. See 26-Across
43. Porridge type, in a nursery rhyme
44. "There ___ joy in Mudville..."
46. ___ *Camera*
47. Upright
49. Castle feature
51. Priam or Paris
54. Egyptian god
56. "Starting Over" singer
57. 1939 Bergman drama
63. Bit of news
64. France, once
65. "There's ___ Out Tonight"
66. Gaelic
67. Diamond gear

68. Costar of 10-Down
69. Hutch moms
70. Tavern choices
71. Gravel ridge

DOWN

1. Back talk
2. "___ You Babe"
3. Pasternak character
4. Take down ___ (humble)
5. Nero's tutor
6. Sing like Bing
7. Exclamation of praise
8. Thespian McCowen
9. Filmed again
10. 1939 Boyer romance
11. Flower recipient in a Faulkner tale
12. Thicket
13. Drenched
21. French nobleman
25. Former surgeon general
26. Genie's home
27. Hautboy
28. Actress Rowlands
29. 1939 Power flick
31. Actor Ken
34. Rocker Clapton
36. Moscow autocrat
37. Salinger lass
38. Prim
40. Numerical prefix
42. Outboard, e.g.
45. Law
48. Riddle
50. Messy, as a bed
51. Made an effort
52. Behind: prefix
53. Stout
55. Emulates Frosty
58. Toe cap
59. Aussie avians
60. Hit
61. District
62. Real lulu

ACROSS

1. Melodramatic sigh
5. On vacation
8. Warm oneself
12. Render
13. Favorably disposed toward
14. Tex. neighbor
15. Plantation bigwig
17. Server's burden
18. After 12:59
19. Make amends for
20. Create a stash of
24. Surrounded by
25. Indian royalty
26. Musical Ant
27. Patronizing treatment
33. In addition
34. Radius neighbor
35. Borden spokescow
37. Turn out awkwardly
38. Kitty's weapons
39. Partake of (a repast)
41. Old Atlanta venue (with "The")
42. Shoeshine Boy's alter ego
47. Low
48. Funny Caesar
49. Assistant
50. Celtic tongue
51. TV spots
52. Track competition

DOWN

1. In the past
2. Ms. Ullmann
3. 5th or Park: abbr.
4. Sun. monologue
5. Frank
6. What lunch never is
7. See 13-Across
8. Simple toast words
9. Rubber capital of the U.S.
10. Idiomatic street talk
11. Danny who played Mitty
16. . . . . _ _ . . .
19. ___ for All Seasons
20. Section of a circle
21. Former Chinese leader
22. Columnist Landers
23. Cause an accident, in a way
24. Summer beverage
26. Feat for Sampras
28. New Haven collegians
29. Five-o'clock dir.
30. Under the weather
31. Three ___ Match
32. Senate vote, maybe
35. Playwright Rice
36. Bowling alleys
37. Marie or Jeanne: abbr.
38. Encipher
39. Arthurian lady
40. Does sums
42. It's a free country: abbr.
43. Smash into
44. Metal mold
45. Pindar's pride
46. Obtain

PUN-JABS

(15)

ACROSS

1. Fail, on B'way
5. Wagner work
10. Nile wader
14. Penultimate fairy-tale word
15. When the Haggadah is read
16. Art subject
17. Ali Baba's ranking?
19. Meaty meal
20. Vestige
21. Opposite NNW
22. Colorado tribe
23. Speaker of baseball
26. Finnish lake
28. Walls of the *Nautilus*?
32. Dynamic starter
35. Santa ___ (California wind)
36. Of pitch
38. Bower
39. Coal holder
40. Something to dress
42. Gardner of the screen
43. Texas show
46. Leg bone
48. Role for Mae
49. Mystery
51. Sing Sing shoemaker's specialty?
53. Do together
55. Capet kings
56. Tippler
57. Limb
59. Belgian town
63. Mine, to Maurice
64. 007 checking shortweights?

67. Cats, e.g.
68. Danube feeder
69. "I'll make ___ to you"
70. Assay
71. Kirstie from Kansas
72. "Smooth Operator" singer

DOWN

1. Tops
2. More than
3. Tableland
4. Small leaves
5. Sugar suffix
6. Footlike part
7. Greek resistance group
8. Brooklyn's Pee Wee
9. Passionate
10. Underwriter
11. Dairymen's dance?
12. Concept: Fr.
13. Stitch
18. Deserve
24. Altar responses
25. French legislature
27. "Take on Me" trio
28. Cavalry sword
29. Kind of suit
30. Toss nuts back and forth?
31. Of some Franks
33. Prime-time fare

34. Doctoral exams
37. Hard work
41. Producer De Laurentiis
44. Self-glorifier
45. Gretchen's grandma
47. Actor's remark
50. Mimosa plant
52. Husband of Isis
54. Norse dwarf
56. *Hook* role
58. Spice wine
60. Toledo pronoun
61. Idaho item
62. Ilk
63. Quick to learn
65. Born
66. Essay

ACROSS

1. Diatonic scale tones
4. Belgrade citizen
8. Barter
12. Altar exchange
13. Lotion ingredient
14. Equestrian sport
15. Play the mediator
16. Table game
18. Healthy breakfast fare
20. Fantastic
21. Legal profession
22. Hot times, in Brest
24. Endure
26. Stages a sit-in
30. Every bit
31. ___ solemnis, Beethoven opus
32. Krazy ___
33. Grassy knolls
35. Hayworth of films
36. Singer James
37. Scarf down
38. With racked nerves
41. More stingy
45. Mat match
47. Do a hen's duty
48. Fabled man-eater
49. Suffix with refer
50. Sister of Magda
51. Anon
52. Archaic expletive
53. Indonesian coin

DOWN

1. Spanish artist Joan
2. Think-tank product
3. Olympic team sport
4. Fencing implement
5. Essayist Lamb's pseudonym
6. Rink pastime
7. Babylonian deity
8. Meager
9. Used, as clothing
10. *The Mephisto Waltz* star
11. Put up (bills)
17. "___ Kick Out of You"
19. Blemish
23. Decide with a coin
24. Scroogian outcry
25. Inventor Whitney
26. Ancient native of Britain
27. British bowling game
28. Make (doilies)
29. Paddington, for one: abbr.
31. Sacred composition
34. Decrease
35. Sound from the bleachers
37. Goaded (with "on")
38. Deuces
39. Word of deduction, to 40-Down
40. Infamous Roman emperor
42. Quechuan
43. Gutter site
44. No-hit specialist Nolan
46. Mr. Iacocca

ACROSS

1. Now's partner
5. Hornet horde
10. Swirl (soup)
14. Dry African waterbed
15. Brouhaha
16. From end to end, to Burns
17. 1922 fiction winner
19. Poetic dusks
20. Makes tough
21. Canal, e.g.
23. Gag reaction
25. Gymnast Comaneci
26. ___ Bell (Anne Brontë's alias)
29. Used to be
31. Carved symbol
34. Thai coin
35. ___ favor
36. Herman or Reese
37. Actress Mary
38. 1988 fiction winner
40. Speech pauses
41. Sluggishness
43. Sara of film
44. Without alteration
45. Sling mud
46. Pouch
47. Plant fiber
48. From Erin
50. Sea raptors
52. Couch for two
55. Burdens
59. Yemen city
60. 1926 fiction winner
62. Gossip
63. Jeweler's lens
64. Hebrew prophet
65. Lip
66. Scornful smile
67. Appear

DOWN

1. "___ brillig, and the slithy toves"
2. Policeman's shout
3. Singer Brickell
4. A ___ cup of tea
5. Huge hit
6. Tied the knot
7. "There oughta be ___"
8. Staffs from scratch
9. D.C. hostess Perle
10. Germ-free
11. 1950 fiction winner
12. Soap writer Phillips
13. Promising
18. Dash
22. Advanced gradually
24. Military status
26. Borders (upon)
27. Strike and rebound
28. 1963 fiction winner
30. Kitchen fume
32. Problem for Pauline
33. Author Hermann
35. According to
36. Pod find
38. Acer Becker
39. Bad habit
42. Life givers
44. Supposes
46. Sexy Stone
47. Rustic motels
49. Circus barkers
51. He rocks the boat
52. Youths
53. Songstress Coates
54. Exam option
56. Label info
57. To be, in Tours
58. Fraud
61. Ajar, to bards

ACROSS

1. Hemingway's moniker
5. Love god
9. Sign of a shark
12. Pearl Harbor location
13. Car corrosion
14. Had one's cake
15. Remedy for an author's headache?
18. Pindar creation
19. Construction bars
20. Rearing at the gate?
24. Tarzan's subject
25. WWII arena
26. Oxlike antelope
30. Sharks or Jets
32. Photo ___ (media events)
34. Square measure
35. Ledge
37. Brew served with scones
39. Paving material
40. Heavenly haymaker?
43. Outstanding, in a way
46. Alma-___, Kazakhstan
47. Advanced degree at Bragg?
52. Breakfast fare for Pilate
53. Actor Ray
54. Priam's domain
55. Turner of American history
56. French river
57. Roll response

DOWN

1. Comic-book smack
2. Bern's river
3. Key letter
4. Detroit exports
5. Che Guevara's given name
6. Living room furnishing
7. Ancient Tiber port
8. Steady
9. FDR's pooch
10. List listing
11. New Jersey team
16. ___ *fixe*
17. Beautiful, to Bellini
20. Crones
21. Colorful, bony fish
22. Philosopher Descartes
23. From ___ bottom
27. Comic Johnson
28. *Hud* Oscar winner
29. Move like a dragonfly
31. Be a bad winner
33. Sam Nunn was one
36. Noted right-hand man
38. In re
41. Golden calves, e.g.
42. *The Sot-Weed Factor* author
43. Second word of a fairy tale
44. Long-running PBS show
45. Exam for Jrs.
48. B–F connection
49. Measurement of land
50. Dartmoor outcropping
51. Seer?

ACROSS

1. Qum one
6. Circle bit
9. Valletta is its capital
14. Captured
15. Wine and dine
16. Use, as influence
17. Exclaimed
18. Rocker's need
19. Inert gas
20. Layer
21. Sabra, for one
24. Bother
25. Put (money on)
26. Star pitcher
28. Journey to the top
31. Lomé's land, formerly
36. *Andrea ___*, ship of note
37. Languish
38. Nice notion
39. Owing
40. Change
41. Some germ cells
42. *___ People,* MacLaine movie
44. Blue hue
45. Sea follower
47. Bhutto's home
49. Comes to a point
50. Light starter
51. Jug
52. Spots on TV
55. Galápagos owner
58. Bleat
61. Used an awl
63. Greek letter
64. Premieres
66. Stuffed fruit
67. Twitch
68. Delight
69. Aden is there
70. Feedbag bit
71. Hafez al-Assad's nation

DOWN

1. Poison ivy symptom
2. One in a million
3. Consanguine
4. Born
5. Pacers' state
6. Emmy or Tony
7. Della's costar
8. Deal (with)
9. Land of Chichén Itzá
10. Hewing tool
11. Ms. Olin
12. Stomped
13. Hydrogen's is 1: abbr.
22. Command to Fido
23. Type of brew
25. Hilo wreath
27. Yalie
28. Make sense
29. The March King
30. Small waterway
31. Saturn's largest moon
32. Early Scott Turow book
33. Worship
34. No way!
35. Sweet people
37. Entreaty
40. Garret
43. Morse code sound
45. North Atlantic islands
46. Lender's abbr.
48. Palme's land
49. Tango requisite
51. Decree
52. Sailor's shout
53. Hand (out)
54. Willowy
56. Capable of
57. Vast continent
58. Kodiak animal
59. Not pro
60. Cruising
62. First lady
65. Layer of cloth

ACROSS

1. Clerical garments
5. Bat wood
8. Scholarly volume
12. Lacking clothing
13. Lithic lead-in
14. Algerian seaport
15. Novel by the featured author
18. Drawing support
19. ___ over (capsize)
20. Sally in space
22. WWII vessel
26. Charge for service
29. Actress Mary Beth
31. Aware of
32 and 34. Featured author of this puzzle
36. Croat or Bulgar
37. Blow a horn
39. "Leave It" band
40. Broke, in a way
42. Cudgel
44. Debauchee
46. Former Secretary of Labor
50. Novel by the featured author
54. Ibsen heroine
55. Curve
56. Sharif of films
57. Start of a football play
58. Beaver's pride
59. Diamond cover

DOWN

1. Parisian priest
2. ___ Flynn Boyle
3. Arm of France?
4. Become distinct
5. Novelist Beattie
6. One on a quest
7. Sewing machine inventor
8. Handyman's chest
9. Bobby of hockey
10. ___ de mer
11. Terminus
16. Nobel-winning statesman Root
17. Tiny
21. Reason to take the Pledge?
23. ___ You, Helen Hunt film
24. To ___ (perfectly)
25. Items in Hellman's attic
26. Observe Yom Kippur
27. First lady of scat
28. Mild yellow cheese
30. Norse hammer bearer
33. Coincide in part
35. Freeway no-no
38. Ukrainian seaport
41. Buck's mate
43. Sired
45. Secondhand
47. ___ Dancer, Nureyev documentary
48. Nicholas, e.g.
49. Celtic bard's instrument
50. USNA grad
51. Over there
52. Period of history
53. Doctrine

KICKOFFS

ACROSS

1. Pacino-De Niro film
5. Tweed-era cartoonist
9. Gave a hand
14. Sailor's saint
15. European capital
16. Where eagles snore?
17. Begin
20. Duty of a kind
21. Teen social
22. Night flier
23. Study frantically
25. Subway stops: abbr.
27. Walker: abbr.
30. Trade, to Sartre
32. Teen hangout
36. Assumed name
38. Endure
40. Eye part
41. Begin
44. Hebrew month
45. Store sign
46. Tea-party crasher of fiction
47. Letter flourishes
49. Pouches
51. ___ es Salaam
52. Salutation start
54. Bowl sounds
56. See 36-Across
59. Bearing
61. Play grounds
65. Begin
68. Inn
69. Roman date
70. Concerning
71. 1984 Derby winner
72. Orator of old
73. Self inflators

DOWN

1. Guess the weight of
2. Actress Raines
3. ___ vincit omnia
4. Subject
5. Milk choice
6. Bottom of my hearth
7. Sty serving
8. Escorted trips
9. "Mama" character
10. Shocker of the sea
11. Bedouin
12. "Firecracker" singer Loeb
13. Trial run
18. From the beginning
19. Take turns
24. Knights of ___ (Hospitalers)
26. Racing boat
27. Actress Irene
28. Avoid adroitly
29. Kuwait coin
31. Coin reverse
33. Steer clear of
34. Old record label
35. USAF general Ira
37. Bitter
39. Daub with grease
42. Go at
43. Kick the bucket
48. NOW member
50. *Jade* actor
53. Dig find
55. Hawkins of Dogpatch
56. Goals
57. Have in mind
58. Hammett hound
60. Nothing, in Mexico
62. Atlantic fish
63. Poi base
64. Shouts for a matador
66. Aviv lead-in
67. Collection

ACROSS

1. TV actor Max
5. Meek one
9. Santa's employee
12. Soprano Gluck
13. "Heat of the Moment" group
14. Kanga's bouncy baby
15. Bruce's ex
16. Absorbed, in a way
18. Gardner of mysteries
20. Patellae
21. Change container
23. Lucie's brother
25. Golf champ Ernie
26. "In Living Color" segment
28. Blabbed
32. Any of several
33. ___ Days in May
35. Sebastian of Olympic fame
36. Nil, in Nicaragua
38. Civil-rights activist Parks
39. Urban conveyance
40. Pocket fuzz
42. Dark, patchy clouds
44. Frogs' maneuvers
47. Dodge City lawman
48. Complicated
51. Green land
54. Brouhaha
55. Roof overhang
56. Ownership document
57. Cut down
58. Laurel or Lee
59. Track information

DOWN

1. Run around restlessly
2. Pub purchase
3. Covered with water
4. Hideaways; haunts
5. Happening recently
6. Cigar residue
7. Eleventh-century date
8. Lenders, frequently
9. Iroquois people
10. The Last Emperor star
11. London forecasts
17. Create a cardigan
19. Minus
21. Landless laborer
22. Arm bone
23. Fairway clump
24. Some seasons, in Lyons
27. Show Boat composer
29. Tied up
30. Fill
31. Socialist Eugene
34. Shuttle overseer
37. Purina rival
41. Keys
43. Confession of faith
44. Jodie's Nell costar
45. Inner: prefix
46. Admit frankly
47. Utopian location
49. Cistern
50. Actress Le Gallienne
52. Cerise, e.g.
53. Wynn, et al.

MINUS SIGNS

ACROSS

1. Villa on the Volga
6. Mop
10. Smug one
14. Improvise
15. "Don't tell me!"
16. One of 18
17. Looks for (truffles)
18. Archaic Spanish coin
19. Let out
20. Benevolent behavior
23. Rocker Adam
24. Compass point
25. Make-believe
27. Busted, at Bragg
31. Operate
32. English river
33. Parisian pronoun
36. Icy dome
40. Canasta combination
41. Jazz high spots
43. Singer of "Fame"
44. Church bigwig
46. Grate upon
47. Claire and Balin
48. Barbecue treat
50. "Hooray for ___!"
52. Stature
57. Olé cousin
58. A long time
59. Hesiod's "good neighbor"
64. Immortal Yankee
66. Shady walk
67. Dumb move
68. Gang chaser
69. Roscoe of old movies
70. Printing tool
71. Chariot extensions
72. Dear, in Roma
73. Despots

DOWN

1. Mend
2. End of a Durante number
3. Simple weapon
4. White Sox team of 1906
5. Missing
6. Service tree
7. Young bear
8. Walking ___
9. Scarecrow player
10. Any ship
11. "___ is an island"
12. Lena and Ken
13. Balzac's Cousin
21. Famed Jesse
22. Needle case
26. Classes for emigrés
27. South Pacific nonpareil
28. First name in stunts
29. Shape
30. Portal
34. Spat add-on
35. Fair
37. Burt's ex
38. Toward the mouth
39. Seine feeder
42. Sudden gush
45. Comic Rudner
49. Fast-food order
51. ___, Run, Updike opus
52. Grayish blue
53. The way to go
54. Pop into
55. Regard: Latin
56. Sniggler
60. And
61. Start of a Durante number
62. ___-do-well
63. Canine caveats
65. Times: abbr.

ACROSS

1. "...market to buy — pig"
5. Swinging Fountain
9. Lowest point
14. Tenderfoot
15. Graceful equine
16. Scale-tipping
17. Love, to Livy
18. — avis
19. Chopped finely
20. Surrounding a TV lawyer?
22. Falco and Brickell
23. Literary monogram
24. Cooler for the summer
25. In the Black?
26. Prevented
29. Sarnoff's legacy: abbr.
32. Did tailoring
35. Former "60 Minutes" man
38. Early Christian
39. Juliet, to Romeo
40. Profession
41. Phone parts
43. Rages
44. — *Lay Dying*
45. Unaffected
47. Highland fuel
50. NCAA post-season event
51. Droop
54. Get gussied up
56. Bad Christie character?
59. Memorize
60. Millstone
61. *East of Eden* son
62. Skylit courts
63. Soil: prefix
64. Trident part
65. Chaucer yarns
66. Prom attendee
67. Iron, et al.

DOWN

1. Conform
2. Noxious vapors
3. Treasure
4. Actress Garr
5. Marched
6. Chalk blotter
7. Edible island root
8. Israeli Abba
9. Bumps
10. Endure
11. $\frac{1}{10}$ of a classic sitcom star?
12. Sinking-in phrase
13. Beatty film
21. Experts, sort of
25. Oklahoma town
26. *Diary of —— Housewife*
27. Cartel
28. Night of romantic poetry
30. Hand over
31. Bellicose Olympian
32. "Very funny!"
33. Epochs
34. Tiny Opry star?
36. Layers
37. Type of test
39. LIRR stop
42. Tolkien creature
43. Harvard color
46. Tentative
48. Macabre
49. Moffo, et al.
51. Small shoot
52. Without peer
53. Chromosome cargo
54. Land plan
55. Actress Shaw
56. Castle defense
57. *Picnic* author
58. Pro chaser

AIR SHOW

ACROSS

1. Applications
5. Postprandial cheese
9. Talk-show host
14. Split hairs?
15. Duty list, at Sandhurst
16. "It's the end of ___"
17. DIVE
19. More pristine
20. Aircraft engine housing
22. Booby trap
23. Late students
26. Emulated Shylock
28. More slippery
29. Freight
31. Flood foiler
32. Arafat's prize
33. NYSE listing
36. Snow jobs
37. More tender
38. Mmes. of Málaga
39. AARP member
40. Spreadable edibles
41. Sheen
42. "White Christmas" composer
44. Awaken
45. Orbital extreme
47. Grade more sharply
49. Smooth engine sound
50. Settle a scrap
53. Shakespearean woods
55. SPIN
59. Angelic Della
60. Burn soother
61. Director Kazan
62. Short and sweet
63. Soviet news agency
64. Bumper boo-boo

DOWN

1. Increases (a bet)
2. James' *Giant* costar
3. Sooner than, in sonnets
4. Straphangers
5. Utah canyon
6. Loungewear
7. Slanted type: abbr.
8. Fatha Hines
9. Stepped lively
10. Single-handed
11. CIRCLE
12. Ryan of TV
13. Like cornstalks
18. Kinshasa's country, once
21. First-born of two
23. Turns turf
24. ___ the hole
25. BANK
27. Paint base
29. Svelte Sophia
30. Burrows and Fortas
32. South winds, in old Rome
34. Lap armor
35. German steel city
37. *The Crucible* setting
38. Having dark peepers
40. Vent opener?
41. Ms. Garbo
43. Way out
45. Separated
46. Blender button
47. Fodder holders
48. Poe pieces
51. Coup d'___
52. Oscar ___ Renta
54. Maiden-named
56. Mug shot?
57. Tenth of a sen
58. "Unforgettable" Cole

ACROSS

1. One of the Leeward Islands
5. Dreary
9. Bounders
13. Religious artifact
14. Of flying
15. Together, to Solti
16. Discharge, as lava
17. Chinese poet Wei
18. Dutch South African
19. Mel Blanc's southern bantam
22. Earth digs
23. Notorious Helmsley
24. Slip by
27. Mixture
29. Magnate Turner
30. Fire follower
32. Trolley sound
36. Bumble Bee rival
40. Squelch
41. Mark, to Caesar
42. President pro ___
43. Concise review
45. Unimportant person
48. Personality classification
50. Field: prefix
51. Wayne's *True Grit* role
57. Cook's trip
58. '60s musical
59. *Ghosts* playwright
60. Circle dance
61. Roman being
62. Flee to a JP
63. Auto pioneer
64. Part of a bar's stock
65. Meeting: abbr.

DOWN

1. Utah's lily
2. Not have ___ to stand on
3. Chessman
4. Role players
5. Grows light
6. Actual
7. English composer
8. Dumbfound
9. Kit's partner
10. Festoon
11. Owner: Sp.
12. Sun. delivery
13. Ring official
20. Pee Wee of baseball
21. 1950 Nobelist in medicine
24. Common abbrs.
25. City near Salt Lake City
26. It might lead to lead
27. Batting result
28. Forgot to take
31. "I," in *The King and I*
33. Concerning
34. Exigency
35. Like venison
37. Linen altar cloth
38. Scrubwoman's support
39. Ballroom dance
44. Author Willa
46. Roman revels
47. Make an error
48. Cavalry unit
49. ___ *in the Navy Now*
50. Land measures
52. Piece-of-cake
53. ___ to the occasion
54. Soldiers' hangouts: abbr.
55. Agents
56. SSW opposite
57. However, briefly

ACROSS

1. Workers' protection gp.
5. Sorrowful word
9. River to the Caspian
13. Norma and Charlotte
14. Riviera resort
15. Campaigner Elizabeth
16. Stale
18. Banyan, e.g.
19. Disregard
20. With 57-Across, definition of "imposter"
23. CIO partner
24. Middle of a palindrome
25. Actress Taylor
26. Brazil resort
27. *King* ___ (1958 Elvis movie)
31. Horace creation
32. Door brass
34. Sound of contempt
36. Author of the definition
42. Western wear
43. Sweet tubers
45. Organ with a drum
48. Demosthenes, e.g.
51. Born
52. Jerk
54. As well
56. Land unit
57. See 20-Across
62. Literary Lamb
63. Feel pity (for)
64. Prufrock's poet
66. Height: abbr.
67. Crowd noise
68. Movie Wilder
69. St. Thomas
70. Hill builders
71. Org.

DOWN

1. Food fragment
2. 1992 Whoopi Goldberg movie
3. Precious hand-me-down
4. City near Turin
5. Moose rack
6. San Marino money
7. Breezes through (a test)
8. Flow slowly
9. Venerate
10. Pasta sprinkle
11. Adjusted
12. Sofa
17. Margo Channing's nemesis
21. Bow
22. A Castle
23. Arrival at Ararat
28. Discharge
29. Globe
30. Him, to Henri
33. UK network
35. Take a stab at
37. Equal-sided parallelogram
38. Paddle
39. Saratoga Springs, e.g.
40. Pet singers
41. Ralph Waldo and kin
44. View
45. High regard
46. Handsome chap
47. Duelist's tool
49. Additional ones
50. Tigger's pal
53. Urbane
55. Wallet filler
58. Yuri's love
59. Holy image
60. Rap
61. Olympian Korbut
65. Decade

ACROSS

1. Penn film, ___ So Lovely
5. First of all?
9. The ___ shebang
14. Termite or gnat
15. Senatorial garb
16. Emanations
17. Book by 51-Across
20. Take advantage of
21. Bid at an auction, perhaps
22. Boston Harbor litter, once
23. Sat in session again
24. Current prefix
26. René of France
27. ___ point stitch
28. Leave out
29. Divides
30. Road curve
31. African lake
32. Topol role
33. Milieu for 51-Across
35. Popeye's rival
37. Makes a choice
38. Part of "RPM"
41. Flower-child guru
42. Chaste
43. Hawaiian hotshot
44. Der ___, Adenauer alias
45. Roman Stoic
46. "What ___ these mortals be"
47. Summer quaff
48. Fire fodder
49. Trucker's aid
51. Chronicler of 17-Across
54. Modern memo
55. Expired
56. Riga native
57. Transmit
58. Pay to play
59. Speedy fliers, for short

DOWN

1. Spend big-time
2. Gats
3. North American natives
4. Stone monuments
5. The gamut
6. Pinscher header
7. The time of your life?
8. Attractive item
9. Prop for Merlin
10. 1963 Newman movie
11. Skill of 45-Across
12. Nursery item
13. Lamb output
18. Wilde quality
19. Tic-tac-toe winner
25. Den of thieves
26. Vena chaser
28. Horrified cry
29. Furry family members
31. Oxford, e.g.
32. Carry
33. Wall in, once
34. Wheel tooth
35. Grandma, old-style
36. Sideways
38. Coiffed dogs
39. Actor Gould
40. Vacation spots
41. Circle the wagons
42. Tiered temple
43. Handy-andies
45. Lettuce type
46. Pt. of "TGIF"
48. Ms. Tomlin
50. Adam ___
52. Inlet
53. Henry & June character

ECHOES

ACROSS

1. Gossoons
5. "To ___ human..."
10. Moscow despot
14. Declare
15. Big Easy gridman
16. Salt's shout
17. Snake charmer
19. Siberian waterway
20. *Guys and Dolls* doll
21. Thespian Brennan
23. Haberdashery display
24. Fresh fellow
25. Affix
28. Diplomatic protest
31. Blackens
32. Terrines
33. Prince of the theater
34. Hints
35. Saturday suburbanite, perhaps
36. Kiss's partner
37. Comic Olsen
38. Bireme hand
39. *Alla* chaser
40. Cane rings
42. Looks daggers
43. Aromatic wood
44. Writer O'Faoláin
45. Has a hankering
47. Aegis issuers
51. Clinton's birthplace
52. Magician
54. Through
55. ___ out (making do)
56. Start for bunny
57. Bouncy
58. *Roma* hill count
59. This, in Tijuana

DOWN

1. Etna effluent
2. Eager
3. Chump
4. Is beat by the heat
5. Made out
6. Sorties
7. Full-blown
8. Argent finish
9. Banner headline
10. Higher up?
11. Joy
12. First-class rating
13. Hanks' frequent costar
18. Drizzles
22. "When ___ a lad..."
24. N.T. angler
25. *An ___ Murder,* March film
26. Anglo ender
27. Counterfeiting job
28. Coolidge's VP
29. Bisect
30. *Les femmes*
32. Sinew
35. Treacle
36. Ooze out
38. Boorish
39. Like an ulcer diet
41. Backslide
42. Actor Arliss
44. Played out
45. Official seal, in China
46. Amble
47. Roast-pig holder
48. Work of art
49. Take ten
50. Maiden, in Madrid: abbr.
53. It's strummed at a luau

ACROSS

1. Mickey's creator
5. Weapon for Little John
10. Former cabinet member Mike
14. Borodin's prince
15. Loom
16. Antitoxins
17. Pave
19. Bear snare
20. Incited
21. Goes with the flow
23. Aphrodite's offspring
24. Pacific ray
25. Dissertation
28. Cardinal's honorific
31. Hambletonian prelims
32. Fasten
33. Typewriter key
34. ___-bitsy
35. Refined
36. Trig function
37. Fanatic
38. Literary specter
39. Having more marbles?
40. Plunder
42. Copse cousin
43. Conclusion
44. Philanthropist Wallace
45. Rennes resident
47. North Dakota neighbor
51. Mother of Castor
52. Pier group
54. Unprotected
55. Boring tool
56. Nerd
57. Playwright Kushner
58. All in
59. Swiss banks?

DOWN

1. Pantywaist
2. Petri-dish medium
3. Batty
4. Burlesque; farce
5. Military dress caps
6. Literary heavyweights
7. Gung-ho
8. Shriner's topper
9. Bizarre
10. Property
11. Twisting
12. Fall start?
13. Chihuahua comments
18. Actress Roberts
22. Odense native
24. Bashed
25. Uses turpentine
26. Excited
27. Story of the Trask family
28. Shake a tail
29. Fops' props
30. Chicago film critic
32. Laminates
35. Logger's lopper
36. 1777 battle site
38. Chinese: prefix
39. Dependable
41. Long prayer
42. Glad rags
44. 1969 Wimbledon champ
45. Splotch
46. ___ *Man*, Estevez film
47. Vast prefix
48. Turgenev's birthplace
49. Page
50. Invites
53. Calendar abbr.

ACROSS

1. Eagerly anticipating
5. Alpha opposite
10. Service for eight, e.g.
13. Money in *Milano*
14. Island dances
15. More
16. Smith of *Twister*
17. Let in
18. Toward the end
19. Beginning of a teenager's plaint
22. DDE's command
23. Carefree
24. Signed
26. Sub finder
28. *Streamers* playwright David
31. Down under bird
32. Afternoon repast
35. Words of approximation
36. Teen column in *Parade*
38. Light carriage
40. Eastern capital
41. Mythical bird
42. Sightseer's route
43. Julius, to Caesar, e.g.
47. ___ *Is Born*
49. Winter mo.
51. Seraglio room
52. End of plaint
57. Glut
58. Fish net
59. Oxidize
60. Malaria symptom
61. Llama milieu
62. Lotion extra
63. Muffin variety
64. Friars do
65. Hamilton bills

DOWN

1. Axis foes
2. Florentine painter
3. Prayer
4. Long cut
5. *Butterfield 8* author
6. Blues singer Waters
7. Sailor's guardian
8. Increase
9. Dog star
10. Goldbricks
11. Regards highly
12. Pigskin holder
15. Panache
20. Consent
21. "For shame!"
25. Steve and Eydie, e.g.
27. Idol add-on
28. Actor Phoenix
29. Egyptian deity
30. So ___ (amen)
33. Concerning
34. Via, briefly
35. Wine: prefix
36. Handyman
37. Shell that echoes the sea
38. Mexican Mrs.
39. Behan play (with *The*)
42. *Due* follower
44. Part of "LEM"
45. U.S. inventor
46. Loire port
48. *A Death in the Family* author
49. Sahara sights
50. Pour forth
53. Romanov ruler
54. Long-jawed late-nighter
55. Opera with elephants
56. Part of "QED"
57. Wilt

ACROSS

1. Campus newcomer
6. Dove for second
10. Earlobe gem
14. Variety show
15. Fork feature
16. John of *Iceman* fame
17. Suspect's way out
18. Economist Smith
19. Ampersands
20. First course for Sagan?
23. Bug header
26. Result of spit and polish
27. Type of sugar
28. Cubist painter Juan
30. Compass point
31. Mosque official
32. The Last Frontier
34. First course for Sartre?
39. Pet
40. Some do it to the occasion
42. Pt. of "NOW"
45. Genetic letters
46. Dane of drama
48. Caviar source
50. Went marauding
51. First course for Greenspan?
54. Saw attachments?
55. French job
56. Excessive
60. Singer Brickell
61. Change, to Cato
62. Antitoxin
63. Letter opener
64. Mouse catcher
65. Splices

DOWN

1. ___ Lippo Lippi
2. Bro or sis
3. Egg: prefix
4. Very, very minute
5. Shady bank jobs
6. Brenda or Bart
7. Resort near Venice
8. ___ uproar
9. Bulldoze
10. Wows an audience
11. This evening, in ads
12. Brings to ruin
13. ___ *Under the Elms*
21. Prop for Faldo
22. Like some colognes
23. Emulate Moe
24. It's got tough fiber
25. Hatch's state
28. Photo finish
29. Hip chats
32. On the Bering
33. Sent *par avion*
35. Slow musical passage
36. Yule hang-up
37. Unctuous
38. Words of understanding
41. LAX listing
42. Toed the line
43. Ebb
44. Gena Rowlands film
46. Polloi header
47. Pique
49. 4-time Indy winner
50. Camera term
52. Believe ___ not
53. Hollow: Latin
57. Cycle starter
58. Groove
59. Morning hrs.

ACROSS

1. Sultry dance
6. "Dream a Little Dream of Me" singer
10. Frame upright
14. Circa
15. Laver rival
16. Poet Khayyám
17. Braxton, Danza, Quinn
20. Took to court
21. Science guy Bill
22. Add basil to, for example
23. Jam ingredient?
25. Aloe recipient
26. Richards, Rice, Potts
30. Zany
32. Unkindly
33. Chromosome component
35. Foil relatives
36. Just do it
37. Solitaire stockpile
39. Andalusian aunt
40. Grate stuff
41. Unfrequented
42. Wallach, Wiesel, Howe
46. Catches
47. Bitter rancor
48. Missouri River feeder
51. Gird up
52. Time past
56. Johnson, Shaw, Miller
59. Bridge post
60. Wrongful act
61. 12th anniversary gift
62. Granny, e.g.
63. Madigan and Carter
64. Sports report

DOWN

1. Uses a shuttle
2. Father: Arabic
3. Afternoon prayer
4. Counselor's offering
5. Giant Giant
6. Eroded landform
7. "___ sow, so shall…"
8. ___ Na Na
9. Voluptuous
10. A Bach
11. Author Oz
12. Hand, to Ballesteros
13. Mawr lead-in
18. Drafty?
19. Sea swallow
24. Merkel and O'Connor
25. Cuff
26. "It's ___!"
27. One's proper place
28. Stays in park
29. Organic compound
30. N.Y. opera house
31. Cap-___ (entirely)
34. Apathetic one's choice
36. Sale caveat
37. Work
38. Logical
40. Canadian province
41. Andes animal
43. Meaning
44. "I could ___ horse"
45. Plume sources
48. Scout's group
49. Author Hubbard
50. ___ time (never)
51. Graceful
53. "Yikes!"
54. Regretful type
55. Shore eagle
57. Nicole's love
58. Literary monogram

ACROSS

1. *Cold Comfort* ___
5. Indian seaport
10. Chatty Larry
14. Prefix for distant
15. The terrible twos, e.g.
16. Biblical birthright seller
17. Former senator Sam
18. Deposes
19. Arachnid creations
20. Early photos
23. Giant armadillo
24. Chi lead-in
25. Way up
28. Tiny Tim's ax
32. Caused by sea surges
33. Cultural no-no
34. Thunder Bay's prov.
36. Geisha's wrap
37. Champagne glass
39. Lao follower
40. Kops' prop
41. Pilsner, e.g.
42. Peter Shaffer play
44. Famed ornithologist
46. Assets
47. Go astray
48. Rural tower
49. George Bush, for one
56. Continental coin
57. Ain't right?
58. Arm bone
59. Pitiful word
60. Shortstop Pee Wee
61. Carte
62. Pretense
63. Harness maker
64. Editor's order

DOWN

1. Manage without help
2. Shade of blue
3. Ladder crosspiece
4. Petty detail
5. Good chaps
6. Freedom, in Swahili
7. Demolish, in Devon
8. In re
9. Lab vessel
10. Cute midway prize
11. Phrase of understanding
12. Collars
13. Astronaut Grissom's moniker
21. British aristocrat
22. Manchurian river
25. Organ pull
26. Leg bone
27. Soissons *sayonara*
28. Driving move
29. Krazy ___
30. Water flower
31. Follow
35. Miss Trueheart
37. Winter time
38. Composer Delibes
41. Actor Young
42. Scat queen
43. Select groups
45. Overthrow
46. *Old Times* playwright
48. Meaning
49. Fiji wrap
50. Noted times
51. Mars: prefix
52. Teen misfit
53. "___ a song go..."
54. Poet Sexton
55. Maritime: abbr.
56. Corn unit

ACROSS

1. Gallant's opposite
5. More than a foible
9. Floes
14. ___ avis
15. Rocker Billy
16. Florida town
17. Neighbor of Turkey
18. Astronomer's glass
19. Outspoken
20. Ski attire
22. Motionless
23. Strapping
24. Overly curious
25. Yeshiva instructor
29. Method
32. Deeps
34. Brazil's ___ Paulo
35. Chilled
39. Kitchen herb
41. High-pitched woodwind
43. ___ Verde (Anasazi site)
44. Bustle
46. Peru packers
47. Endangered felines
50. Exclusively
51. Rosalind's wooded hide-out
54. Becomes faint
56. Tunes in
57. Pass bills
62. Spry
63. Coffee containers
64. Observe
65. Toughie
66. Fodder veggie
67. Gemstone cut
68. Rendezvous
69. Pianist Duchin
70. Paris pronoun

DOWN

1. Fodder box
2. Pasternak heroine
3. Viva-voce
4. *Two Years Before the Mast* author
5. Riviera rental
6. Lofty principles
7. Makes known
8. Fashion's Schiaparelli
9. Related to Bossy
10. Thrifty
11. Camptown events
12. Dazzle
13. Like feta cheese
21. Spode, for example
25. Hotel booking
26. State in western Brazil
27. Active pollinators
28. Trifles
30. Maple product
31. Keep one's nose to the grindstone
33. Hitch
36. Crooner Perry
37. Verve
38. Portion
40. Keats creation
42. Refinement
45. Bid
48. Gore, for example
49. Used ASL
51. Conform
52. Precision
53. Simple bloom
55. Garner theme song
57. Garage job
58. Bound
59. Eve's second
60. Dabbling duck
61. Brontë heroine

ACROSS

1. Asian nanny
5. Actor Robert of *Tru* fame
10. Satiate
14. South American monkey
15. Native Alaskan
16. Revolutionary Luxemburg
17. Sean Lennon's maternal side
18. Stretch (for)
19. Distressing device
20. Nothing
23. With, in Orléans
24. Female ruff
25. Sovereign-related
28. Hebrew letter
30. Map abbr.
33. Jai chaser
34. Regan's father
35. Small cont.
36. Nothing
41. *Juin, juillet et août*
42. River in Belgium
43. A Roberts
44. Some, on the Somme
45. Notorious tsar
46. Petite
48. NNW opposite
49. Floating ice
50. Nothing
58. Soft muslin
59. 1936 film, ___ *Three*
60. Yawn inducer
61. Prussian article
62. *The Pumpkin* ___, Bancroft film
63. Arab land
64. Dutch treat
65. Word with "up" or "down"
66. A.G. Janet

DOWN

1. The gamut
2. Skirt style
3. On
4. Latin-American
5. Taciturn Marceau
6. Pertaining to a fatty acid
7. Garner
8. So extreme
9. Very delicate
10. Munch on pasturage
11. Theater section
12. Computer operator
13. Starchy root
21. Gametes
22. Prepare beans in Baja
25. Leveled
26. Special group
27. Dangerous winds
28. Pilgrim suitor
29. Was an usher
30. Hear
31. The call of the IRS
32. Dick Dick
37. Raise aloft
38. Got rid (of)
39. O.T. Hebrew prophet
40. The guy next door
46. Inhibits
47. Sun's path
48. TV's talking feline
49. Military posts
50. Hook's crony
51. A sovereign
52. Radius' mate
53. Blacken
54. Network
55. City on Seward Peninsula
56. Pahlavi's land
57. Alien: prefix

ACROSS

1. Yarn spinners
6. Service tree, for example
10. Equine hues
14. Ait
15. Poker holding
16. Actor Estrada
17. Epithet of Napoleon I
20. See 60-Down
21. Cloy
22. Yellow-orange fruits
26. Author Gay
30. Field of conflict
31. *Black Magic 1*, e.g.
33. Since Jan. 1
34. Send a check
35. Brit's thank-yous
36. Converge
37. 1972 Peter O'Toole film
41. Rudolph of the Met
42. Charged particle
43. Antoine's academy
45. Eastern sea
46. Over
48. Charles' principality
49. Sink ___
51. Colleague
53. Music halls
55. Debatable
56. TV spy spoof of the '60s
63. Auger
64. New Mexico resort
65. Asian kingdom
66. Perceived
67. Signs of a hit
68. Twos

DOWN

1. Ignited
2. Pun ending?
3. Porter's kin
4. Left over
5. What dots signify, in music
6. Uneven
7. Lout
8. Eliminates
9. "___ ware that will not keep" (Housman)
10. Asian pepper
11. Uris hero
12. Feminine influence, in China
13. It's the limit
18. Sarge, e.g.
19. PDQ, to a doc
22. Swiss river
23. Foremost
24. Returns to custody
25. Word in a Rushdie title
27. Mask cutout
28. Kleptomaniac
29. Hot time in N.Y.
32. Asymmetrical wheel
36. One of the Fab Four
38. Imaginings
39. Mauna chaser
40. Just-acquired
41. Sis' sib
44. Language suffix
46. Verdi classic
47. What Mick Jagger gathers?
50. *Two* ___ (Loren film)
52. ___ de plume
54. Remotely
56. Cable network
57. Weed whacker
58. Prior to
59. Aussie hopper
60. Busy one in Apr.
61. Stripling
62. Loop sights

ACROSS

1. Rizzuto of Cooperstown
5. Harrier's home
9. Kshatriya, for one
14. Emilia's husband
15. Rio Branco's state
16. In progress, to Holmes
17. Start of a truism
20. Private place
21. Our, in Orly
22. Brief response?
23. *The Devil's Dictionary* author
26. *Exodus* hero
28. Guffaws
32. Aero ending
33. With 41-Across, Prime Minister of 1868
35. Tender spots?
37. Evangelist ___ Semple McPherson
38. Middle of truism
39. Mini egg
40. Pindar, e.g.
41. See 33-Across
43. Monarch capturer
44. David's dad
45. AAA recommendation
46. Grand landholding
49. Wee dram
51. "___ told by an idiot"
53. French dance
57. End of truism
60. Ancient Andean
61. Wrath, to Ovid
62. Cubic Rubik
63. Noble, to a chemist
64. Bastes
65. Bay relative

DOWN

1. Quay
2. Wealthy one
3. Start of a Porter title
4. Certain quiches
5. Tolstoy lass
6. Genuine, in Germany
7. Hindu title
8. Gore's home: abbr.
9. Nopal, et al.
10. Prior
11. Cartwheel's cousin
12. Sock part
13. French connections?
18. Kyoto kale
19. U.S. tars
24. Sheep dog
25. Otherwise
26. Tolerates
27. Mailed money
29. Nitrogen compound
30. Sound buys
31. "With the jawbone of ___" (Judges)
34. Black rock
35. Indian region
36. Vanquish
37. Smashing
42. Flea-market transactions
44. Crystallize
47. Fighting
48. Sully
50. Wall climber
52. Cantabs' foes
53. Chew on
54. Poi plant
55. Editor Brown
56. Scholar's collar
57. CLXVII x VI
58. Ms. Richards
59. Lode load

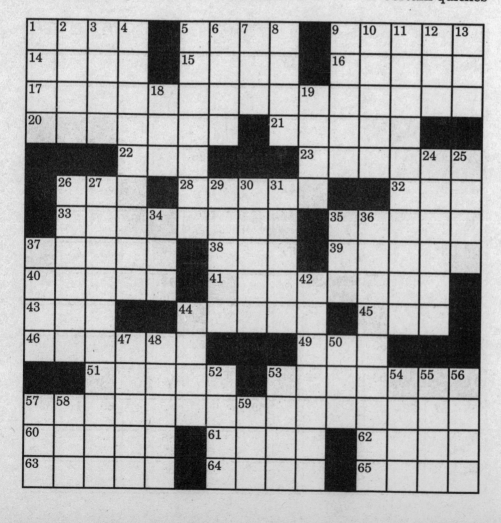

ACROSS

1. Tyrrhenian isle
6. Turbulent
10. Fuji flow
14. Steve or Mel
15. Against
16. Tucked in
17. Theme of this puzzle
20. "Runaround" girl of song
21. Canasta card
22. Geezers
23. "___ Hunt," adventure series
24. Vichy water
25. Eastwood film
34. She fell for Narcissus
35. Court statements
36. CSA member
37. Open to debate
38. La Scala's locale
39. Seed case
40. Printer's measures
41. Chips of film
42. On the summit
43. Vow segment
47. Ms. Gardner
48. Spike of note
49. Edible fungus
51. Antilles island
53. Near the fantail
56. Hedonist's creed
59. Instrument for Bream
60. Territory
61. Speak
62. Columbia gridder
63. Legion
64. Ziti sauce

DOWN

1. Gives a pink slip to
2. Expo manager
3. Ballet movement
4. Court enforcer
5. Conforming
6. Diminish
7. *Raiders...* hero
8. Some are JG
9. Bishop
10. Attlee's party
11. Keep in contact
12. Drs. Dolittle and Herriot
13. TV pitches
18. Uzbek sea
19. Lanes
23. Ear or eye follower
25. Macho ones
26. Image: prefix
27. Whoopi film
28. Mimicking
29. ___ ease (uncomfortable)
30. Below, to a bard
31. Estonian city
32. *Middlemarch* author
33. Actor Bellamy
38. Louvre lure
39. Interlaken river
41. Pearl fetcher
44. Solidify
45. Hamburg waterway
46. Join forces
49. Hawaiian isle
50. Hall-of-Fame QB Graham
51. Milk variety
52. With skill
53. Liberal follower
54. Worry
55. Neophyte
56. Cockney underworld?
57. NATO nation
58. Nice season

ACROSS

1. Pear variety
5. Sherpa encounter
9. Italian game
14. ___ about (circa)
15. Pull down
16. Barrow abode
17. Hawaiian bird
18. B ___ boy
19. Hogan's hazards
20. Working mother's stop
23. Journalist Lesley
24. Sandusky sight
25. Beauty Gardner
28. Spiritedness
31. Delved into
33. Mil. address
36. Intestinal section
39. Janet in D.C.
40. Ann Martin book series (with *The*)
44. Cathedral projection
45. French legislative body
46. Shaker Ann
47. Common herd
50. Attic walkway
52. "___ was saying…"
53. Too
56. Agave fiber
60. Early education
64. Humiliate
66. Flu symptom
67. Birth covering considered lucky
68. Lessened
69. Patrick Dennis' Auntie
70. Against
71. "Art for art's sake," e.g.
72. Piece of cake
73. Wall St. org.

DOWN

1. Stocks' mate
2. ___ a time
3. *War and Peace* girl
4. Yuletide scene
5. 2525, e.g.
6. Loosen
7. Fleeting moment
8. Deep-seated
9. A basic taste
10. Troll's kin
11. "Howdy Doody" clown
12. Beat pounder
13. Dawn deity
21. "…calm, ___ bright"
22. Puppy bite
26. Trial site
27. Sunburnt brick
29. Foreman's foe
30. Jersey cagers
32. Killer whale
33. Manila hemp
34. Irene of *Z*
35. Pigheaded
37. Shoshonean
38. Part of "YMCA"
41. However
42. Clavell's *King* ___
43. Unperturbed one
48. City on the Rio Grande
49. High rails
51. Alley item
54. Junctures
55. Hymn accompaniment
57. ___ degree (at all)
58. Bozos
59. JR's mom
61. Pre-owned
62. Arizona city
63. Dribble out
64. Letter trio
65. Ice-cream treat

ACROSS

1. Bass brass
5. Rice cakes
10. We, in Wiesbaden
13. M __ mouse
14. Lopsided
15. Japanese aborigine
16. Shopper's reminder
17. Salisbury steaks
19. Herbal-brew plant
21. Keaton and Lane
22. *A Man and a Woman* star
23. Sergio of directing fame
24. FDR's first Vice President
26. Trumpet fanfares
29. Ascot events
30. Craves
31. Snow, to Burns
32. Refuges of a sort
33. Judges' wear
34. MIT degrees
35. Japanese drama
36. Sample recordings
37. Glass ovens
38. "__ knows"
40. "Town Without Pity" singer
41. Pitcher's aid
42. Student of Masaccio
43. Walked
45. Kind of cheese
48. Light vintages
50. Poet Pound
51. Tanker weights
52. Remove with a solvent
53. Penny
54. A dog days mo.
55. Boca chaser
56. Otherwise

DOWN

1. Powder
2. American propaganda org.
3. Piscine hors d'oeuvre
4. Saint-Exupéry, et al.
5. Notebook, in Nice
6. __ *of Two Cities*
7. Rickey flavoring
8. Priest's duds
9. Collegians
10. Cutlet entrée
11. Anent
12. Actor Tamblyn
15. Capital of Guam
18. Violent protests
20. Married Mlles.
23. Bowlers' aisles
24. *Cum* __ *salis* (with a grain of salt)
25. Moses' aide
26. Small drum
27. Previn or Gide
28. Insolent
30. Part of "NOW"
33. Rex Reed, for one
34. Stage scenery item
36. From, in Barcelona
37. They meet in a kiss
39. Middays
40. Czech city, in Bonn
42. Give the __ (prove false)
43. Sp. miss
44. Biblical pronoun
45. Bolting device
46. Shore eagles
47. Estimate
49. Dockworkers union: abbr.

ACROSS

1. Four before E
5. Within an ___ of (close to)
8. Moviedom's horror street
11. Some are revolving
13. Licensed radio operator
14. Commonplace caviar
15. Snack with a hole
16. Exist
17. Cold or cream commencer
18. Title for Jacobi
19. First course in Kiev
21. Pentateuch book
24. Waiver for the first round
25. Biceps location
26. Japanese dramatic form
28. Mild oath
32. Force (through)
33. First course in Shreveport
36. Bar draw
37. Novgorod negative
39. Upon, to Yves
40. *Medea* actress Caldwell
41. Acorn's future
44. Smartly dressed
46. First course in Boston
50. TV's Peeples
51. Sass
52. French article
53. Little lizard
56. Humorist George
57. Soap substance
58. Patriot Allen
59. Daniel was thrown here
60. Little boy
61. Cellist Ma

DOWN

1. Append
2. Heckle
3. First course in Cannes
4. Celtic priest
5. Jezebel's husband
6. Chocolate substitute
7. Manicurist's abrasive
8. A Roberts
9. Lomond or Ness
10. Rendezvous
12. High-___ (nervous)
20. Take in, in a way
21. Merit
22. Medical photograph
23. Old French coin
27. ___ *Pinafore*
29. First course in Catalonia
30. Curative succulent
31. November game
34. Fella; guy
35. Florida produce
38. Remove an illegally parked car
42. Mature individual
43. Nairobi's land
45. Religious devotion
46. Clothed
47. Go under cover
48. Word on a shop door
49. Clarinet need
54. Ms. Medford
55. Lennon's lady

THE BIRDS OF SUMMER

ACROSS

1. "Pow!"
5. One of the Aleutians
9. Bible tower town
14. Roof lip
15. Blow your own horn
16. Where *Carmen* plays
17. Bird of east Pennsylvania
20. Small amount
21. Fateful date for Caesar
22. Balkan capital
23. Hied
24. Redactor's word
25. Athena
28. Work out with Foreman
29. Dandy preceder
32. Moslem ruler
33. Kim's hubby
34. Feeling yesterday's workout
35. Bird of south California
38. Singles and doubles
39. Unauthorized disclosure
40. Current fashion
41. Year: Sp.
42. German town
43. Tasks
44. Engrossed
45. Causing joy
46. Have high hopes
49. Author Ambler
50. Kind of trip
53. Bird of west Pennsylvania
56. Author Blixen
57. Roman Stoic
58. Melville opus
59. Getting on
60. Dash
61. Actor Billy

DOWN

1. Bawled
2. Gag response
3. Eager
4. Baseball's Ott
5. Puts up with
6. Cornered aloft
7. Bugle call
8. Groan of disgust
9. More like a skeleton
10. Not together
11. Carotene header
12. Ireland, to Yeats
13. Alençon product
18. Island group north of Sicily
19. Fasten
23. Winter transports
24. Mote
25. Turkish title
26. Fast, to bards
27. Slowly, to Solti
28. The Eight painter John
29. Wild card
30. Actress Worth
31. Repairs
33. Sales rep
34. Young haddock
36. Romeo, e.g.
37. Ionian isle
42. Exposing
43. Bow-tie type
44. Mature
45. Actress Scacchi
46. Another of the Aleutians
47. Catch (flies)
48. Actress Gilpin
49. Etc.'s cousin
50. Columnist Bombeck
51. Thug
52. Sioux
54. Perfect serve
55. 48-Down's role

ACROSS

1. Dried watercourse
5. Hold up
8. Ship's yard
12. Moran of "Happy Days"
13. Springsteen's birthplace
14. Computer plug-ins
15. Wherewithal for sundries
17. Concerning
18. Golden Horde member
19. Like nuts, at times
21. Math subj.
24. Poet's field
25. Cat's-paw
28. Argentine's agreement
30. Grist for a cyclotron
33. *Exodus* hero
34. Bar in Fort Knox
35. Movies' Myrna
36. Opposite of max.
37. 30-Across, for one
38. Court ace of the '70s
39. Sty dweller
41. Shorebird
43. Courtroom recorders
46. Bar folk: abbr.
50. Periods of time
51. Fireworks device
54. Staff officer
55. Japanese veggie
56. Ms. Macpherson
57. Misplaced
58. Catch (a thief)
59. Card combination

DOWN

1. Lamented lachrymosely
2. Part of a Met score
3. Drive in with force
4. Attica occupant
5. Kennel adjunct
6. Carbohydrate suffix
7. Serenades à la Lassie
8. Photographer's request
9. Some long-necked ducks
10. 160 square rods
11. *Reds* subject John
16. Boston hockey great
20. Landed
22. Ain't kin?
23. Gleason title role
25. Aswan sight
26. Site of the Tell legend
27. Silly fools
29. Certain ones
31. La la preceder
32. Bill of Saturday-morning TV
34. Venetian villain
38. National song
40. Beginning
42. Cold and damp
43. Circus performer
44. Quartet with an absentee
45. Whirled
47. Start to phone?
48. Holler
49. Iditarod racer
52. Mountain in Crete
53. Brit with social standing

PRIVATE PROPERTY

ACROSS

1. 200-milligram weight
6. Irritable
11. Sword beater?
14. Pedro's pal
15. Do a taxing job
16. Land unit
17. Senator's handout?
19. Singing syllable
20. Curve shape
21. Gunpowder ingredient
22. Trencherman
24. Tubs
25. Marathoner's necessity
26. Texas city
29. Camelot stable dwellers
31. Maine town
32. Paris pal
33. Church section
36. Cinema swine
37. Throw into the street
38. ___-pie (entirely)
39. Do a Child-ish chore
40. Exploit
41. 1995 Horse of the Year
42. Indigenous
44. Library tools
45. Soft shade
47. Guinea pig
48. Kitchen gadget
49. Crystalline stone
51. Bud's partner
54. Single's last words?
55. Baseball player's sweetie?
58. Corp. honcho
59. Talk from a soapbox
60. Twangy
61. AK native
62. Emulated Liz
63. Echidnalike

DOWN

1. Give a hoot
2. Hebrew prophet
3. Joshes
4. Wine's asset
5. Plains storm
6. Play groups
7. Rustic
8. Bakery emanation
9. RSVP part
10. Addison's partner
11. Singer's summons?
12. Was human
13. Approaches
18. Josip Broz
23. Nerve
24. Put on a pedestal
25. Sleepers features
26. Court shots
27. "I smell ___!"
28. Author's employee?
29. Look up?
30. Clock sound
32. Tel tailer
34. Mast or gaff
35. Some double features?
37. *Herr* Jannings
41. Carlsbad attractions
43. Craven's forte
44. Tzara's art
45. Diva Leontyne
46. Staff workers
47. Enciphered
49. Bite and bite
50. Italian noble family
51. Actress Virna
52. ___ even keel
53. Far from fair
56. It's all in your mine
57. Pool length

ACROSS

1. Mushrooms, for example
6. Blubber
9. Headliner Davis
12. Certain exams
13. *Printemps* month
14. Gardner of Hollywood
15. First name in a Vegas headline
17. Capitol figure: abbr.
18. Buddhist center in Japan
19. Farm unit
20. Rat Pack headliner
25. Addams' cousin
26. Musical compositions
30. Supplies
34. Lure
35. Two-deck card game
37. Shea player
38. Headlining yenta
42. Headliner Paul
45. *Arabian Nights* number
46. Headliner Zadora
47. Headlining group, The 5th ___
52. Sea raptor
53. George's brother
54. Author Calvino
55. Buck's better half
56. Late headliner Tormé
57. Flogged

DOWN

1. Opponent
2. Big planter
3. Harass
4. Former senator from Ohio
5. Major world faith
6. Daubs
7. Scull
8. Curb, for one
9. Painter Franz
10. Declare
11. Mantle
16. Lingerie buy
19. Med. school course
20. Harrow blade
21. Sundance's Place
22. Like ___ of bricks
23. Pound in at a slant
24. New England vacation stop
27. Weekly news magazine
28. Pete Sampras, at times
29. Adjusts (one's alarm)
31. Madhya Pradesh royalty
32. That, in Toledo
33. Terminus: abbr.
36. Zoologist's concern
39. European cervine critter
40. Ancient Greek dialect
41. Panorama
42. Emulated Rich Little
43. Actor Robert De ___
44. Citizen of cinema
47. Adjust a rheostat
48. Dander
49. Singer/songwriter Janis
50. *Corrida* accolade
51. Auction signal

ACROSS

1. Manger
5. *Metamorphoses* writer
9. Funnyman Sahl
13. Classic villain
14. Stack of chips
15. Gods' blood
17. With 55-Across, an opening-night comment
20. Ballpark figure
21. Concurrence
22. Give ___ chance
23. By means of
24. Social niche
27. With 41-Across, actress who reportedly made the comment
32. Letts, e.g.
33. Taboo
34. Reasonable
35. Ruin
36. Printer's need
37. Prod
38. Amorous look
39. Seasons, by the Seine
40. Carried on, as a war
41. See 27-Across
43. Where van Gogh painted
44. Cobbler's tool
45. Alfonso's queen
46. On land
50. Moves like a boa
55. See 17-Across
57. Dancer Cunningham
58. It beats ace high
59. Winged
60. Property paper
61. Geometry calculation
62. Actress Daly

DOWN

1. Refer to
2. Bowl shouts
3. "By the Time ___ to Phoenix"
4. Soprano Lucrezia
5. Narcotic
6. Outlook
7. Latin pronoun
8. Ruby of screen fame
9. Prayer book
10. Singer Phil
11. Korea's Syngman
12. Shredded
16. Soak (flax)
18. Discharges
19. Tar or salt
23. Roof sights
24. Crete's capital
25. Standish's stand-in
26. Baby bearer?
27. Hit the bottle
28. Customary
29. Sweater size
30. Chartres cherubs
31. Pay attention
32. Future tulip
33. Brazilian seaport
36. Runt's moniker
40. Fury
42. Did injury to
43. *Peer Gynt* character
45. Fictional Dinsmore
46. Bank feature: abbr.
47. Lean-to
48. Fabled loser
49. Tale starter
50. Luminary
51. Miami cagers
52. Hard to hold
53. Tatum's dad
54. Parched
56. Superfund org.

ACROSS

1. Home to Baylor U.
5. Chopin's beloved
9. Turner of history
12. Not care ___
13. Musical collection
14. *A Chorus Line* song
15. Zany one
17. ___ *a Cockeyed Wonder*
18. Loch of note
19. Emulate Gutenberg
21. Cut wood
24. Loquacious
25. Enthusiastic
26. Unwell
28. Sidekick
29. Chekhov of the theatre
30. To the stern
33. Moved quickly
35. ___ *patriae* (patriotism)
36. Hoglike mammals
38. Dame Kiri's métier
39. Omit in pronunciation
40. Envelope sealer
42. Hold a session
43. Roger Clemens' aim
48. Varnish ingredient
49. Low digits
50. First letter in code
51. ___ Wednesday
52. Fountain request
53. Bolshevik Trotsky

DOWN

1. Used to be
2. Arrow's trajectory
3. Flivver, for example
4. Unlocked
5. Is loudly lachrymose
6. Woeful response
7. Nothing
8. Small toothed cetacean
9. Nolan Ryan specialty
10. Regarding, once upon a time
11. Peevish
16. Celebrated at the altar
20. Campaigned for office
21. Fool
22. Clark's *Mogambo* costar
23. Greg Maddux error
24. Nincompoop
26. Echidna treats
27. Inhabitant: suffix
29. Takes into custody
31. In favor of
32. Refrain syllable
34. Give alms, e.g.
35. Charm
36. Noted Croatian-born inventor
37. Nom de plume
38. Furniture wood
40. Ricky's TV landlord
41. Leslie of the WNBA
44. As well
45. *Corrida* shout
46. Aircraft of sorts: abbr.
47. *The Joy Luck Club* author

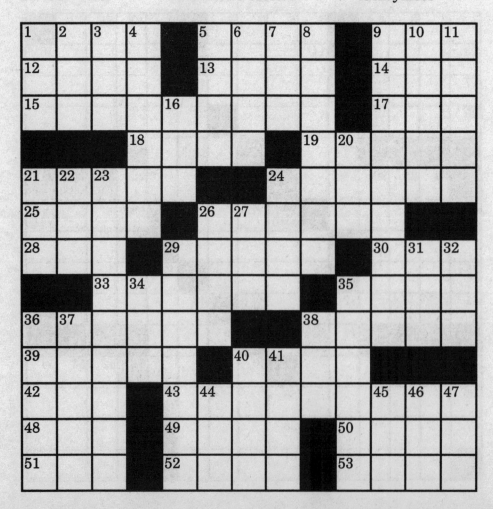

ACROSS

1. Power unit
5. Greek letter
10. Scrape roughly
14. On ___ with
15. Measuring the same
16. "...___ saw Elba"
17. Very alluring
18. Calms
20. Another Greek letter
21. Two-sided
22. Visit a bistro
23. Meddlesome youngsters
26. Throughway egress
27. Agreeably biting
29. Kin of PDQ
31. Gave info to (with "in")
32. Stealthily
35. Acapulco aunt
36. Bluesy
38. Former Mideast org.
40. Paper VIPs
43. Accomplished ones
45. Unruly groups
46. At which
48. Military rank, for short
50. ___ the neck
52. Glossy fabric
54. Peeves
55. Actress Arthur
58. Eight-oared galley
60. Schoolbook
61. Ait
62. In the future
63. Takeback
64. Exigency
65. Dries up
66. "The Heat ___" (Glenn Frey hit)

DOWN

1. Waisted bug
2. Cornelius and Zira
3. Football playmates
4. Stab
5. Dress shiner
6. 32 ounces
7. Remorse
8. West of Brooklyn
9. German epithet word
10. SOP complications
11. ___ *With a View*
12. Monopolize
13. Pub measure
19. Isaac's mother
21. Pair
24. Can. province
25. Hit bottom
27. %: abbr.
28. Nastase of tennis
30. Junior's room, often
32. Switch settings
33. Elizabeth's quilting parties?
34. O'Hara home
36. Watch pocket
37. Major or Minor constellation
39. Q–U filler
41. Obstructed
42. Copier need
43. TV sites
44. Limit: prefix
46. Closer to the target
47. Path followers
48. ___ célèbre
49. Start of a Dickens title
51. Holy sculpture
52. Geo. meas.
53. Guitarist Lofgren
56. Montreal fair
57. Lots
59. *Norma* ___
60. Angle starter

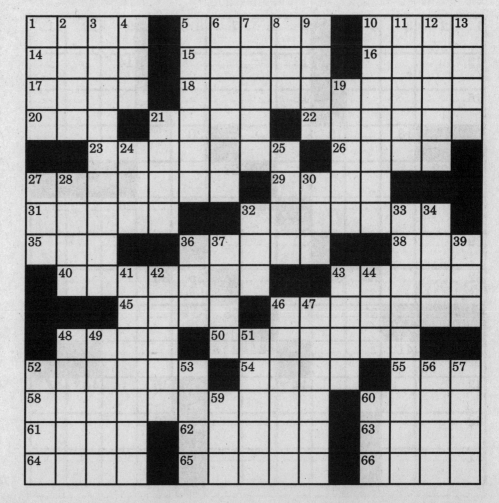

ACROSS

1. Lowdown
5. Golden follower
9. Burrows of Broadway
12. Uttered
13. ___ time (PDQ)
14. Cargo unit
15. Brutish fellow
16. Conclusive statement
18. Scatter here and there
20. Officiates at a track meet
21. Squealed (on)
23. Layer in the coop
24. Hebrew patriarch
25. Attentive
29. Sorority letter
30. Break a fast
31. Claire of *Ninotchka*
32. Street fixture
35. Ornamental floral bit
37. Land measure
38. Brutal individuals
39. Irritate by friction
42. Wide-awake
43. ID essential
45. West of Hollywood
48. "___ Got a Secret"
49. Tavern offerings
50. 1993 Kline film
51. Pod occupant
52. Moral lapses
53. Like a needle

DOWN

1. Bar opener
2. Play the harridan
3. Emergency service
4. Folk singer from Birmingham
5. Felt under the weather
6. Use the teeth
7. USNA graduate
8. Spoiled
9. Modern power source
10. Party pooper
11. They catch passes
17. Zephyr, for example
19. Pt. of "RV"
21. Rolling in dough
22. Having a pallid hue
23. Success on Broadway
25. Wrestling site
26. When "there was light"
27. Apartment rental
28. Falls off the pace
30. Vane direction: abbr.
33. Mississippi floater
34. The Garden, et al.
35. Get it
36. Ticker-tape event
38. Ask divine favor for
39. Cut hair
40. Wealthy individual
41. Lost, in a way
42. Grace concluder
44. Richard's *Goodbye Columbus* costar
46. Greeting from Caesar
47. ER art?

ACROSS

1. *Cherchez la* ___
6. Exclusive
10. Elbe tributary
14. Mountaineering tool
15. Call (a cab)
16. Zenith
17. Blazonry
19. Translucent silicate
20. Carpenter, for one
21. Flop
22. Blathered
24. *All Quiet on the Western Front* hero
27. Was troubled
28. Tick away
30. Small amphibians
33. The law, to Dickens
34. Happy tune
35. Talks a blue streak
37. Vietnam War movie
43. Cultured product
44. Incite
45. Compass point
48. Walden, e.g.
49. Picturesque
51. Preacher's place
53. Caches
55. "Frasier" radio personality
58. Wish undone
59. ___ polloi
62. Myanmar's locale
63. Top secret
66. Remainder
67. Pradesh royal
68. Flip-chart support
69. Fill to the gills
70. Ruth's sultanate
71. Patriot Silas

DOWN

1. Pay deduction inits.
2. MBA's class
3. Schmo
4. Become entangled
5. Mass transit?
6. Nuance
7. Get in a row?
8. Branch
9. Cinema roarer
10. Metrical feet
11. Bulbous bloom
12. Roast hosts
13. Double-checks the check
18. Do a slow burn
23. Iraqi port
25. Appropriately
26. Bounties
28. Shoemaker's helper
29. She plays Ling on TV
31. Had a hunch
32. Dervish's cap
35. Flabbergast
36. Gravelly waste
38. Mini-hog?
39. Swellhead's excess
40. African capital
41. Samuel's mentor
42. Gumshoe
45. Cages
46. Sartre classic
47. Sign up
49. Vinegary
50. Was in a regatta
52. Agenda
54. Doctor
56. Bear, to Pierre
57. Emulate a cavy
60. Receptive
61. Elba, e.g.
64. Genetic letters
65. Charlotte of TV

ACROSS

1. Ginnie in a portfolio
4. Swedish automaker
8. Shuttle yarn
12. Grill
13. Golden rule word
14. In fine fettle
15. Borscht belt favorite?
18. Muckraker Tarbell
19. Erich von Stroheim classic
20. Beatles album for cobblers?
25. Eurasian range
26. Reverence
27. Toady's response
30. Groundless
31. Groan producer
32. Godfather, to Brando
33. Math abbreviation
34. Pose
35. Southwest dwelling
36. Remington's rhythm section?
38. Bloodline
41. *¡Viva torero!*
42. Baker's favorite musical?
48. Profit prophet Greenspan
49. Irish Rose's lover
50. Street, of Rheims
51. Carry on
52. Use an atomizer
53. Aardvark's morsel

DOWN

1. Tatami, for example
2. Cigar fallout
3. Squeeze by (with "out")
4. Nappy materials
5. Close, to Coleridge
6. Shapiro or Clark: abbr.
7. Quagmire
8. Lost-one's query
9. Comfort
10. Arctic slab
11. Care for
16. Septuagint or Vulgate
17. The look of love?
20. Bring down
21. Pakistani language
22. Unguent
23. Brown in butter
24. Possess
27. Eastern discipline
28. Panache
29. Convey
31. Slapstick prop
32. Items in Ginsburg's closet
34. Betelgeuse, for one
35. Montana's topper
36. Evel deed
37. Heavyweight great from Lafayette
38. Way out there
39. Spicy Spanish stew
40. Colt of a different color
43. Broodmare
44. Diamond stat: abbr.
45. Time, to Sophia
46. One with a habit
47. Procure

ACROSS

1. Construction info
5. "___ Buddies"
10. Mediocre marks
14. Kyrgyzstan range
15. Ms. Astaire
16. Evaluate
17. Regions near the Arctic Circle
19. Italian noble family
20. Request
21. As early as, in Arles
22. Bloom's support
23. Adjectival suffix
25. Important person
27. Compensated
32. Lively dances
35. Aussie fools
36. Stared
38. Samovar
39. Kid
40. The end of France?
41. The Supremes, e.g.
42. Formicary dweller
43. Giant
44. Tendon
45. Come to pass
47. Cabal members
49. Sharpens
51. Title for Hopkins
52. Sorry sigh
54. Resort of a sort
56. Coated with leaf
61. Roll of cloth
62. Detroit burb
64. Soft cheese
65. Pyle or Els
66. Tra following
67. Jewish month
68. Intimidate
69. Salver

DOWN

1. Yemeni capital
2. Fall heavily
3. Role for Costner
4. Quote
5. Love song
6. Part of a harem
7. Thrill
8. Ancient
9. E-mail transmissions
10. Coal distillate
11. Sussex city
12. Major ending
13. Appear to be
18. Small increments
24. On the up and up
26. Vile
27. Indian VIP
28. TV's Verdugo
29. Site of a 1648 treaty
30. Play part
31. Carvey and Delany
33. Snoop
34. Deceives
37. Galvanizes
40. Outwitted in bridge
41. Actor Allen
43. Decimal base
44. Letter ornament
46. Kiosk paper
48. More exalted
50. Germ
52. Swedish group
53. Manor master
55. Family member
57. Merry tune
58. Pricey
59. Ms. Fitzgerald
60. June 6, 1944
63. Cravat

ACROSS

1. O'Neill shade providers
5. Old-age nest egg
8. Realizes fiscally
12. Standardbred's movement
13. Land of dreamers
14. Precinct
15. *All Creatures* ___
18. Monica's first name?
19. Dog star
20. Gerund concluder
22. Being, in Brittany
25. Print
31. Alpine flower?
32. Gramm or Christie
33. Jailbird
34. Ethical concerns
39. Black, to Balzac
40. Trifling amount
41. Related to disco dancers
44. Noted Broadway slob
48. Landscapist's concern
52. Blackguardly
53. Day of the wk.
54. "By Jove!"
55. Naysay
56. Canton closer
57. Rookie's recording

DOWN

1. Quiche ingredients
2. Zhivago's beloved
3. Way of carrying oneself
4. Reception interference
5. ___ tizzy
6. Columnist Barrett
7. Tacks (onto)
8. Broadway Joe
9. A time to remember
10. Aviv lead-in
11. Mineo of the silver screen
16. Transport for Patton
17. Worry over time
21. Festal pomp
23. Loaded, Spanish-style
24. William's alma mater
25. Lawyer's hangout?
26. Reclined
27. Golden Fleece carrier
28. *Oui* alternative
29. Casual clothes
30. Chang's other half?
35. To a great extent
36. Pony pace
37. Goes a-courting
38. Felt the pressures of time
42. Total attendance
43. Burden
45. *La ___ aux Folles*
46. Genesis gent
47. Go back to square one
48. Was in the vanguard
49. Product ender
50. Cotton cleaner
51. Ruby of *The Stand*

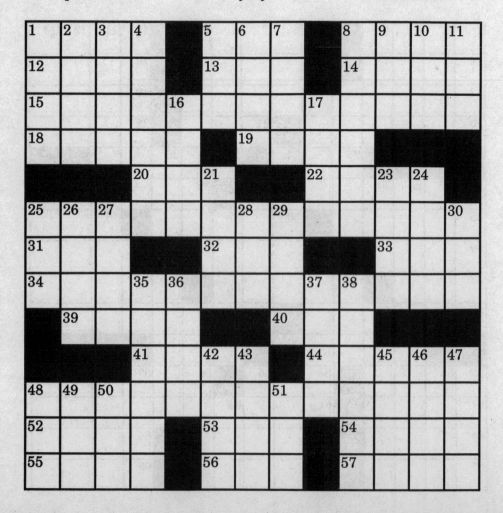

ACROSS

1. Parisian flatfoot
5. Put up with
10. Rhode Island player
13. Confute
15. Shire or Morgan
16. Verb-forming suffix
17. English nurse
19. Hound for cash
20. Curtain tufts
21. Dawdles
23. Kind of cake or meal
24. Jazz pianist Chick
25. Fr. miracle worker
32. Intense pain
33. "Mine!" said Fifi
34. Landon who lost in '36
37. Embellish
38. Built rapidly, as a tab
40. Phone
41. Newt
42. Sculptor's creation
43. *Picnic* lass
44. Late Nobelist
47. Bower
50. Shore eagle
51. Emulated a sibyl
54. Winter wear
59. Waterfront union: abbr.
60. American philanthropist
62. Gun (the engine)
63. Sanctuary
64. Tadpole, e.g.
65. Devon river
66. Fad
67. Wampum

DOWN

1. Guitar bar
2. Helen's mother
3. Nile denizen
4. Skips class
5. Mount in the Cascades
6. "Mazel ___!"
7. Turgenev's hometown
8. Ibsen's home
9. Corpus chaser
10. Contract addendum
11. Blue hue
12. Neighbor of Dorado
14. Physicist's formulation
18. Sept
22. Reinforced shoe part
25. Wise one
26. Relief initials?
27. Dash out
28. Wrap up
29. *Divina commedia* author
30. Flightless avian
31. Outshine
34. ___-de-camp
35. Tosses marbles
36. Market variety
38. Worn track
39. Grill dust
40. ___ es Salaam
42. Russian dish
43. Telepathy preceder
44. Skier Tommy
45. Send back to jail
46. Chicago paper, briefly
47. Blazing
48. Posh watch
49. Atlanta player
52. With wings
53. Surfer's conveyance
55. Links bunker
56. French I word
57. Bright star
58. Glitch
61. Stimpy's pal

ACROSS

1. ___ impasse
5. Crèche threesome
9. Elation
12. Baby's first word, perhaps
13. ___ arms (ready to fight)
14. Stone or Iron
15. Verbose
17. Ancient god of heaven and earth
18. Sabrina, for one
19. Nonconformist
21. Carried on (a campaign)
24. Set by for later
25. General Bradley
26. Quibbled
30. Kids' card game
31. Misaddressed piece of mail
32. Chemical ending
33. Cried like a ghoul
35. Short cut
36. Exhort
37. Leaves at the library
38. Lively dance
40. Banana coating
42. In history
43. Verbose
48. Neighbor of Arg.
49. Canal of song
50. "I Dream of Jeannie" star
51. Article, in Normandy
52. Accomplishment
53. Carries out

DOWN

1. Equipment for the Stones
2. Mariner
3. Ecclesiastical chalice
4. Be verbose
5. Stubborn individual
6. Symbol of neatness
7. Whitney invention
8. He doesn't appreciate
9. Verbose
10. Arch with a point
11. Outcry
16. Turner of network fame
20. The night before Christmas
21. Slays 'em
22. Oriental servant
23. Verbose
24. Went down a chute
26. Medieval weapon
27. Woodchopper's need
28. Chanteuse Adams
29. Sheriff's aides: abbr.
31. Canceled out
34. Get under one's skin
35. Like most pretzels
37. Fabled princess tester
38. Artist Gauguin
39. Hideous monster
40. Ballet position
41. ___ out a living (got by)
44. Contemporary art?
45. Altar sentence
46. Neckline shape
47. USNA grad's rank

ACROSS

1. Posts
6. Comedian Wilson
10. ___ *Off Place*, 1993 Disney film
14. 1978 Nobel laureate
15. Letterman rival
16. Sit
17. Fruity drink
19. Galileo's hometown
20. Lively wit
21. Of greater height
23. Edit
26. Takes five
27. Wandering Polo
31. Seeps
33. The Beehive State
34. Regional weather
36. Upon
40. Muscle condition
41. Stair part
42. Prod
43. Eastern VIP
44. Dispatch boat
45. Shout out
46. Cordage fiber
48. Thrust back
49. "Law & Order" types: abbr.
52. Took the Mustang
55. Werther's creator
57. Torment
61. Culture medium
62. Fruity burlesque item
66. Domesticated
67. Barbra's 1968 costar
68. Plains home
69. Being: Latin
70. Diamond count
71. Bonus

DOWN

1. Food additive, for short
2. Swiss river
3. Ms. Lupino, et al.
4. Northern European
5. Sound system
6. Woodwind
7. Fragrant garland
8. Business abbr.
9. Keats or Shelley
10. Fruity side
11. Prevents
12. Valuable item
13. Brings up
18. Conrad's Lord
22. Exist
24. More clamorous
25. Stadium tops
27. Silent
28. Bit that matters?
29. Indian royalty
30. Fruity part of a Washington legend
32. Real nowhere man
34. Study at the eleventh hour
35. Very mad
37. Snare
38. Sly look
39. Mell lead-in
47. Tray type
48. Evaluate again
49. Marble rock
50. Latin garb
51. Reds and Blues
53. Major airport
54. Moving vehicle
56. Bard's black
58. Peak
59. Virgo's mo.
60. Prophet
63. A Dolenz
64. Bobbsey twin
65. Pastoral spot

ACROSS

1. Crony
4. Advisor to Balaam
7. Computer-store customer
11. Scheherazade's Baba
12. Bakery grouping
14. Fountain of jazz
15. Country star Davis
16. Tourist mecca in India
17. Australian mine find
18. With aplomb
21. Antelope cousins
22. In the manner of
23. *Beowulf*, for example
25. Hellion
26. Bath of England, e.g.
29. Disinterested
33. Human end?
34. With peaked pallor
35. Rather and Fogelberg
36. Alley roamer
37. Stadium level
39. Happy-go-lucky
44. Say with conviction
45. Macpherson of *Sirens*
46. A lyrical Gershwin
48. French artist Lalique
49. 21-Across, for example
50. Pinch
51. Calls it a wrap
52. Soon-to-be alums: abbr.
53. Command for Dobbin

DOWN

1. A Shriver
2. King of stand up
3. Black sweet
4. Briskly
5. Longs (for)
6. Antivenins
7. *Once ___ Time*, Cary Grant film
8. Celtic clan subdivision
9. Inclusive phrase: abbr.
10. Look to for support (with "on")
13. Deli purchase
19. Arrow feature
20. They cover most of Switzerland
23. Wallach of film fame
24. Mexican poet Octavio
25. Author Fleming
26. Traumatizing for life
27. Skillet
28. Hirt and Jolson
30. GI miscreant
31. Stopped up, in a way
32. Brainstorm
36. Gets worn down
37. He ran with Harrison
38. Baking specialists?
39. Buck the odds
40. Like two or four
41. Sell
42. Pub round
43. View from Ashtabula
47. Copy humorously

SAYS ZOO?

ACROSS

1. Section of Tel Aviv
6. *Inter* —
10. At the summit of
14. Egg-shaped
15. Bando and Mineo
16. Elegance
17. Deer, to a hunter?
20. Govt. agency
21. On the left side
22. Quantity
23. Edberg of tennis
25. Magnon header
26. Use polar transport?
33. Wild cat
36. Bridge sweep
37. Present, as a case
38. Flop or flip
40. Wrath
41. *Casablanca* actor
42. Time being
43. R.I. neighbor
45. Onetime Berlin sight
46. Wildebeest calf?
49. Portable bed
50. Iberian city
54. Mars, e.g.
58. Actor Rickman
60. Lea lady
61. Memoirs of a doe?
64. Role for Shirley
65. Pleasure
66. Relaxed
67. Shoe form
68. Flair
69. Like some rural roads

DOWN

1. Actress Glynis
2. Salt's yell
3. Coerce
4. In shape
5. Hebrew word for God
6. Movie terrier
7. Cowardly Lion player
8. Le Havre holm
9. Eritrea's capital
10. Sax range
11. Nobel-winning bishop
12. They get the yoke
13. Forward
18. Parries
19. Sans ethics
24. Composer César Auguste
25. Join firmly
27. Bring out
28. Peer
29. Earthy tones
30. Jumna River town
31. Sneer
32. Hull part
33. One-horse sleigh
34. Fairy-tale word
35. Computer list
39. Winter auto need
44. Actor Lloyd
47. Mental decline
48. Actress Debra
51. Critter
52. Young hooter
53. Indigent
54. Marlo's mate
55. Zhivago's love
56. *A Farewell to* —
57. Nifty
58. On the briny
59. Legal claim
62. Poorly
63. Greek letter

Rearrange the letters of each ACROSS answer into a new word before entering it in the puzzle grid.

ACROSS

1. Cabbage cousin
5. Female deer
8. Kissers
12. Actual
13. Osiris or Apollo
14. Art ___ (1920s style)
15. Scalene, for example
17. Wander
18. Glacial deposit
19. Spud
20. Olympic skater Jansen
21. Shade
23. Horse color
25. Harvests alfalfa
26. Once around the track
29. Disperse
31. Laud
33. Bath place
34. Beginning of Durante's theme song
36. Step ___ (hurry)
37. Fires
38. Writer Anaïs
39. Bamboozle
42. Shore
46. Aromatic spice
47. Fixing a tire
48. Clue
49. Afternoon social
50. "Thanks ___"
51. Proboscis
52. Mystery writer Josephine
53. Prophet

DOWN

1. Shakespearean royal
2. Woody's offspring
3. Capital of Nepal
4. King John's mother
5. Norse deity
6. Grant beneficiaries
7. It gets the yolk
8. Derision
9. Lawrence opus, *Women in* ___
10. Cartoon light bulb
11. Chic and jaunty
16. Get ___ of (scrap)
19. Some Christmas presents
22. Comparison word
23. Police call: abbr.
24. Informer
25. "___ silly question..."
26. Pointed formation
27. Columnist Buchwald
28. Summer zodiac sign
30. Apiece
32. Substance on Brett's bat
35. Put down on paper
37. Part of a movie
38. Somewhat: suffix
39. Makes dainty doilies
40. She faded away to nothing
41. Ex-dictator Idi
43. Understanding words, "___ it!"
44. Fill completely
45. Oral-verse collection
47. Vote from the floor

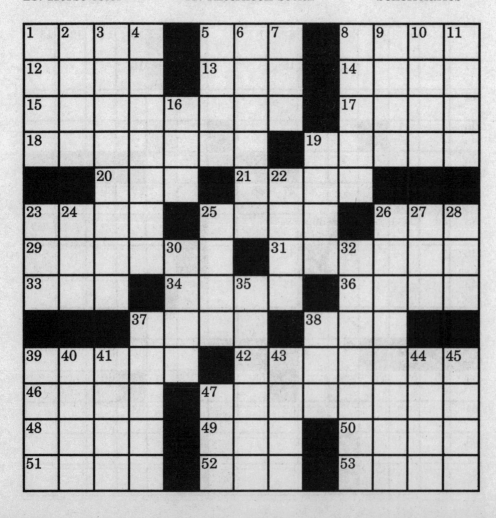

ACROSS

1. Thinker Blaise
7. Bistro's kin
11. Saturn's mate
14. S. American rodent
15. Plains people
16. Symbol of one's job
17. Actor Mickey
18. "Golly, that man is bent over," said Tom ___
20. Saddle plate
22. *Hud* star
23. "The chimney is clogged," said Tom ___
26. Decorous
28. Tennis shot
29. Peruvian coin
30. Lingered anxiously
31. Exploited
33. "___ of wealth and taste," Jagger lyric
35. "I've just run over my father," said Tom ___
40. Leavenings
41. Brown
43. 1962 World's Fair site
46. Common contraction
49. Reverence
50. Revolt
51. "The thermostat is set too high," said Tom ___
53. Keats product
54. Traumatized
56. "I just love sleeping outdoors," said Tom ___
58. Of a modern spiritual movement
62. TV science guy
63. Showy trinket
64. Slurs over
65. Print measures
66. Yoked ones
67. Generator

DOWN

1. Links score
2. Before now
3. Old French coin
4. Hex
5. Chet or Eileen
6. "You ___ me, Blanche"
7. Comic Bill
8. Leaf-cutting ant
9. Golf group
10. Mental power
11. "Goodness!"
12. Sense of taste
13. Fashioned
19. Slight hollows
21. Oval
23. Winter woe
24. Was an also-ran
25. Above: German
27. Author Hunter
30. More severe
32. Dawn to dusk
34. Bathroom staple
36. Seines, e.g.
37. Retail extra
38. Soft metal
39. Small sailboat
42. Spanish king
43. Lying face upward
44. Name source
45. Mountain crests
47. Merited
48. Stern
51. Papa of music
52. A Booth
55. Hint
57. ___ Dinh Diem
59. Nabokov novel
60. Rare rock
61. Madrid pronoun

ACROSS

1. Long in the tooth
4. Seth's boy
8. Talented; skillful
12. Court
13. Japanese statesman Hideki
14. Canadian Indian
15. Awards affair, perhaps
17. Old Spanish coin
18. Dutch painter Frans
19. Campus bigwigs
20. The Parthenon is here
23. Peril
24. Poetic grazing grounds
25. Romaine
26. To's mate
29. Nosher's network
33. Butt bit
34. Rustic stopover
35. Small landmass
36. Angel's aura
38. Tip-off participant
40. Words from Stein
42. Crosspiece
43. Show displeasure
44. Prepare for market, in a way
48. Threat word
49. Dust Bowl fleer
50. Dos Passos opus
51. Stag
52. Theoretical jury member
53. Hot off the press

DOWN

1. Sage bird
2. Slugger Gehrig
3. An Everly brother
4. Hawke of film
5. Carols
6. Spanish eyes
7. Beau or Jeff, to Lloyd
8. Land measures
9. Meal at Tiffany's?
10. Depend (upon)
11. Slippery swimmers
16. Box for one's hopes?
19. Record
20. Opening letter, in code
21. Tiffin followers
22. Lutèce it ain't
23. Bard McKuen
25. Prisoner, briefly
27. Irritate
28. Unique individual
30. Arrange alphabetically, e.g.
31. Lennon's love
32. See 10-Down
37. Daisy's relative
38. Shrewd maneuver
39. Sign up for
40. Parroted
41. Actor's plum
42. Leaf collector
44. Beau Brummell, for one
45. Woman with a habit
46. Employ
47. Handle like a lout

ACROSS

1. Simoleon
5. 1977 U.S. Open champ
10. Tell all
14. Eugene O'Neill's daughter
15. Defeatist's words
16. Greased
17. Racehorse, slangily
18. Backbone
19. Straight up, at a bar
20. Get some Z's
22. With praise
24. Get-up-and-go
26. Like
27. Buddy, briefly
29. Novelist Shute
31. Tiny insect
34. Draw a bead on
35. Simper
36. Organ features
38. Pirouette
40. *Same Time, Next Year* playwright
42. Night shade
43. Lady of Spain
45. Traditional teachings
47. "___ Lazy River"
48. Actress Talbot
49. Make a choice
50. Means of support
51. Syria, once upon a time
53. Nick name?
55. Word for word
59. Put two and two together
62. N.Y. tribe
63. Excuse

65. Call one's bluff
66. Pianist Petri
67. Permitted
68. ___ now (from here on)
69. Fixed routine
70. Eucalyptus lover
71. Concluding

DOWN

1. Real-life police show
2. Cuckoo bird?
3. In the year of the Lord
4. Urban VIP
5. Conversely
6. Berlin pronoun
7. Secular
8. High-school memento
9. Stops up
10. Authentic
11. Place, in Paris
12. "When I was ___"
13. Computer unit
21. Vigor
23. Green fruit
25. Malevolent
27. Fish in a dish
28. Age
30. Total
32. Clean slate
33. Marry sub rosa
36. For each person
37. Hindrance

39. Mark well
41. Bucks' mates
44. Avis lead-in
46. Sicilian peak
49. Charlie's brother
52. Give ___ (speechify)
54. Sea-surge related
55. Swerve
56. Therefore
57. Wild time
58. Isinglass
60. Amorous archer
61. Dexterous
64. Puppeteer Baird

ACROSS

1. Xiamen, once
5. Larson cartoon, "The ___ Side"
8. Like Superman near Kryptonite
12. PBS show
13. "Gotcha!"
14. Ms. la Douce
15. A k a Mike Connors
18. Part of "HRH"
19. Susan of "L.A. Law"
20. Chaps
21. Digital watch device
23. Howl at the moon
24. Tunisian port
26. *Little ___ of Horrors*
28. Creek
31. A k a Eve Arden
34. As well as
35. In case
36. Acorns' futures
37. Highland hat
38. Peter, Paul and Mary: abbr.
39. *Batman* villain
42. Corrode
44. Took a load off
47. A k a Sandra Dee
50. Actress Rowlands
51. Time past
52. Cartoonist Peter
53. Any minute now
54. Church seat
55. Cries of surprise

DOWN

1. Egyptian symbol
2. Additional
3. Not by sea
4. Run off at the mouth
5. Hack rider
6. Gob's greeting
7. The old college cry
8. Similar to port
9. Gray of "Silver Spoons"
10. Latin I word
11. Jayhawker's state: abbr.
16. Byrnes of TV
17. Christian love feast
22. 111, Roman-style
23. Pugilistic matchup
24. Vast lunar expanse
25. Joyful amusement
26. Appear
27. Main offices: abbr.
28. Calm
29. Squid squirt
30. Beast of burden
32. *Nutcracker Suite* girl
33. Polka chaser
37. Man from Laredo
38. Metro stop: abbr.
39. Ragged tears
40. Dairy-case purchase
41. Atlantic City game
42. Lip
43. "Pretty maids all in ___"
45. Bane of adolescents
46. Ring decisions
48. Kindergarten rest
49. Sharp turn

ACROSS

1. The Great Compromiser
5. Part of "GATT"
10. Verne hero
14. Carson's replacement
15. Breeder's Cup events
16. Old Mogul capital
17. Sherlock Holmes' debut
20. Director Craven
21. Highest rating
22. Maintain
23. Wildebeests
24. Very, in Vichy
25. Walk proudly
27. Nicknames
28. Hip network
31. St. John's-bread
32. Grain elevator
33. Positive
34. Crossword editor's complaint?
37. Fully developed
38. Deserve
39. Observes
40. Network initials
41. Andre's court rival
42. Author Lessing
43. Secrete
44. Swiss river
45. Historic county of Scotland
48. Boffo Moffo
49. Jeer
52. Onetime land of the Giants
55. Romanov ruler
56. Room
57. Vicinity
58. Coarse bristle
59. Less loco
60. Trust

DOWN

1. Scratch
2. —— majesty
3. Aardvark's staple
4. Uncle Sam's desire
5. Audition
6. Downpours
7. Teen problem
8. Moines header
9. French appetizer
10. Scottish scones
11. Eye a thigh
12. Diver Louganis
13. Modern scandal suffix
18. Budapest's river
19. Falstaff favorites
23. Copse kin
24. Eagle gripper
25. Sir, to Sabu
26. Snares
27. Animal in a French zoo
28. More than two: prefix
29. Aligns
30. Some necklines
31. Round: prefix
32. Condition
33. Goal, for one
35. Gratuitous
36. Arctic attire
41. Boring person
42. Alvin Ailey, e.g.
43. Libra neighbor
44. "What's —— girl like you…"
45. N.T. book
46. Demolish, in Devon
47. Midge
48. —— impasse
49. Unadorned
50. Oka port
51. Slangy assent
53. Upscale gym
54. Face value

ACROSS

1. Gas-station fixture
5. Business letter abbr.
8. Dusting powder
12. John Glenn's bailiwick
13. Old card game
14. Dairy-case item
15. Tumbler's move
16. Line lead-in
17. Done
18. All or most
21. Years and years
22. Singer Sayer
23. Brahman, for one
26. Hibernation times
30. Unrefined stuff
31. Strawberry's lid
32. Belly
33. Maker
36. Like some trendy pants
38. Tuck's partner
39. Highland head warmer
40. Plays the clown
47. Sinister
48. Wally of "Underdog" fame
49. Huron neighbor
50. Rational
51. Malt drink
52. Hotel checkout item
53. "Too bad!"
54. RB's scores
55. Bewildered

DOWN

1. Fortified red wine
2. "Oops!"
3. Distance for Bannister
4. Took a straw vote
5. John who sang "Daniel"
6. Palindromic time
7. Yellow marsh bloom
8. ___ to handle
9. Middle name in Menlo Park
10. Lecher's look
11. Essence
19. Promissory note
20. D.C. VIP
23. Present, to Pliny
24. Sale-item notation: abbr.
25. Society-page word
26. Onetime Cabinet department
27. Did it come first?
28. Toupee
29. Porcine home
31. Me-tooer
34. Leg joints
35. Reason for overtime
36. Tended locale
37. One-cell organism
39. One sure thing
40. Southwest outcropping
41. Racetrack shape
42. One of Columbus' trio
43. Auctioneer's word
44. *Trinity* novelist
45. River through Khartoum
46. Crème–crème link

ACROSS

1. Guilt ___ (feeling of self-reproach)
5. Radio jock Howard
10. Butts
14. General's helper
15. Fortune-telling deck
16. N.Y. native
17. Spotless
20. Sri Lanka's major export
21. New Testament book
22. Doesn't have
23. Lake fish
24. Quilt filler
26. Mounts for Lawrence
29. Perry's maker
30. Sharkey's rank: abbr.
33. Sheltered
34. TV studio sign
35. Abner's epithet
36. Age of the flappers
40. Jog
41. Loud alarm
42. Fairy-tale starter
43. Gridiron divs.
44. Maple genus
45. Oral
47. Fortas and Vigoda
48. Encounter
49. Birdie beater
52. Eye drop
53. Sellout sign
56. Basic teacher
60. Actress Gershon
61. Trap
62. Roof lip
63. *The Big* ___
64. Judean king
65. Needle holes

DOWN

1. Diplomacy
2. Get one's dander up
3. Concept
4. Soup legume
5. Library shelving
6. Take a bite of
7. Noted times
8. Propel a shell
9. To the ___ degree
10. Bowling button
11. Johnson of "Laugh-In"
12. Not pungent
13. Matches, as a bet
18. Brad
19. Student doc
23. Ibsen's Gynt
24. Strength
25. "It's a sin to tell ___"
26. Tote
27. Vocally
28. Financial resources
29. PC key
30. Hoosegow
31. Rook or bishop
32. Comic Ole
34. Monsters
37. Actress Sanford
38. Delicate
39. Play a horn
45. Scorched
46. Vermont resort
47. Put to rest
48. Montreal underground
49. Border
50. Diva's solo
51. Cotton-processing machines
52. Autocrat
53. Stick around
54. Wander
55. Raw rocks
57. Mr. Kabibble
58. Compass point
59. Fair grade

ACROSS

1. Basinger's Baldwin
5. Baba of lore
8. Hoodlum
12. Trevi tender
13. Golfer Hogan
14. Seine tributary
15. Boston's nickname
17. London architect
18. Sunday talk: abbr.
19. Nobelist Hemingway
21. Fashionable
24. Rubbernecks
26. Passed into law
28. Sandal strap
32. River in Siberia
33. Beetle
35. Billy of rock 'n' roll
36. Ramble (through)
38. Breathe
40. Most blanched
42. Fabray, familiarly
43. Snuggle
46. Western alliance initials
48. Sonja Henie's hometown
49. Burg boundary
54. Get burned up
55. Bauxite or galena
56. Baker's essential
57. Chopped
58. Say okay tacitly
59. Unit of PC data

DOWN

1. Mass attire
2. Illusion, of sorts
3. Period to remember
4. Lets go
5. Cut short
6. Alcindor or Ayres
7. Hidden
8. USS *Burg*?
9. Engage for a wage
10. Applies
11. Well-mannered fellow
16. Rorschach, for one
20. Out to pasture: abbr.
21. Dissolve
22. Remarkable person
23. Comic Bill, a k a Jose Jimenez
25. Place on a pedestal
27. Burg at an army base
29. Norse deity
30. *A Doll's House* heroine
31. Singer Campbell
34. Spread more seed
37. Crony
39. Cartoonist Lee
41. Indicate awareness
43. Snack
44. Lucrezia Borgia's second husband
45. Large number
47. Unkempt individual
50. Gold, in Granada
51. Wall climber
52. Clear as profit
53. Compass dir.

ACROSS

1. Minimum
6. Chinese fraternity
10. Travel trippingly
14. Rosie competitor
15. Roman route
16. Mandlikova of tennis
17. Column projection
18. Describing a *dama* of means
19. Makes a blunder
20. Basil Rathbone's *The Adventures of* ___
23. Noted Chairman
24. Gloomy
25. Summer cooler
26. WNW opposite
29. Undiluted
32. Drs.
34. Hepburn Broadway role
36. Cougar
38. Rustic hotel
42. Eddie Hodges' *The Adventures of* ___
45. *Turandot*, e.g.
46. Therefore, to Titus
47. Sch.
48. Hubbub
50. Hindu mystic
52. Visitors from afar: abbr.
53. Pie ___ mode
56. Taper off
58. I, to Claudius
60. Dan O'Herlihy's *Adventures of* ___
66. Fashion house
67. Penn. port
68. Ghana port
70. Wagner goddess
71. ___ *Fein*
72. Brazil port
73. Was
74. Tormé's forte
75. Got up

DOWN

1. Madrid article
2. Heroic poem
3. St. Louis sight
4. Oregon city
5. Beat ___ (escape blame)
6. Amateur, in London
7. Of hearing
8. Sites for ties
9. Ordained Billy
10. Author Silverstein
11. Fate
12. "The Lady ___"
13. Totally old
21. Jeweler's aid
22. In a weird way
26. Reverberate
27. Meal starter
28. "___ homo!"
30. Hayseed
31. Polishing material
33. Davenport
35. Gumbo veggie
37. Jason's craft
39. Casino cubes
40. Wee pest
41. Remnants
43. Afflicted
44. Aviator's "OK"
49. Fixate
51. Williams title creature
53. Egyptian measure
54. Orléans river
55. Domicile
57. Acid variety
59. March handout
61. Qum's land
62. Spanish lass
63. Lincoln coin
64. Number prefix
65. Generations
69. Pub order

ACROSS

1. Hardwood source
4. Beau's brother
8. Molt
12. Land measurement
13. Jump for Kerrigan
14. In excellent health
15. Christmas evergreen
16. Stubborn cuss
17. Woody's scion
18. Kildare's mentor
21. Fisherman's item
22. French holm
23. "___ boy!"
26. Yoko of music
27. Oriental sauce
30. Sellers role in a Kubrick classic
34. Spruce juice
35. Meritorious pilot
36. With 33-Down, *Shane* star
37. Barbecue residue
38. Total up
40. Earp's *Tombstone* partner
45. Engrossed
46. Bring down
47. He had a salty wife
49. Medley
50. Egg (on)
51. Ripen
52. Roe
53. Thrill to the max
54. Rocker Vicious

DOWN

1. Fellow with two left feet
2. Dry, plus
3. *Tea and Sympathy* star
4. Farr of "M*A*S*H"
5. Be joyful
6. Took a tumble
7. On the run from
8. Contour
9. Rhodes of "Daktari"
10. Paris pronoun
11. ___ *volente*
19. Pesky insect
20. Wild plumlike fruit
23. Personals, for example
24. Refrain starter
25. Cookbook abbreviation
26. Loneliest number?
27. Helios, in Latium
28. Eggs
29. Japanese currency
31. Allergic reaction
32. ___ *Line* (Broadway hit)
33. See 36-Across
37. Cattle-call attendee
38. Adjust, as tires
39. Had an evening meal
40. Influential Carnegie
41. Ronny Howard role
42. Spinner, for one
43. Word of lamentation
44. Baseball's Berra
45. Stewart of music
48. Kennedy on the Hill

ACROSS

1. Astonish
6. Start of a birth announcement
10. Penultimate Greek letter
13. Walked to and fro
14. ___ parle français (Montreal shop sign)
15. Brit's sweetie
16. Words of approximation
18. Actress Mary
19. Riga citizen
20. "...partridge in ___ tree"
21. Small snakes
22. Compass pt.
23. Meager
24. Steelers' org.
25. Morse-code sounds
26. Was on the bench
29. ___-Penh, Cambodia
31. Denominations
34. Employ
35. Replay technique, for short
36. Outer: prefix
37. Wasted
39. Bleed
40. Crow's places
42. Actress Marion
43. Fish hawk
45. Bible pronoun
47. Foxy
48. Runs away for love
51. Nev. neighbor
54. Papal name
55. Quiet times
56. Tender
57. Some NFLers
58. The finest
60. French article
61. Needle cases
62. Mythical trio
63. Draft letters
64. Being: Lat.
65. Egg-shaped

DOWN

1. Student's offering
2. Virile ones
3. Grave
4. Piquancy
5. Nigerian tribe
6. More aloof
7. Louise and Turner
8. Most tart
9. Reply: abbr.
10. Knickers
11. Excesses
12. Currier's partner
14. Deadlocks
17. Absorbed
21. Grasshopper's fabled antithesis
23. Singer Nina
25. Lisbon title
27. Texas team
28. Actor Knight
29. +++++
30. Perplexes
32. Outside: abbr.
33. Government contract word
35. Good sign for angels
38. Debtor's letters
41. Peepholes
44. Found chasers
46. Dame Myra
49. Wolf constellation
50. Stan's mate
51. Short surplice
52. Stop, on a rue
53. Rental contract
54. Asset
56. Eastern European
58. Born
59. Eerie sighting

ACROSS

1. Element of reality
5. Annoying one
9. Attention getter
12. Composer Stravinsky
13. Fabled man-eater
14. Fury
15. *Nautilus* captain
16. Self-obsession
18. Castle defenses
20. Be half the battery
21. Cowboy gear
23. Pluto or Poseidon
24. Campaigned for office
25. Point in the Arctic
28. Word in a syllogism
32. *Same Time, Next Year* costar
34. He's central to this puzzle?
35. In a sec
36. Sound from a cannon
37. Small bit
39. ___ de tête
40. Behave
42. Suspicious
44. Goddess of the moon
47. "Suddenly ___"
49. Poor Richard's book
51. Disturbance
54. ___ *Te Ching*
55. Skin-cream ingredient
56. Yearn (for)
57. Pro votes
58. Congressional output
59. Con game

DOWN

1. Fiver
2. Lifetime
3. Schwarzenegger flick of 1985
4. Military subdivision
5. Rhymester
6. Coop harvest
7. Good sign for a show
8. Beat
9. Clue
10. Comic actor Idle
11. Affirmative, casually
17. Adjutants
19. Cleopatra's bane
21. Zodiac crustacean
22. Iconic headwear
23. Fellow
26. Leave out
27. ___-tze, author of 54-Across
29. Like Valentine's Day
30. Prod
31. Merely
33. Iowa religious community
38. Pack animal
41. Love or Erie
43. Chest closings
44. Computer input
45. "Now ___ me down..."
46. Eighth-century Hebrew prophet
47. Coal transport
48. Hawaiian instruments
50. In the style of
52. Claire of Hollywood
53. Sleep-state acronym

WHY RHYME?

ACROSS

1. Trims (a photograph)
6. Heavy sigh
10. Hart's mate
14. London measure
15. Kapaa dance
16. Nasty Nastase
17. Thespian
18. *Baby Take —*, Temple film
19. Proffers, to Burns
20. *Oliver!* song
22. Literary drudge
23. *Der —* (Adenauer)
24. Dodge
26. Fanfare
30. Showed a second time
32. Ending for comment
33. Various: abbr.
35. Home of the Nez Percé
39. Farrell's Studs
41. Track-worker's transport
43. Go
44. Awl or maul
46. Annulus
47. Big name in bauxite
49. "— Now"
51. Dom DeLuise film
53. Mitchell manse
55. Sector
56. Holiday dessert
62. Roused
63. Make ready
64. Hotelier Helmsley
65. — May Clampett
66. Level: Fr.
67. "To — human…"
68. Understanding words
69. Count (on)
70. Daft

DOWN

1. Pincer
2. Loaded
3. Preminger of film
4. Figurehead's spot
5. Ongoing story
6. Come to — (stop)
7. Clumsy sailors
8. Manager Felipe
9. "GMA" anchor
10. Stranded
11. Ancient war epic
12. Elizabeth II, to Edward VIII
13. Anchor's post
21. Alpaca's kin
25. Conceited
26. Public room
27. Siouan
28. Chaplin's wife
29. Spade or Hammer
31. Canyon reverb
34. Absorbed by
36. Vitriolic
37. Ms. Mandlikova
38. Bacchanal
40. Sets
42. Happy as —
45. Hot cereal
48. Man in blue, to Cagney
50. Caught in the act
51. Deceives
52. One of Grable's well-turned pair
54. Pertain (to)
55. *Eins* follower
57. Importune
58. Claudius' heir
59. Anchorage
60. "What's — for me?"
61. Lenient

ACROSS

1. Seethe slowly
5. Showdown command
9. Belfry hanger?
12. Boundary
13. City on seven hills
14. Wing
15. Straight
17. Buddy and Sally's boss
18. New Zealand native
19. Mechanical devices
21. Doris or Laraine
23. Gore, for one: abbr.
24. French article
27. Maiden-named
29. PDQ's cousin
33. Basic
37. Route for Vespasian
38. Pop
39. At some future time
40. Communications giant, for short
43. *Culpa* header
45. Arbitrator
49. Ho's hello
53. Mentor to Samuel
54. Clean
56. Tricky curve
57. Luminary
58. On the Sargasso
59. Do-over, at Wimbledon
60. Avoid religiously
61. Dean Martin's Matt

DOWN

1. Urban-renewal target
2. Ike's ex
3. Inside: prefix
4. Strikingly unusual
5. Joanne of films
6. Medieval instrument
7. Improve
8. Piece (of cake)
9. Bovine digs
10. Soothing lotion
11. Flaps
16. Climbing tropical vine
20. Leader of a mosque
22. Hankering
24. News agency: abbr.
25. Hardware-store purchase
26. Prior to, once
28. "Kookie" Byrnes
30. Mole
31. Beverage on tap
32. Ferret, at times
34. Cleveland waterfront
35. Actor Waterston
36. Platonic conception
41. Tie up
42. Tither's portion
44. Islamic deity
45. Projectionist's unit
46. Besides
47. One of your dukes
48. One of Isaac's kids
50. Belgian river
51. Achilles' soft spot
52. Musical Ant
55. Coffee container

IF IT ITCHES . . .

ACROSS

1. Plunge
5. Deep horn
9. Belgian town
12. Carpathian range
14. States firmly
16. Low character
17. Making the grade
19. Carioca's city
20. Flower: prefix
21. Weather-map line
23. Choppers
26. Scrap for Spot
27. Allison of jazz
30. Month subset
32. Australian rock band
35. Surrounds
38. Bones on which we sit
40. Word in a salutation
41. Chides vehemently
43. Tiger, to the Bradys
44. Maine park
46. Bargaining advantage
48. Pharaoh after Ramses I
49. Ash or birch
51. Stink
52. Urban transport
54. Declare
57. Plant tissue
59. Real cool
62. Classical Japanese drama
63. Allergist's diagnostic tool

67. Ms. MacGraw
68. Selected
69. Angelic Della
70. Range item
71. Norse deity
72. Hied

DOWN

1. TV's Erwin
2. Mulberry cloth
3. Letter abbr.
4. Bordello
5. Sticky substance
6. Cavaliers' sch.
7. Absurdity: Fr.
8. Arrow paths
9. Spot for notations
10. Sock set
11. Bother
13. '70s tennis great
15. "Take off, fly!"
18. Intimidate
22. Bric-a-___
24. Pitcher
25. Realtor's joys
27. Plateaus
28. In reserve
29. Cheap single
31. City on the Dnepr
33. Zorro's mentor
34. Provide food for
36. Kimono sash
37. Chair
39. Compass point

42. Golf-bag items
45. Old phone feature
47. Goes around
50. Strict overseer
53. Pear variety
55. PC key
56. German river
57. Charles' sport
58. Repeat
60. Prez's backup
61. Being, to Brutus
62. Cat chaser
64. ___ Lay Dying
65. Bo's rating
66. Spread (hay)

ACROSS

1. Mantle's weapon
4. Owned
7. Jonathan of "Dark Shadows"
11. Jurist Fortas
12. Gardner in the movies
13. Jimmy's *Rear Window* costar
14. That girl
15. Dotrice of "Picket Fences"
16. Actress Taylor
17. Hedren of *Marnie*
19. Youth
20. Scads
22. Vichy water
25. Bud pot
28. Kreskin's gift, for short
29. Stocking mishap
30. *North by Northwest* star
34. Asian coin
35. Hollywood union: abbr.
36. Executive power
37. Tally (up)
38. Plot
41. Grant's counterpart
42. With 6-Down, *The Man Who Knew Too Much* star
45. With 21-Down, *Psycho* victim
48. Come in first
49. Calendar abbr.
51. Presses
52. Tread the boards
53. Onassis, to chums
54. "Fly ___ the Moon"
55. Sow palace
56. *Vertigo*'s Novak

DOWN

1. "Phooey!"
2. Aid
3. Actress Hatcher
4. A Marx
5. Steer clear of
6. See 42-Across
7. Couples of links fame
8. Spread, like color
9. Diamonds, to a felon
10. Welsh river
13. Clutches
18. Yeats creation
19. Majesty header
21. See 45-Across
22. Iroquoian Indians
23. Polly, to Tom
24. "For ___ you is born…" (Luke)
25. Miles of *Psycho*
26. Eager
27. Chopin's beloved
31. Dear possessions
32. Indy 500, for example
33. State positively
39. Proclamation
40. Game show's Hall of fame
41. Comedian Jay
43. Writer Dinesen
44. Calcutta wrap
45. Muppeteer Henson
46. Exist
47. *Wayne's World* interjection
48. Used to be
50. Baseball's McCarver

SAUCY ONES

ACROSS

1. Played tricks on
6. Inactive
10. Thyme, for example
14. Coeur d'___, ID
15. Dupe
16. Barbra's *Funny Girl* costar
17. Dark sauce for meat
19. Judy's daughter
20. Tennis unit
21. Shock
22. Soda-fountain treat
24. Leopard in a Hepburn/Grant comedy
25. Cava header
26. Complies with
28. Good will
32. Doughnut-shaped solid
33. Old-fashioned blow
34. Title for Agatha Christie
35. Kuwaiti VIP
36. Ceremonies
37. Sills solo
38. Rich Little, e.g.
39. Sups
40. Diner freebies
41. With canniness
43. Oater band
44. Apiary residents
45. Chess win
46. Slender
49. Reckless
50. Command to Fido
53. Rabbit's kin
54. 10-Down, plus whipped cream

57. Utopia
58. Composer Satie
59. Sculptor Auguste
60. CD part
61. Scout groups
62. Bergman or Borg

DOWN

1. Pokes
2. Lily plant
3. Impudent
4. Wrap up
5. Alan Freed and others
6. Calabria's country
7. Old Dutch coin
8. Spanish article
9. Constituents
10. Rich eggy sauce
11. Give off
12. Demolish
13. Actor Pitt
18. Easy tosses
23. Moreover
24. Creamy sauce for seafood
25. Wall climbers
26. Energy
27. Prickly shrub
28. Card-players' pool
29. Deserves
30. Strike down
31. Bering and Beaufort

32. Brewed drinks
33. Watch parts
36. Bought back
40. May honorees
42. Drenched
43. Montana move
45. Oct. 31 wear
46. Stepped on it
47. "I saw," to Caesar
48. Increases
49. Havoc
50. Dwell
51. Oklahoma city
52. Heredity unit
55. Metal source
56. Moo

ACROSS

1. Took care of one's tab
5. Hairstyling stuff
8. Child, for one
12. Unoccupied
13. Pierre's comrade
14. Heavenly headgear
15. 9 iron or 3 wood
17. Too
18. D.C. clean-air group
19. Paris tower engineer
21. Groucho's trademark
24. Gunning for it?
25. Said or Royal
26. Peruse
27. Frequently
30. One ___ time
31. Film producer Ponti
32. Bronx attraction
33. Diego preceder
34. Gallic souls
35. Mr. Sprat's diet
36. Helps with the dishes
38. Masculine
39. Go-ahead
41. Kirk, to Bones
42. Tree trunk
43. 3 little words
48. Mil. fliers
49. Kitten's sound
50. Rather's beat
51. Brokaw and Bosley
52. Slippery one
53. "A ___ told by an idiot…"

DOWN

1. Greedy individual
2. Turmoil
3. Under the weather
4. Give a drubbing to
5. Festive
6. Big Australian bird
7. Those left of center
8. Rub the wrong way
9. 6
10. Word in an ultimatum
11. Touchstone, for one
16. Paramedic's course: abbr.
20. ___ Angel, West film
21. Busy folks on 4/15: abbr.
22. #9 in the Greek alphabet
23. 4-RBI 4-bagger
24. Farmland measures
26. ___, Next Year, Slade play
28. Mare's baby
29. Franciosa of film
31. Dean who plays Kent
35. Wail
37. Coral constructions
38. 1004, for Claudius
39. Place adjacent to
40. 5, on a scale of 1 to 10
41. Cheek
44. Bruce of "The Green Hornet"
45. Pro vote
46. Athena's winged familiar
47. Take advantage of

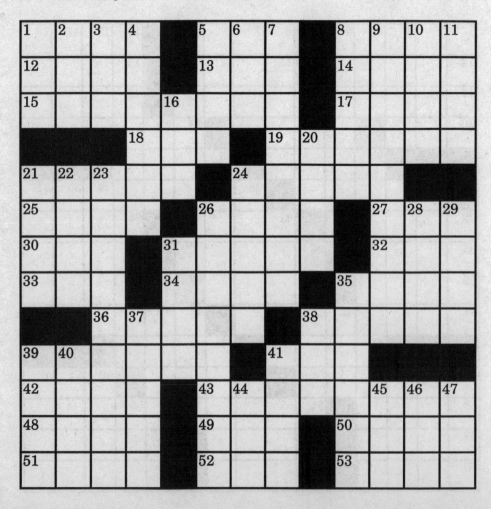

ACROSS

1. Old Atlanta arena (with "The")
5. Arrived
9. Rich soil
13. Executor
14. "Bad Animals" group
16. Novelist Tyler
17. Frightful viper?
19. Paving stone
20. Poured forth
21. European region
23. Votes against
24. Afrikaner
25. Dwarfed shrub
29. Ordered
30. Fortas of bench fame
33. Marilyn Horne's forte
34. NCO reacts to bumbling rookies?
37. Kitchen item
39. Strong alkali
40. Initiate
41. What to do when frustrated?
44. Make angry
45. Onager
46. Arab sultanate
47. Actress Ella
49. Valhalla host
50. Hold up
51. OPEC, e.g.
54. Wee spinning animals
59. Tons
60. Belittle boyfriends?
62. Preserve
63. Town in Ohio
64. Waste allowance
65. Layer
66. British actor Leo
67. Likewise

DOWN

1. Tout's data
2. Cartoonist Drucker
3. At no time, poetically
4. Dies ——
5. Soft leather
6. Mosquito genus
7. Safe-driving org.
8. Before, before
9. Surgical beam
10. Humdinger
11. Opponent
12. After: prefix
15. Vacuum tube
18. Actor Andrews
22. Porters
24. Roll with a hole
25. Small boat, in Barcelona
26. PhD hurdles
27. Foch and Simone
28. Declines
29. Rocker Adams
30. One more time
31. Uncle Miltie
32. Kefauver of politics
35. Highway to Fairbanks
36. Abruzzi commune
38. Lyric poem
42. Greenbrier
43. Very changeable
48. Old Hebrew month
49. Ichthyophagous mammal
50. Bow rub
51. Dramatis personae
52. Jai chaser
53. Ramble
54. Norse letter
55. Salty cheese
56. British peer
57. Wishes undone
58. Considering
61. Cadge

ACROSS

1. 1040, for example
5. News bit
9. "Chicago Hope" network
12. Wrath, to Claudius
13. Wise herb?
14. "___ note to follow sew"
15. Recreational lanes
18. Explosive initials
19. At ___ for words
20. He captured Valencia in 1094
23. Fire
25. Boxer Spinks
26. Fabled race loser
27. Purpose
30. Little Richard hit
33. Fool
34. Grooves in the road
35. Gothic author Anne
36. David Copperfield's wife
37. Catcher's gloves
38. Paris parting
41. Gam
42. Shea Stadium happenings
48. Period of note
49. Put down, as carpet
50. Oliver's request
51. Actor Ayres
52. Mrs. Sundance
53. Actress Skye

DOWN

1. Lie
2. ___ y Plata (Montana's motto)
3. Rarer than rare
4. Last word from the Wicked Witch
5. "___ It Romantic?"
6. Child's game
7. I
8. Threats
9. Singer Laine
10. Equine colors
11. Stewed fruit dish
16. Neither Rep. nor Dem.
17. Large antlered animal
20. Queen of scat
21. Signs of summer
22. Prisoners
23. Polar employee
24. Hostile Olympian
26. Sixty minutes
27. Part of a set
28. Splinter group
29. Seed-potato features
31. What they had in River City
32. Art of paper folding
36. Sandra of Gidget
37. Ryan of I.Q.
38. Object of Cain's ire
39. Challenge
40. "___ Three Ships"
41. Clytemnestra's mother
43. Quaker offering
44. Dolt, in Devonshire
45. Meadow sound
46. White-tailed eagle
47. Bishop's jurisdiction

ACROSS

1. Mornings: abbr.
4. Thin mason's wedge
8. Little boys
12. Nonsense
13. Nettled
15. Charles, the composer
16. Brouhaha
17. Goddess of sorcery
18. ___ *la vie*
19. *On the Town* song
22. Hold a session
23. So far
24. Assn.
26. Spicy flavor
29. Brazilian title
32. Start of a Christmas hymn
38. Deep sigh
40. Spartan magistrate
41. Lulu
42. Gets specific
44. "___ clear day you can..."
45. Gambling game
46. "Come again?" sounds
49. Saying
53. On a grand scale
56. Faulkner novel
61. 1/640 square mile
62. Hordes
63. Ms. Hogg
64. Marshal's emblem
65. Provoke
66. Toward the stern
67. Slitted flat bread
68. "Rats!"
69. Color

DOWN

1. Irish islands
2. Computer phone device
3. Vermont ski area
4. Crystal-ball visionary
5. Common euphemism
6. An ex-Trump
7. Allots (with "out")
8. Carmen Miranda favorite
9. Assert
10. Secretary, e.g.
11. JFK sight
13. Brownie output
14. Freshly moist
20. Okay
21. Hokkaido, once
25. *Fargo* director
27. Taboo
28. Some agents
29. Title for Cupid
30. Norwegian saint
31. Doll's cry
33. Pro with 1040s
34. Resistance unit
35. Curly's cohort
36. Gaelic
37. Noted time
39. "*Que* ___"
43. Prom beverage
47. 1946 Nobelist
48. Health resort
50. Bates or Hale
51. Nailed by the Veep?
52. Wild wheat
54. Homeric opus
55. Denlike
56. When Hamlet's ghost appears
57. Impish kid
58. Radames' love
59. Punch
60. Chum
61. Horned viper

ACROSS

1. Plantations
8. Makes a decision
12. The communications officer: abbr.
13. Czech capital, to natives
14. Portrayer of 29-Down
17. John, the piano man
18. Watch leave
19. Luge
20. The ship
24. Small fry
25. Wall creeper
26. He called Eve Grandma
27. Prophet
29. Yucatan natives
31. Swedish actor Kjellin
34. The first officer: abbr.
36. Caustic substance
37. Most urgent
39. Year in the 17th century
40. Writer Oz
41. Lengthy period
42. Body duct
45. Chief Engineer Scott
50. Thaw
51. Prickly plant
52. Oberon on film
53. He played the captain
56. Fiery places
57. *Profiles in ___*
58. Bauxite and pyrite
59. Shoe parts

DOWN

1. Firstborn
2. Stanley's pained cry
3. Bunched, as hairs
4. Man in ___ (monk)
5. Rotate
6. Before
7. Overseas airline monogram
8. Lowest deck
9. Lady's gentle mount
10. With 33-Down, "Space"
11. Utter
13. Look long
15. "Be quiet!"
16. *The Green Flag* author
20. Turn inside out
21. Louis and Bill
22. Walkman maker
23. Being, to Cato
25. Doctrines
28. Turntable abbreviation
29. The doctor
30. Related
31. Grandpa of 26-Across
32. VIP's car
33. See 10-Down
35. European river with a scent?
38. Actress Parsons
42. Springlike
43. Claim
44. Metric units of volume
46. Irritates
47. Suffix in medicine
48. ___ *culpa*
49. Shade tree
50. Paris tube
52. Rhineland rodent
53. One of the five W's
54. ___-fi
55. Term of affection

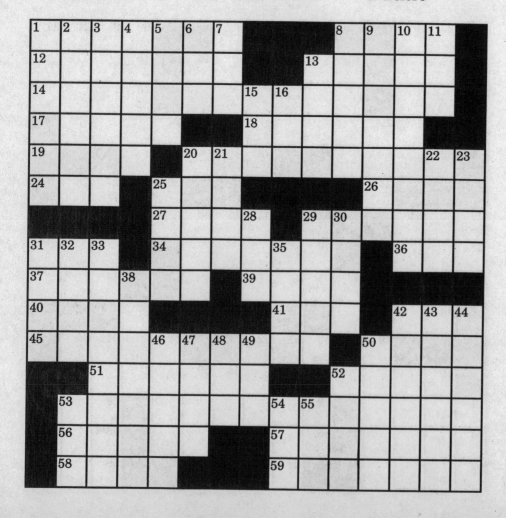

ACROSS

1. Skillful
5. Act fishy?
9. Lots
13. Genesis sellout
14. Staffer
15. Hawk-headed god
16. Shaw titular hero
18. ___ Triomphe
19. Critic Maltin
20. Wriggle
22. Digit
23. Asian range
24. Embarrass
28. Nietzsche's Übermensch
32. Stomata
33. Encrusted
34. Samuel's teacher
35. Old Brit
36. Nickel-copper alloy
37. Aesir VIP
38. Hard wood
39. Roof overhangs
40. Musician Winwood
41. Province in Ireland
43. Auto equipment
44. Le Moko of the Casbah
45. Full-house abbr.
47. Moderate (over)
50. Iron partition?
55. Income: Fr.
56. Tutor of Alexander the Great
58. Signed
59. Run amok
60. Sir Guinness
61. "___ grief!"

62. Bad reviews from 19-Across
63. Computer floppy

DOWN

1. Work at the Sands
2. Slave to crosswords?
3. Lisbon folk song
4. Crank
5. Iliac lead-in
6. Earnest Dublin author
7. Edible freshwater fish
8. Jumble
9. Short cannon
10. Screw maker

11. Art model
12. North Sea feeder
15. Summoned, as a cab
17. Pledges
21. Jacket part
24. Dismay
25. Ada Co. seat
26. Walking Woman sculptor
27. Part of a match
28. More rational
29. Hilo strings
30. Vibrant
31. Diamond counts
33. Sheltered bay
36. Finished off, à la Karpov

37. Nebraska tribe
39. Caught a glimpse of
40. Brusque
42. Built an aerie
45. Descendant
46. Becomes oxidized
47. Mrs. Grundy, for one
48. Clinton's A.G.
49. Costner role
51. Garden hopper
52. Gudrun's mate
53. Paris holms
54. Belmont margin
57. Narrow inlet

ACROSS

1. Breathless
6. 33-cent purchase
11. Bikini upper
14. Guangdong enclave
15. *Silver Streak* star
16. Squabble
17. Chickens out for a stroll?
20. Surprise hits
21. Winter warmer
22. Andalusian affirmative
23. In conformity with
25. Fate
28. Earthenware
31. "___ Dinka Doo"
32. Walk-on
33. Shutterbug, for short
34. Right time for chicken?
38. Antiseptic prefix
39. Pouting person
40. WWII's General Wingate
41. Imitates Porky Pig
43. Canine-related
45. "___ say, not..."
46. Arrangement: prefix
47. Insert
49. Like Grandma's chicken soup
53. Chicken dinners for award winners?
56. Make larger
57. Indian leader
58. Corrupt
59. Crossed (out)
60. Greenish blues
61. Cut sharply

DOWN

1. Rocker's needs
2. London slammer
3. Give ___ (prompt)
4. Vendor
5. Chicken entree
6. *Heidi* author
7. Noted Speaker
8. Writer Rand
9. TLC pro
10. Diplomat's code of behavior
11. Connecticut city
12. Cross
13. Bearded
18. Take ten
19. Honky-___ (dive)
23. Iron clothes?
24. Old-time movie magnate
25. Wellington natives
26. ___ water (up the creek)
27. Made tracks
28. Eateries
29. "Mary Tyler Moore Show" spinoff
30. Alpine tune
32. Italian isle
35. Inherent
36. Turndowns
37. Math expression with only one term
42. Drudgery
43. Humid
44. Puts into action
46. Bagel-shaped figure
47. High point
48. *The Miracle Worker* star
49. Toss
50. Continental biggie
51. Hangouts
52. Balt: abbr.
54. Driving mound
55. ___ Na Na

ACROSS

1. Change for Eliza
6. Reindeer herdsman
10. Phoenician deity
14. Manco Capac's people
15. Mountain feedback
16. ___ Stanley Gardner
17. Cheat
18. Red shade
20. In vogue
22. Prim ones
23. Artist's subject
24. *Den* ___, World Court site, to Germans
25. Least bold
28. Composite pictures
32. Dynasty
33. Bumppo craft
34. Carpet pile
35. Invites
36. Clinton pet
37. Melchior and company
38. Corp. head
39. *Star Wars* director
40. Rank
41. Aussie bounder
43. Greeted the villain
44. Green moth
45. Some paintings
46. Tracy's topper
49. Bible temptress
53. Assay
56. Teresa's town
57. Ice and Stone

58. Jacob's sib
59. Nobs
60. Nectar-eating parrot
61. Watch winder
62. Bar legally

DOWN

1. Tuscan city
2. Business-letter abbr.
3. March Madness gp.
4. Placidity
5. Advocate
6. River landing
7. Expert
8. A few wds.
9. Gulf food fish
10. Finest caviar
11. Extra dry
12. Burn soother
13. Steichen's "eye"
19. Incensed
21. Banned bug spray: abbr.
24. Nene noises
25. Shanty
26. Minor Old Testament prophet
27. Whitehorse's territory
28. Hong Kong neighbor
29. Punkies
30. Armstrong's craft
31. Scouted

33. Wintertime warmer
36. Smith and Jones
37. Church letters
39. Glass menagerie collector
40. Farmland
42. Photo finish
43. Hasten
45. Music hall
46. Stable baby
47. Hence: Latin
48. Fast buck?
50. Fluffy stuff
51. Sax range
52. Door hardware
54. Wash. zone
55. Papua port

ACROSS

1. Predicament
7. Hebrew letters
13. Symbol of the Resurrection
14. Ushers to a new chair
16. "My heart ___ when I behold a rainbow..."
17. Medicinal hybrid?
18. Feel poorly
19. British tar, slangily
21. Snead need
22. Tundra transport
24. Silent Negri
25. Spell start
26. Shocking hybrid?
29. Breach of security
30. Song ending
31. Eureka, for one
33. Sneak attack
36. Royal entertainer
37. Gala celebrations
39. Sexton, for one
40. On the house
41. Mad hybrid?
46. Statutes
47. "That makes sense"
48. Seized car, informally
49. Ego, to Freud?
50. Goofed
52. Pen tip
53. Heightened hybrid?
55. Scrooge's sin
59. ___ apart (identify)
60. Current
61. Netted fish
62. Nail coating

DOWN

1. Aussie gal
2. Certain railroad car
3. DDE or RMN
4. "Jeopardy!" ques.
5. More, in music
6. Use unfairly
7. Semitic language
8. Majesty header
9. See from a distance
10. Sermon seat
11. Pulsating hybrid?
12. Cheapest ship section
13. Mud puddle
15. Canvas shoe
20. Parisian pronoun
23. Stops a bomb
24. Turkish bigwigs
25. Diamond stud
27. Remainder
28. "Seriously!"
32. Lusty look
33. Distress greatly
34. Wondrous things
35. Mournful hybrid?
38. Roused
39. Happen at an earlier time
42. Sugary suffix
43. Doge city
44. Heroic
45. Chemist Alfred
50. Black, to a bard
51. Mystical writing
54. 1,051, to Hadrian
56. German preposition
57. Shrink's org.
58. Brink

ACROSS

1. Complain
5. *Ten North Frederick* author
10. Ladies of Spain: abbr.
14. Baltic feeder
15. Astronomer Carl
16. Newcomer
17. Billionth: prefix
18. Usurp
19. Serves a winner
20. Actors' wheels?
23. Advantage
24. Virginia Clemm's husband
25. Malay island
28. Helen's adopted home
30. Squeal
33. Chilean port
34. Like Yale
35. Lawsuit
36. Lawyer's wheels?
39. Glide
40. Pindaric works
41. Light-bulb gas
42. Say further
43. Billfold items
44. Linens
45. Can
46. Chimney grime
47. Jock's wheels?
53. Nastase of tennis
54. Kick the bucket
55. Tumbler turners
57. Check
58. Veil fabric
59. Norse treatise
60. Rent
61. Trapshooting
62. See stars

DOWN

1. Felon
2. Eliot's Bede
3. Attorney General Janet
4. Troubadour's tongue
5. N.Y. river
6. Actor Presnell
7. *Let Us Now Praise Famous Men* author
8. Foolhardy
9. Exact opposite
10. Flat
11. Lestat's creator
12. Martial Olympian
13. Mayday
21. Paragon
22. Coquettish
25. Model wood
26. Mountain nymph
27. Unbending
28. Tints
29. Guns (an engine)
30. Gamut
31. British racetrack
32. Difficult years
34. Napoleonic, for one
35. Custodian
37. Links
38. Swift brute
43. Black gold
44. Eye holder
45. Essay
46. Set of wage rates
47. Choir voice
48. Row
49. Caroline Islands group
50. Hercules' love
51. Grant
52. Jekyll's alter ego
53. Social suffix
56. Mineo of film

ACROSS

1. Timothy Hutton film
5. Dickens lad
8. Noun suffix
12. Wee hour
15. Stars
16. Tennis defeats?
17. Apples of a sort
18. Seine landmass
19. Salt Lake City team
20. Fancy
21. Organizer Chavez
23. Anatomical wrinkle
25. "... __ o'clock scholar"
26. Optical ailment
28. Actor Knowles
30. Instincts
34. Popular tournaments?
37. Crete peak
38. Nabokov novel
39. Private eye, for short
40. Guido's high note
41. Specialist in lofty shots?
43. Accumulates
45. Gives in
47. Journey part
48. Prison space
50. Baltic res.
52. Clan symbol
56. "I had wild Jack for __" (Yeats)
58. Speed contest
60. Pindaric poem
61. Footloose one
62. Misjudged a good serve?
64. Musical work
65. Conclusion
66. Gershwin girl
67. Harem room
68. Birds' associates

DOWN

1. Mentally stimulating
2. Anoint, in the Bible
3. Seeger and Sampras
4. Peru coin
5. Puzzle
6. Gets frosty
7. Decks of cards: abbr.
8. Shelley elegy
9. Bad news at a wet Wimbledon?
10. One of the Boyers
11. German city
13. Tennis appointment?
14. WWII craft
15. Vb. variety
20. Breakfast food
22. "__ was saying..."
24. Stomach: prefix
27. Alpine vocalist
29. Tennis player?
30. Diamond __
31. Altar vow
32. Infant tennis scores?
33. Chalcedonies
35. A Wallach
36. Diego header
42. Famous Phil
44. Self-esteem
46. Beach
48. Candy coating
49. Marry on the sly
51. "__ loaf is..."
53. Odds words
54. Bring forth
55. Doles (out)
57. Time to note
59. Key: French
62. AFL's mate
63. Ingenue

ACROSS

1. Talented
5. "You can ___ horse…"
10. It's mostly a lot of junk
14. Calliope sound
15. Reference book
16. Four roods
17. Live luxuriously
20. Chemical compounds
21. Charter
22. Annapolis grad, for short
23. Ripped
24. Mongolian tribesmen
26. A ways away
28. Passed
32. "Let him step to ___ which he hears" (Thoreau)
37. Gymnast Korbut
38. Avoiding extremes
42. Baldwin
43. Mists
44. Sergeants, e.g.
48. Room lead-in
49. Sulking
51. Numbered work
55. Mimic
58. Svelte
59. Pencil end
61. FHA offering
64. Appeal
65. Noodles
66. Conceits
67. Variety
68. It's a plus
69. Experiment

DOWN

1. To ___ (exactly)
2. Crow
3. Gambling game
4. Anesthetic of yore
5. Trails
6. Numerical suffix
7. Hi, to Ho
8. Early Hebrew tribesman
9. Of the stars
10. Ginnie in a portfolio
11. Pine
12. *Monitor* material
13. Trip sections
18. Rancorous
19. Olympus matriarch
24. Supremes or Bee Gees
25. Squash, for one
27. Big Board's cousin: abbr.
29. Wild plum
30. Actor Richard
31. Ward and Ozzie, on TV
32. Revenuer
33. Hawaiian town
34. Adam's apple locale
35. Year in the reign of the Sun King
36. Gas flow meas.
39. Legal wrong
40. Hurry
41. Duenna
45. Aware of
46. Actress Mason
47. Is malicious
50. Lazarus and Samms
52. Surgeon Sir James
53. Custom
54. Utah lilies
55. Gstaad sight
56. Chukker game
57. Pitcher
59. Formerly, formerly
60. Kick back
62. Alley roamer
63. Poetic work

ACROSS

1. Scoria
5. Geraint's lady
9. Dueling memento
13. Old-fashioned buckle
14. Abundant supply
15. Squash variety
16. Black-and-white treat
17. Throw in the towel
18. *Guy Rivers* author
19. Classic dog story
22. Genealogy chart
23. Meshed fabric
24. Dieter's choice
26. German pronoun
28. Dit's partner
31. Pole, at sea
32. Comical Kabibble
33. Copperfield's wife
34. Boris Badenov's nemesis
38. Spillane's ___ *Jury*
39. Tiller's site
40. Adjoins
41. Compass point
42. Gets to
43. Antiquated
44. Summer tones
46. Troubles
47. Classic horse story
53. H.B. Stowe contemporary
54. Coral collection
55. Wordy Webster
56. Bergen's Mortimer
57. Retail complex
58. Past
59. Letter encl.
60. Suit to ___
61. Flute part

DOWN

1. Convertiplane acronym
2. Actress ___ Flynn Boyle
3. Crackerjacks
4. Somewhat spectral
5. Hosted
6. Family member
7. China leader?
8. Reckon
9. Heir
10. Vanderbilt, et al.
11. French weapon
12. Roles on "ER": abbr.
15. Pallid
20. Seeing red
21. Statesman Root
24. Notices
25. Original models
26. Sprays
27. Attorney's honorific abbr.
29. Lofty ridge
30. *The Smoker* painter
31. Assam addresses
33. Bandages
35. Anklebones
36. La Guardia alternative
37. "___ ears!"
42. *The Woman ___*
43. Poppycock
45. Ere
46. Fred's sister
47. Polynesian power
48. Author Bombeck
49. Sans mixer
50. Crotchety one
51. *Citizen ___*
52. Interjection
53. Lisper's bane

ACROSS

1. Wearing wedgies
5. Loose Arab robes
9. Gala
13. Preside at tea
14. Model Macpherson
15. Bert's buddy
16. Con man
17. Kind of miss
18. Spud
19. Bird sternum?
22. Amen
23. —— nous
25. Terhune canine hero
26. Rotten
28. Type type: abbr.
30. Desert ruminant
33. West Indian chest cover?
35. Geisha wrap
36. Pair
38. U.N. agency
39. Fish orb overlay?
41. Saint and queen
43. Shuttle overseer
44. Chess pieces
45. Ike's command: abbr.
46. *Le Louvre, par exemple*
48. Permits
51. Sprig's thorny feature?
55. *Soldats'* weapons
57. Upon
58. Actress Merrill
59. Reagan Attorney General
60. Francis, e.g.
61. Roman hails
62. Haven
63. Feels poorly
64. Bow trees

DOWN

1. Match wits
2. Sharpens
3. Get the better of
4. Emulate Magic
5. Virgil classic
6. Cry from Lamb Chop
7. "——! poor Yorick"
8. Spanish artist
9. 1957 Louis Malle film
10. Amuse
11. Link
12. Ballad ending
15. Harrow rival
20. Property
21. Obscure
24. Philadelphia gridder
26. Sink
27. "...rule them with —— of iron"
29. Thirteen popes
30. Schmaltz
31. At right angles, at sea
32. Time for Puck's revels
33. Porter of song
34. John or Paul
37. "The day and the way ——" (Swinburne)
40. Least hard
42. Twelve
45. Becomes one on the run
47. Roman being
48. Coral creation
49. Surrender (rights)
50. Tendon
52. Asian monk
53. Small case
54. Glasgow girl
55. Guitar adjunct, briefly
56. Vintage car

ACROSS

1. *Femme fatale*
5. Low-cal lunch
10. Lovable person
14. Overdo the barbecue
15. Soap plant
16. Theater-door sign
17. Indian royalty
18. 1982 Barry Levinson film
19. Give in, to a degree
20. Area in front of home plate?
23. Koala's hangout
24. Son of, to Faisal
25. Renowned
28. Sultanate's relative
33. Troy, to Caesar
34. See 14-Across
35. Gessler's bailiwick
36. Bit of 9th-inning drama?
40. Illuminated
41. *Bene* lead-in
42. Cotton-blend fiber
43. Alpine tops
46. Salutation finales
47. Sound from Sandy
48. Stripper Sally
49. Three Alous, once?
55. Meal course
56. Containing gold
57. ___ *Man* ('84 Estevez film)
59. 1984 Nobelist
60. Hit
61. Tennis term
62. Teens' ball
63. Dancer Carol
64. Zero on court

DOWN

1. TV adjunct
2. Captain of the *Pequod*
3. Script heading
4. Hard copy
5. *Funny Girl* married ladies
6. Ammonia derivative
7. "Cheers" star
8. Something to give up
9. Tush
10. Expose a quack
11. The yoke's on them
12. *Barnum* role
13. Inc., in Leeds
21. Bridge play
22. Geisha's accessory
25. Tops off the tank
26. Actor Delon
27. Mixed, in Pisa
28. Splinter groups
29. Joke response
30. Cathedral, in *Roma*
31. Politico Hatch
32. Wee pests
34. Period, in a telegram
37. As quick as a wink
38. Back's back
39. Nonsense
44. Cash
45. *Dernier* ___
46. Contagious
48. Wage increase
49. Half an octet
50. Indy racer
51. Arizona city
52. Cereal fiber
53. Upholster anew
54. British ne'er-do-well
55. NASA abbr.
58. Prime

MIXED VEGETABLES

ACROSS

1. Train component
8. Not fatal
15. On the loose
16. Like some concerts
17. Tear-jerking message?
19. Sprinkled
20. ___ song (final performance)
21. Top-notch
22. Director Reiner
24. 500 lead-in
26. That guy
29. Playwright O'Casey
31. ___ and took notice
35. Keats' output
37. Leaves' home
39. Yoga position
41. Hot looker?
44. Ladd classic
45. Seaweed product
46. Video-game flick
47. Invocation start
49. Fateful March date
51. Compass dir.
52. ___ Free
54. Follow closely
56. Stumble
60. Started (with "off")
62. Tournament type
66. Parents' supper song?
69. Gelid
70. Oakland team
71. Ancient finds
72. Categories

DOWN

1. Country music star
2. HRE ruler
3. Word of woe
4. "See ya!"
5. Statements of belief
6. Past
7. They wear stripes
8. "Over There" composer
9. Knocks over
10. Antique car
11. Dancer Pavlova
12. Actor Scott
13. Celebrity
14. Coastal raptor
18. Matched motors
23. March sister
25. Lock inscription
26. ___ d'oeuvres
27. The Gem State
28. Silver Star, e.g.
30. Price performance
32. Suit ___
33. About-face, in traffic
34. Don
36. Chinese: prefix
38. "Zounds!"
40. Since, to Burns
42. Belgrade native
43. Originated
48. "Is that so!"
50. Loren of films
53. Understands
55. Mortarboard tossers
56. End-of-the-week comment
57. Wealthy: Sp.
58. Currier's mate
59. Some muscles, for short
61. *Jeanne* ___
63. Wee bills
64. Brazil state
65. Army chow
67. Luau paste
68. RMN's home

TUMBLING ACT

ACROSS

1. Olsen of vaudeville
4. Thingamajig
9. Somersault in the air
13. Ex-NYC mayor
15. Skiers' mecca
16. Designer Gernreich
17. God's ___ (burial ground)
18. Thinker's distraction
19. Carolina campus
20. Part 1 of a Thurber quote
23. Plumlike fruit
24. Actor Linden
25. Part 2 of the quote
32. Tackles a brook
33. Fielder's choice?
34. Vane dir.
35. Ruing the run
36. Aspirations
38. Author of *The Counterfeiters*
39. California judge
40. Bay
41. Supped in style
42. Part 3 of the quote
46. Luncheonette letters
47. Bones
48. End of the quote
55. Cook book

56. Overcharge
57. Not shut
58. Give illegal aid
59. Ant, once
60. Fluctuate
61. Cartoonist's needs
62. Fresh
63. Uh-huh

DOWN

1. Endorsement
2. Toxic range weed
3. Wall-paint shade
4. China's ___ Four
5. Sun line on a map
6. Gyro holder
7. City in Arizona
8. Singular happenings
9. Without restrictions
10. Calm before the storm
11. Role model
12. Golfer's target
14. "Amen" star
21. Woes
22. Need
25. Deeds: Lat.
26. For this case
27. Plentiful
28. Draw
29. Cat–tails connection
30. Subordinate to
31. Clarinet attachment
32. Homeless child
36. Held ones
37. Barn resident
38. Collapse
40. Moiety
41. Join in space
43. Axis vessels
44. Saws
45. Fastidiousness
48. Option for Hamlet
49. Sign
50. Actress Downey
51. Sponges
52. "...is ___ forever"
53. Comical Martha
54. Tumble
55. Climax

ACROSS

1. Gulliver's creator
6. Don Rickles specialty
10. Finger
14. Zeal
15. Bring up
16. Milky gem
17. Majorca seaport
18. Song for Tetrazzini
19. Asta's master
20. Cartoon character
23. Pedagogues' org.
24. Olden days
25. Bonkers
28. Existed
31. Fraternity letters
35. Down under fowl
36. Blokes
38. Béarnaise, for one
39. Paul Newman character
42. Hannibal Smith's group
43. Playwright Chekhov
44. April 15 initials
45. Tasty treat
47. Merry, to Mimi
48. Teen trouble spot
49. ___ B'rith
51. Very blue
53. Ghostly ship
60. French fuzz
61. Cranny companion
62. Rib
63. New Age halo
64. Major end
65. One of Thalia's sibs
66. Help a heister
67. John and Jane
68. Fiend

DOWN

1. Undermines
2. Blanket
3. Python Eric
4. Stir up (trouble)
5. Clientele
6. Boast
7. Of planes
8. Pluvious
9. Texas river
10. Illicit
11. "Baked in ___"
12. Some overcoats, for short
13. Lodge member
21. Seesawed at sea
22. Out of the sack
25. Skim off the schmaltz
26. Stradivari's teacher
27. Soldered
29. Time ___ half (wage rate)
30. Police chief?
32. The food of love, to the Bard
33. Mast nut
34. Taste is one
36. June sign
37. Bristle
40. Striped feline
41. Palm off (on)
46. Caught some rays
48. Stick (to)
50. "___ Pieces"
52. Behaved
53. Botch
54. Trevi finds
55. Be too fond of
56. Luau strings
57. Polite address
58. About
59. Light gas
60. Airport grp.

ACROSS

1. Stitch temporarily
6. Nitty-gritty
10. Flow's converse
13. Before
14. Ashtabula's waterway
15. Eye
16. Midge's sports group?
19. Plug spots
20. More recent
21. Mass of ice
22. Chestnuts
25. Polished
26. Gold place
28. Duelist's tool
30. Calendar pgs.
31. Beleaguers
34. Legal thing
35. Troll classification system?
38. Stool pigeon
39. Vientiane inhabitant
40. Cager's hoop
41. Chance descriptor
42. Says yes, to a host
46. Fred's early partner
48. Half the Sprats' larder
51. Goldfish
52. Penny pinchers
54. Mogadishu's land
56. Headline that led to SPCA protests?
59. Cunning son of Farbauti
60. Andalusian appetizer
61. An artful Dodger
62. Chemical ending
63. Adult cygnet
64. *Awake and Sing!* playwright

DOWN

1. "Beat it!"
2. Ringlike marks
3. Rotor's complement
4. Boxer's golden opportunity
5. Nobelist Wiesel
6. Stellar table
7. Shea stat: abbr.
8. Cause pain
9. Bowman of note
10. Kitchen gizmo
11. Puritan
12. Actors Wallace and Noah
15. Court avowal
17. Tiebreaking pers.
18. Affluence
23. Mat message
24. Ancient wheat
27. Skye cap
29. Morales of *La Bamba*
32. Hawk
33. Slowpoke
34. Be cautious and spooked
35. Good spot to make a pass
36. Junior, often
37. Salt
40. Go off on a tangent
41. Withered
43. Rudy of radio
44. Shaman
45. Digging tools
47. Son of Jacob
49. Egyptian dam site
50. Tokyo drama
53. NCO club VIPs
55. Surrealist Joan
57. Dogpatch denial
58. Put ___ fuss

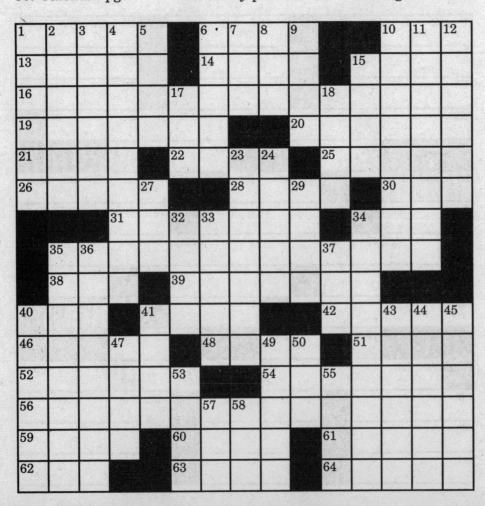

ACROSS

1. Winger of *Shadowlands*
6. Hunk of concrete
10. Expanded
14. Logan and Fitzgerald
15. Dynamic start
16. Pasternak character
17. Peck plays float importer?
20. Ruckus
21. Turkey's neighbor
22. Put on finery
23. Downtime
25. Cover
26. Orson plays Michael?
33. Debatable
36. Pantyhose pull
37. Fall bloomer
38. Map folio
40. Chaplin's title
41. Vanilla
42. Its capital is Accra
43. Vicinity
45. Macpherson of *Sirens*
46. Kate Nelligan plays Betsy Ross?
49. Bunyan tool
50. Closed, in a way
54. *M.* Abélard
58. Borscht base
60. Swiss river
61. Hamilton plays computer wiz?
64. Lift man
65. London aristocrat
66. Rural ways
67. Mickey's maker
68. Took the train
69. Utopias

DOWN

1. Exclude
2. Outwit
3. Hit a high fly
4. Moonbeam
5. From whence Francis came
6. Poet Teasdale
7. Central Mexico city
8. The law's is long
9. Thread spool
10. Very willing
11. Tear down
12. Author Ambler
13. Pathway
18. Guitar bars
19. Station porter
24. 45° angle
25. Uncle Tom's tormentor
27. More than disturbed
28. Mobutu's domain
29. In dreamland
30. *This style:* abbr.
31. Playwright Simon
32. Sea eagle
33. Wise men
34. Roman emperor in 69 A.D.
35. Nordic king
39. African desert
44. Relatives of 49-Across
47. Devon town
48. Rich or Stuart
51. John of old films
52. Gone, in a way
53. Pour on the Russian
54. Deere product
55. Jot
56. Satanic ill
57. See 23-Across
58. Celtic great
59. Della's creator
62. UN agcy.
63. Naughty

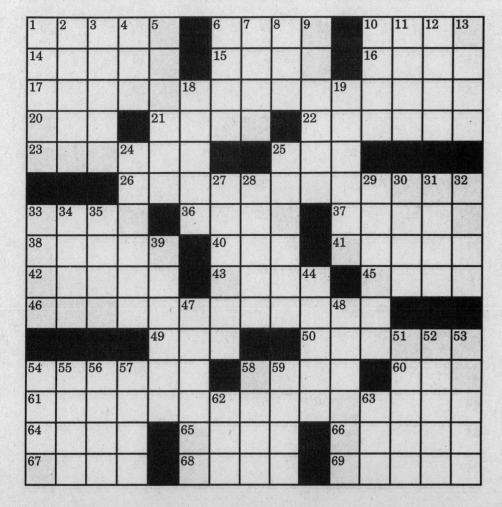

ACROSS

1. Campaigned for election
4. Amerind of the Southwest
7. One of a Chekhov trio
11. Swivel
13. Type of tense
15. Aged, to a Glaswegian
16. NO WAY
18. Chimney feature
19. Pakistani seaport
20. Balloon filler
22. Ex-Tarzan Ron
23. Crankcase need
24. Lambs' guardians
25. NO END
30. Raise a red flag
32. Always, poetically
33. Approving of
34. Say it isn't so
35. ___ *Runner*, '82 sci-fi flick
37. Turkey seasoning
38. Get on
39. Pack it away
40. Chanteuse Natalie
41. NO LIE
46. Actress Archer
47. Zilch
48. Recently pilfered
51. Binges
53. Guacamole base
55. Layer
56. NO MORE
58. Division word
59. Dorothy's companion
60. Beauty parlor
61. Slant
62. *The ___ of the Roses*
63. Johnson or Jonson

DOWN

1. Competitor
2. *The Color Purple*'s Margaret
3. Ibsen heroine
4. Arduous
5. ___ chi
6. Avoided
7. Lunkheadish
8. Dilly
9. Down in the mouth
10. Humorist George
11. Chinese pup
12. Mogul
14. Get in under ___
17. Smooth-running sound
21. Serve to replay
25. Ironic
26. "___ shall have no dominion"
27. October stone
28. Egg (on)
29. Fraction of a foot?
30. "Here ___ again"
31. Once again
34. Cosby bomb, *Ghost* ___
35. Crooner Tony
36. Midnight movie
37. Bawl
40. '88 Penn film
42. Straight mate
43. Single
44. Captivate
45. Swing style
48. Selassie
49. "___ a Grecian Urn"
50. In tatters
51. Invest
52. Red Rose
54. Grouse
55. McCourt book
57. Airport abbr.

A DAY LATE

ACROSS

1. Surrounded by
5. Glance at
9. Consumer affairs org.
12. Turns white
14. Inferno visitor
15. Mauna chaser
16. He preached a day late
18. Swiss canton
19. Acts the stool pigeon
20. Provide with an overhead
21. Chess moves
24. Sets one's makeup
26. Cry "Uncle!"
27. "Wheel of Fortune" purchases
28. Gentiles, to Singer
29. Jots
31. Ready follower
32. Future alumnae
34. Knucklehead
36. Parallelogram-shaped
39. What tanners tan
41. An archangel
42. Himalayan residents
44. Shady shelter
45. Andy and Mickey
46. Posh knob
47. Frequent flier
48. Western fort
49. Other cops did his job yesterday
55. Call ___ day
56. Boleyn, et al.
57. Golfer Calvin
58. Place
59. Denote
60. Cannon of note

DOWN

1. Cop abbr.
2. *Printemps* time
3. Poorly
4. First state: abbr.
5. Twinges
6. Calls it quits
7. Socratic vowel
8. West, for one
9. Day-late Fats Domino song
10. ___ *Godunov*
11. Prisoner's security
13. Orderly method
14. Recipient
17. Lamblike
20. Impassive
21. Happy dove
22. Day-late '66 film farce
23. Chem., e.g.
24. Plays the ponies
25. Ignited
26. Metric meas.
27. Pitch in
29. Gumshoe
30. Composer Saint-___
32. One with a handle?
33. Make slick
35. Greek letter
37. Spheres
38. Padua pronoun
39. Look for
40. Native suffix
42. Gaucho's gear
43. Laugh sneeringly
44. Master artery
45. Expanded, as dough
46. Seethe
47. Catcher Tony
49. Snarl of cars
50. Nine ninths
51. Florid
52. Barbary VIP
53. Alma-___, Kazakhstan
54. Japanese cabbage?

ACROSS

1. Mil. decoration
4. Take the stage
7. Rigg role
11. Summary from Rather
13. Stylish
15. Mindless memorization
16. Work your fingers to the bone
17. Get wind of
18. Nephew of Cain
19. Garr's stand?
22. Former global org.
23. Tending to entertain
27. Arledge's stand?
30. Gained a dependent, perhaps
33. Lead
34. Sitcoms and soaps
35. USAF heroes
37. Cohort
39. To be, in Brest
40. Mini-beard
43. Nurses a drink
46. Method: abbr.
47. Burstyn's stand?
50. Cold War ease-up
51. Expire
54. Herman's stand?
58. Lasso makings
61. Royalty of scat
62. Wear away
63. Parrots
64. Eyesore
65. Seductive singer
66. Canvas home
67. Diary page
68. Guam, to the U.S.

DOWN

1. Strikes out
2. Give a start to
3. Roe
4. Long (for)
5. *Silkwood* star
6. Beauty crowns
7. Bottom-of-the-ninth feeling
8. Almost forever
9. WWII battle area
10. ___ *Misérables*
11. Q–U link
12. Pasta sauces
14. Makes wavy
20. Leeds trunk
21. French river
24. Monogram ltrs.
25. American thrush
26. Figure-eight halves
28. Downy surface
29. Use art gum
30. Carried on
31. Simone's academy
32. Gave out
36. Most nearly vertical
38. Abner's adjective
41. Nine: prefix
42. Regard
44. Ward heelers
45. Sidewinders, e.g.
48. Whimpered
49. Specter
52. Took an oath
53. You might get down from it
55. Lanchester of films
56. A snap
57. D.C. VIP
58. Squealer
59. Unseal, in verse
60. Porker pad

ACROSS

1. Eyewear
6. Kiddies' resort
10. Garb for the Phantom
14. Comic Minnie
15. Bus-jumper Knievel
16. Making a crossing
17. Grand lobbies
18. Cast opening?
19. Prevents
20. Start of quote
23. Job, to a yuppie
26. Salty drop
27. *Exodus* hero
28. Balderdash!
30. Respond (to)
34. Await decision
36. Author of quote
40. Thesaurus man
42. Second Amendment grp.
43. Pester
44. Middle of quote
47. Tolkien beings
48. Life principle
49. Assortment
51. Obtain
52. Posterior, in slapstick
55. Begins the day
57. End of quote
62. Cinder finish?
63. ___ *facto*
64. Property, e.g.
68. Incline
69. Sluglike
70. Looks lustfully
71. New Mexico art colony
72. Coop residents
73. Pitfall

DOWN

1. Reduction site
2. Guinea pig, perhaps
3. Listening device
4. Felony
5. Assassin
6. Jobs-program initials
7. Ward off
8. Free-for-all
9. Absolute; complete
10. Ancient Hebrew measures
11. PDQ
12. Llama land
13. Dawnward
21. Ship's nose
22. Entertain
23. *Meet John Doe* director
24. Small leaf space
25. "...the old, ___ the new"
29. Muscle quality
31. Toward shelter
32. Trolley sounds
33. Exam taker
35. Consort of Siva
37. Golden State fort
38. June honorees
39. Fits into snugly
41. Musical paces
45. Besmirch
46. Wine-label number
50. Ordeals
53. Sufficient
54. Actress Cicely
56. *A Doll's House* playwright
57. Wallop
58. Lamb, in print
59. What's more
60. Pied Piper prey
61. Browbeats
65. Vast expanse
66. Misplay
67. Mao ___-tung

ACROSS

1. Actress Teri
5. Fraudulent operation
9. Got underway
14. *Dies* —
15. Showed up
16. "Sorry, — at the office"
17. *Star Wars* princess
18. Oodles
19. *Andrea* —, ill-fated liner
20. "Unrespected" comic
23. *Silent Spring* subject
24. Analyze ore
25. Hall-of-Famer Pee Wee
27. Condor condos
31. Valencia, e.g.
34. Patriotic org.
37. Connecticut city
39. TV tuner
40. Step — (hie)
42. Este hideaway
43. Chip in?
44. "Warning: this bag is not —"
45. Away from the bow
47. Pearl, e.g.
48. "Peanuts" slob
50. Family car
52. Equine hues
54. Action
58. Health haven
60. Glance
64. Medieval guild
66. *The King* —
67. Menlo Park name
68. Hot blood
69. Nailed at a slant
70. Goes right
71. Tearful
72. Slave to crosswords?
73. Goofs

DOWN

1. Ms. Radner
2. Subjects
3. Actor Claude
4. 1989 retiree
5. Duel memento
6. Bovine baby
7. Mine: Fr.
8. A bit more than a yard
9. One who doesn't pass
10. Self
11. Soil sport?
12. Enthusiastic
13. In apple-pie order
21. Examined
22. A Woolf of note
26. Thompson of "Family"
28. Treeless grassland
29. Speaker of Cooperstown
30. Sediments
32. Way in
33. Sch. for Holmes?
34. Laving need
35. Con
36. Border river
38. Robert —, CSA hero
41. Proofreader's quarry
46. Nil, to a *niño*
49. Diner
51. Immaturity
53. Ray fish
55. Goldbrick
56. No way!
57. Author Günter
58. Ava's Artie
59. Whittle
61. "Country" Slaughter
62. Mideast gulf
63. 1947 Nobelist
65. Drench

ACROSS

1. Rice dish
6. Braided closure
10. Haruspex
14. Swiss poet
15. Equity plum
16. Mr. Rochester's governess
17. First-year astronaut?
19. Try for a part
20. Cold War abbr.
21. Samuel's mentor
22. Secular
24. What igloos provide?
29. Singer Gilley
33. Gaelic
34. Born
35. Critic James and family
36. Drives the getaway car
37. Popeye, for one
38. In proper manner
39. Peru article
40. Stand open
41. Stalwart Ripken
42. *Ivanhoe* author
44. Olympic events
45. Anecdotage
46. Solitary
47. Speakers' platforms
48. Injection that styles hair?
51. Pith helmet
52. Buckeyes' inst.
53. Perfect serve
56. Noted inheritors
58. Travel like Dracula?
62. Out of town
63. A Saarinen
64. Fearless one
65. Verne skipper
66. Colonial sewer
67. With wings

DOWN

1. Masher's move
2. Mischief makers
3. Pinocchio, at times
4. NRC's predecessor
5. Bilks
6. Not strong
7. "... ___ and thy staff"
8. Cheer for Escamillo
9. Scram!
10. Letter flair
11. Certain lenses' M.O.?
12. Time to note
13. Flushed
18. Satiate
23. Actor Ed
25. Wrangles
26. Wave top
27. Grim scythe-bearer
28. Singer Brewer
29. Zany
30. *The Night of the* ___
31. Wine steward's aides?
32. Important
36. As an escort
40. Xenon or argon
42. Berth
43. Pine, e.g.
44. Domed building
47. Promising
49. Godzilla attack site
50. Train stowaways
53. Taj Mahal town
54. Anchor Huntley
55. To be: Fr.
56. Staff
57. Merino miss
59. Actor Gorcey
60. Cent. parts
61. Baron tail

ACROSS

1. Downstairs employee
5. Athenian
10. Poet Robert
13. Put two and two together
15. Stiller's partner
16. *Fists of Fury* star
17. Cowardly messengers?
19. Detroit-based group: abbr.
20. Yale attendee
21. Stay in style
22. More stylish
24. Ill will
26. Footnote term
28. Threads
29. Slangy chap
30. First zoologist?
33. Spherule
35. Abélard's affirmative
36. Play the prophet
39. Shenanigans
43. Pique experience?
44. Nondairy shake?
46. Taylor's third
48. Nursery item
49. Rocker Collins
51. A famous loch
53. Tailor's stat
56. Ottoman minister of state
57. Supreme leader?
59. Gardner from Grabtown
60. Shake a tail
61. Envious wasp?
64. Old flame?
65. Rosinante, e.g.
66. French pronoun
67. Nevertheless
68. Head lock?
69. The man

DOWN

1. Goldwyn's partner
2. Forster's Miss Quested
3. In neutral
4. *La Fanciulla ___ West*
5. Van Halen valuables
6. London break
7. Handle
8. Pacific
9. Reviewed for a hit
10. Sad satellite?
11. Regan's father
12. Taxus
14. Actress Del Rio
18. Trill
23. Skin problem
25. Headland
27. Immerse (in)
31. Razorbill or dovekie
32. "To ___ Coy Mistress"
34. Show you know
36. Conniption
37. Granada gold
38. Bolshevik brew?
40. Mischievous
41. Last name in dictionaries?
42. Pupil regulator
45. Satisfaction
47. Egg ct.
48. King's domain
50. Shack
52. Main partner
54. Maintains
55. Smee, et al.
56. Ming thing
58. Change of five
60. Tao
62. Hitherto
63. Lowe of "West Wing"

ACROSS

1. Pea jacket?
4. Like Friar Tuck
9. Wet blanket
13. Swiss canton
14. Novelist Shute
15. Not so ordinary
17. Severe, as a storm
18. MacArthur's "I"
20. Like a leopard
22. Question mark
23. Mosey
25. Brazos River city
26. *Lundi* follower
27. Oh de Cologne?
28. Tuned in
31. River in Scotland
33. Reeve role
35. Belafonte song
36. Singer's contemporary
37. Exploits
38. Like Steven?
39. Temple's first husband
40. Lighthearted
41. The pits
42. Dog size
43. Cruise ship for couples?
44. Message board?
46. Tract unit
47. Dismantled
49. Bomb
52. *Heidi* author
53. Lennon's "I"
57. Tomorrow's turtle
59. Wiped out
60. Upright, e.g.
61. "Gotcha!"
62. Ms. Daly
63. Control
64. Etna and Ida, in brief

DOWN

1. Place to get stout
2. Certain examinations
3. Anka's "I"
4. Landward
5. Feasted one's eyes
6. Saintly Stowe heroine
7. ___ *vous plaît*
8. Pipe shape
9. Steep
10. Mathematical proportion
11. As snug as a bug in ___
12. Origin
16. Genetic abbreviation
19. Behaves chemically
21. Wall St. worker
24. Campaigner's "I"
25. Uncle Sam's "I"
28. Dr. King's "I"
29. Took a look
30. Soprano Lily
31. Roosevelt specialty
32. Trademark
34. Drum container?
35. Record player
37. Three little pigs?
41. Bart or Lisa
43. Yield
45. Anonymous
46. Washed out
48. Two cubed
49. See 4-Across
50. Tag cry, maybe
51. "Give it ___!"
54. Loan abbr.
55. Be on the level?
56. Heyerdahl boat
58. Beetle juice?

ACROSS

1. Crack-up sounds
5. Merchandise
10. T-men, e.g.
14. Fleur-de-lis
15. Sonic start
16. Salmagundi
17. Store due for change?
19. Consumer
20. It couldn't be better
21. Ret
23. Trifle
26. Dungeonesque
27. Rakish month?
31. Villanelles, for example
35. Put on
36. Guinness and Waugh
39. Undergarment
40. Asiatic arum tuber
41. Shy
42. Japanese export
43. Thoroughbred's kin
44. *Embraced by the Light* author
45. *The Brass Bottle* star
46. Charity events
48. Docked
50. Wee drams
53. Dimmesdale spec.
54. Chair
58. Deal with a ham
63. Osmonds' state
64. Small-size weapon?
67. Nobelist Morrison
68. Blue hue
69. Stingy
70. Plumb
71. Violinist Mischa
72. Sets

DOWN

1. Rock hound's need?
2. Like an erg
3. Honey of a home?
4. Addled
5. Side arm
6. Vintage
7. Diamond dynasty
8. Fear
9. Yule gift-giver
10. Bed, figuratively?
11. Ms. Martinelli
12. Tokyo assembly
13. Boil
18. Vocal range
22. Plate watcher
24. Demean
25. Actress Burke
27. *Pal Joey* writer
28. Sea or snake
29. Half a homer?
30. Dips into
32. Become scarce
33. Was a collier
34. Attention measure
35. No does?
37. Acts babyish
38. Eydie's partner
47. Salutation word
49. Therefore, logically
51. Dated
52. Photo type
54. Pound puppy
55. Siouan
56. Dailey and Rather
57. June happening
59. Vowel type
60. Suit to ——
61. Gung-hoism
62. Goes astray
65. Dep.
66. Lady lobster

ACROSS

1. Cherry variety
5. Civvies
10. Overstuff
14. What the nose knows
15. Lend ___ (listen)
16. 1982 Disney film
17. Myrna, several times
18. Stockholm Sigma Chi's date?
20. ___ it (be careful)
22. Simple shed
23. Oxlike brush bounder
24. Damage seriously
25. Sinks
27. "A ___ your thoughts"
31. Almost orange ape?
32. A, B, C or D
33. Nectar chaser
34. Piaf's pal
35. Sullies
36. Opie's pa
37. Garnet hue
38. Crooked
39. Els of U.S. Open fame
40. Shag
42. Disobeys flagrantly
43. Sales agts.
44. Fill the tank
45. Put ___ (act uppity)
48. Romantic figure?
51. Copenhagen Cub Scout leader?
53. Forgo the fettuccine
54. Big Daddy player
55. *Paradise Lost* figure
56. Hoarse horse?
57. Pond wiggler
58. Good enough to eat
59. Maned deer

DOWN

1. Head start?
2. "Would ___ thing like that?"
3. Oslo candy striper?
4. Power film, *The Long ___*
5. Brick pros
6. Single
7. Fiefs
8. Littlest child
9. John and Jill
10. Tropical
11. Irish isles
12. Suit material?
13. Inside: prefix
19. Poet Heinrich
21. Durn!
24. Farinaceous
25. Directors' group
26. *Soldat*'s branch
27. Fall predecessor
28. Helsinki Playmate?
29. Rumor, in Rouen
30. ___ syndrome
32. Gretzky stats
35. Departs port
36. "Put your arms ___, honey…"
38. Whale variety
39. Film lioness
41. Cleric
42. By the rules
44. Welcome
45. Frigga's hubby
46. Church part
47. Once more
48. *Este*
49. Welsh veggie
50. Depot abbrs.
52. La-la lead-in

ACROSS

1. Russet winter pear
5. Street sound
9. Light pastry shell
13. Town in north Wales
14. Perfume
15. Biblical twin
16. See title
19. Plate eyers
20. College buildings
21. Chimney residue
22. Stun
24. Assumed information
26. Miner's quest
27. Thickset riding horse
30. Hot drink
31. Prepare fish
32. Summon
33. See title
36. Movie unit
37. Cupidity
38. "As ___ and breathe"
39. Continue
40. Tony's poor relation?
41. Supple
42. Tribe
43. Dart
44. *Seascape* playwright
47. Hard on the nerves
50. See title
54. Dill herb
55. ___ and a leg
56. First person
57. Melees
58. Sup
59. Byronic corsair

DOWN

1. UK network
2. Locale for a luau
3. Urban eyesore
4. Folding chair
5. Poet Stephen Vincent
6. Remnants
7. Lawyer's title: abbr.
8. Little, on the Loire
9. Tea variety
10. Computer pro
11. Raise crops
12. Stir
14. Cushion shot
17. Dakota, for example
18. Cutting tool
22. Chips player
23. Middle East gulf
24. Was overly fond
25. Pined (for)
26. Untethered
27. Carp
28. Vaulted arch
29. Venerable theologian
30. Uncas's beloved
31. Orr was one
32. Campaign-minded
34. Exile isle
35. Fingers: prefix
40. Table spread
41. False follower
42. Highlanders
43. Marseille monk
44. Way off
45. Fine fabric
46. Stormed
47. Fed
48. Nothing, to Pedro
49. Growl
51. Roll of bills
52. Blackbird
53. Wee

TALK TO THE ANIMALS

ACROSS

1. Ziti, e.g.
6. Armor bashers
11. Goof up
14. Customary
15. Stop, at sea
16. Curly poker?
17. Simply ducky mystery?
20. Poet Hughes
21. ___ regni
22. Penury
23. Bizet's father
25. The brains, often
28. Low-ly film?
32. Saw
33. Start to freeze?
34. Riot participants
37. Former Belgrade leader
38. Kegler's hangout
40. Surface
41. Print measures
42. Malay native
43. Goneril's sib
44. Novel to crow about?
47. "I" popping?
49. Klutz's comment
50. State
51. In re
53. Lettuce layer
56. Waggish movie?
61. Chemical suffix
62. Patois
63. Horse tail?
64. Lifesaver's center
65. Orders
66. Blocking order

DOWN

1. Move on the green
2. Service man?
3. Made a case
4. Calpac's kin
5. Mr. Baba
6. Eliot's weaver
7. Severn tributary
8. A Kennedy
9. Atty. title
10. Actor Erwin
11. Barker, for one
12. Roxie of "The Jeffersons"
13. Funny Foxx
18. Distinctive
19. The King ___
23. Walt Kelly creation
24. Holiday threshold
26. Viands
27. Paris playmate
28. The other sock
29. Valhalla bigwig
30. Cigar's grub
31. ___ La Mancha
34. O. Henry's gift givers
35. Elliptic
36. Acquiesce
38. Weather words
39. Incensical?
40. Cathedral features

42. ___ tai
43. Agt.
44. Port stopper
45. Pole stars?
46. Miss Piggy's piggies?
47. Dame Edith
48. Actor Richard, et al.
50. Busy as ___
52. Shell partner
53. Wheat disease
54. Irish
55. Darling animal?
57. It's old-fashioned?
58. Gray lay?
59. Function
60. Minyan minimum

ACROSS

1. Stringed instrument
5. Thick liqueur
10. Theda Bara, for one
14. Atop
15. Actor/war hero Murphy
16. On the briny
17. The joys of Orville
20. Mayday kin
21. Rebel Allen
22. Party attendee
23. Entirely
24. Signal for lines
25. Magical TV show
29. On-campus coed
33. First-rate
34. Throughway no-no
36. Galena, e.g.
37. Excuses from Jackie
41. Guido's high note
42. ___ deck (any lower deck)
43. Dill herb
44. Natives of Damascus
46. Marlowe's "___ towers of Ilium"
49. Literary monogram
50. Soak flax
51. Pacific isles
54. Noted designer
57. Notorious Fawkes
60. Pitfalls for Stewart
63. Mah-jongg bit
64. Doctrine
65. *Picnic* penner
66. Luge or pung
67. Coeur d'___
68. Barley brew

DOWN

1. Solemn words
2. Japanese box
3. Elevator man
4. Janeway's record
5. Range rovers
6. *Shine* star
7. Old Norse opus
8. Bearing
9. Grown elver
10. Less distinct
11. *Days of Grace* author
12. Shea nine
13. Gone
18. Position of control
19. T. Williams reptile
23. Tract
24. Reactor part
25. Lovebird abodes
26. Yule plant
27. Close, to bards
28. Sand ridges
29. Cauterized
30. Blackmore's Lorna
31. Pelagic birds
32. Staff signs
35. Mao chaser
38. ___ *17*
39. Has
40. Grainy cellar contents
45. ___ out (cleared up)
47. Rococo
48. Hammer part
51. NCOs
52. Seed covering
53. Macho
54. Balladeer Jacques
55. Early serf
56. P.M. Anthony
57. Drummer Krupa
58. Yen
59. North Sea feeder
61. Athens letter
62. Male cat

MULTIDIRECTIONAL

ACROSS

1. Major faith
6. Tinned meat
10. Piece of legislation
13. Commemorative slab
14. Mountain cat
15. King Mongkut's language
17. Mob group
18. Advantageous position
20. Bilko's rank: abbr.
21. Beatty, et al.
23. Best bunch
24. Kennel names
26. Adores
28. Shows joy
30. French impressionist
31. Mecca mogul
32. Central seating
36. Suffer from ague
37. Skirt styles
38. Ethan Allen's bro
39. Mr. In-between
42. Ale relative
44. Modern designer
45. Draw off (gas)
46. Grouped military style
49. Thesaurus man
50. Hollow stone
51. Lover's sound
52. Airline monogram
55. Secret
58. Make impure
60. Solar disk
61. Not a dup.

62. Singer Rabbitt
63. Sward
64. Yawn
65. Barn dances

DOWN

1. Doctrines
2. Bambi, in time
3. Remote diamond position
4. Clay, now
5. Wander
6. Maine exports
7. Young seals
8. Electrical unit
9. Busch of Hollywood
10. Olympic entrant
11. Notable design of 44-Across
12. Aunt, in Nantes
16. Bad day for Caesar
19. Live it up
22. Goddess of the dawn
25. Seine sight
26. *The Kiss* sculptor
27. Means justifier
28. Stratum
29. 21st-century year
30. Mythical Phrygian king
32. Acted tacitly
33. Starboard
34. Sweet sandwich

35. Put on guard
37. Same: Fr.
40. Bowery Boys debut
41. Hen
42. Large barge
43. Copy
45. Soak
46. Pablo's quaff
47. Leases
48. Cowboy fun
49. Arête
51. Scissor sound
53. Indigo source
54. Holy fems.
56. Porcine one
57. Sky altar
59. Punchless punch

ACROSS

1. Singing style for Ella
5. Did something
10. Jewish month
14. Ineffectual; weak
15. Gower's dance partner
16. Have brunch
17. Yogi's in "divergence"
19. Renaissance Italian family
20. Contests
21. Harnessed together
23. USNA grad
24. Sun. talk
25. Actress Nazimova
26. Little, in Lille
27. Vend
29. Suns' org.
32. Cantina coin
35. Spellbound
37. ___ *Laughing*
39. Entertain
41. Degenerate
42. Nick of Hollywood
43. Measured, in a way
44. Mine yields
46. Beginning
47. Nightmare street of film
48. Ex-Yankee Bucky
50. VP of the '60s
52. "It's ___ to Tell a Lie"
54. Bishopric
55. Scale tones
58. Hose holder
60. Scaremonger
62. Director Kazan
63. Whitey's in "within one's means"
65. Aerosol output
66. Run amok
67. Stratum
68. Surfeit
69. Went astray
70. Soviet news agency

DOWN

1. *Susan* ___, 1961 film
2. Rustic home
3. Vague amount
4. Maryland gridder, shortly
5. Open player
6. Provide food
7. Hall-of-Famer Speaker
8. Conceit
9. Floss variety
10. "Let's Make ___"
11. Mickey's in "take apart"
12. Part of "a.m."
13. Critic Rex
18. Stratagem
22. Actress Terry
26. Sit
27. Big spender
28. Cigar end?
30. ___ *noire*
31. "Pluck ___ rose from off this thorn"
32. Golfer Jerry
33. Writer Ludwig
34. Roger's in "recapper"
36. Elvis' middle name
38. Snack
40. Actor Murphy
45. Cut fleece
49. Infuriate
51. Rustlers' target
53. Union member
54. Skier's haven
55. Shinbone
56. Aits
57. Gang followers
58. Lapidary items
59. *Inter* ___
60. Remote
61. Marshal Dillon
64. In favor of

ACROSS

1. Self-sufficient: abbr.
4. ___ au rhum
8. Length of leather
13. Nixon VP
15. Plenty, to a poet
16. Baby Doc's country
17. By any chance
18. ___ boy!
19. Eve of TV
20. Start of advice to writers
23. Tenant
24. Horned cervine
25. Cleopatra's bosom buddy?
28. Nest egg, of sorts
30. Olympia or bluepoint
32. Middle of advice
36. Counterfeit
39. Top of the line
40. He lived by the advice
43. Actor Penn
44. Leander's love
45. Fender woes
46. *The Flies* author
48. ___ Paulo
50. Cent. parts
51. Icelandic epic
54. Token
59. End of advice
61. Ill-fated ship, *Andrea* ___
65. Grad
66. Eager
67. Water jugs
68. Kenya river
69. Park performer
70. Meat
71. Omen
72. Artist ___ Borch

DOWN

1. "___ Pretty"
2. Bright stars
3. Habit
4. Safari employee
5. Con
6. Fly larvae
7. Anticipate
8. Unbarbered
9. Popeye is one
10. Disencumber (with "of")
11. Goddess of mischief
12. Skittle
14. Teetotalers
21. Houdini's real name
22. Ruth's mother-in-law
25. ___ *Like Alice*
26. French governing body
27. Quarries
29. Arthur of court fame
31. Wise one
32. Unkempt
33. Toward the back
34. Wood knots
35. Medical specialty: abbr.
37. That ship's
38. Hebrew prophet
41. Siren Bara
42. Zambian city
47. Work over again
49. Tarzan, e.g.
52. Mild oaths
53. Dwight's opponent
55. Waxed cheese
56. Finger or toe
57. Pithy saying
58. Tent caterpillar
60. Supporting crosspiece
61. For sure, for short
62. Lear seafarer
63. Female ruff
64. April agcy.

BODY MOVEMENTS

ACROSS

1. Chew the fat
5. Sideburns trimmer
10. "...mercy on such ___"
14. Went by bus
15. An Astaire
16. Contemptible person
17. On French leave
18. Snoop
20. Approach
22. Insincere
23. Make a choice
24. First Shiite caliph
25. Flat-bottomed boat
28. Lost one's head
33. Pick over
34. Wears with pride
36. Here, to Henri
37. Vamoose
40. Promotional items
41. Penurious
42. One of the Websters
43. Be sure of
45. Players
46. Underworld god
47. Clock number
49. Those in opposition
52. Reach the lowest price
58. Follow orders
60. Bridge support
61. Biblical preposition
62. Blouse part
63. Yarn
64. Pub offering
65. Fumes
66. Bates of film

DOWN

1. Bisque tidbit
2. Poet Julia Ward
3. Molech, for example
4. Dickens girl
5. Sewed quickly
6. Choose and follow
7. Enthusiasm
8. Toast topping
9. Singer Chris
10. Nuclear
11. Chowder
12. Dearth
13. MacDonald's frequent costar
19. Delight
21. Pained outcry
24. Fed the kitty
25. Soft leather
26. Embrace
27. One quarter of a bridal need
28. Metal plate
29. Arthur from Richmond
30. Metric units
31. Dazzling show
32. Antenna shape
33. Libya neighbor
34. Chemical connections
35. "Is it yes ___?"
38. Complete
39. Actress Claire
44. Film splicer
45. AFL's partner
47. Murrow show, "See ___"
48. Bits of news
49. "Three men in ___"
50. Zilch
51. *Homme*'s head
52. Moral stain
53. Seine tributary
54. ___ Hari
55. Exam type
56. Bruins' sch.
57. Soon afterward
59. Compass direction: abbr.

GRANDMASTERS

ACROSS

1. Playing marble
6. Pol Kefauver
11. Underworld diamonds
14. Misrepresent
15. Ballpark move
16. Scandal sheet
17. Ralph Bellamy detective role
19. Hellenic letter
20. Simple Simon's desire
21. Street performer
22. Little Edward
23. On all sides
27. Harpies
29. Cities in Spain, Mexico and Nicaragua
30. Ques. follower, hopefully
32. Circle part
33. Priestly togs
34. Disraeli, e.g.
36. Gratify
39. Philippine island
41. Burst of applause
43. French river
44. Bloomsbury economist
46. Stumbler's cry
48. FDR creation
49. Mr. Carson
50. Hill dweller
51. Burton's birthplace
53. Scorn
56. Unisex
58. Kyoto sash
59. Noted journalist
61. Assembly of anecdotes
62. Trip part
63. Natalie's pop
68. Hearth find
69. Vigorously, to Byron
70. Sea duck
71. Harden
72. Speech flaws
73. Lethal element

DOWN

1. Jurist Fortas
2. Salon goo
3. Everybody
4. Cravat ornament
5. Most weird
6. Atty. title
7. Run-down area
8. Relationships
9. Plant swelling
10. Dakar's land
11. Vernon's partner
12. Provide food service
13. Mild oaths
18. Strong desire
23. Woe is me!
24. Riot
25. Hall-of-Fame cager coach
26. O'Hara abode
28. Lady Jane
31. Synthetic fiber
35. CIA predecessor
36. Lichtenstein's art style
37. Natural number
38. Clear the slate
40. Monad
42. Show of hands
45. Always true
47. Hip hedonist
50. Baker and Loos
52. Locust tree
53. Soft drinks
54. Corpulent
55. Dade Co. town
57. Bad review
60. Miss
64. Electees
65. Funny
66. August one
67. Sea raptor

ACROSS

1. *Invasion of the Body Snatchers* sights
5. A continent, to Milton
10. Metric measure
14. Dram ending
15. Anatomical prefix
16. Custer's comrade
17. Start of a Butler quote
19. Anent
20. Base clearers
21. Used henna
23. Kin to durn
24. Q–U link
25. First name of the author
28. Narrow shoe width
30. From ___ Z
33. Beard colleague
34. The quote continued
36. Tops
37. Nosy Parker's feature
38. Forward
39. More of the quote
41. Far from verbose
42. Consume
43. The Tramp's mate
44. Iowa town
45. Tenor Peerce
46. Strained
47. Where the Vistula flows
50. Altercations
54. Sistine ceiling figure
55. End of the quote
57. Vanished
58. Shop tool
59. Part of "QED"
60. Societies: abbr.
61. Fiennes role
62. Vicious and Caesar

DOWN

1. Byway
2. Roman emperor
3. Per ___
4. On the docket
5. Yearly
6. Ploy
7. Actor Tamblyn
8. Nest-egg initials
9. Set off
10. Artist Wood
11. What's left
12. Pay to play
13. Humor
18. Made blunders
22. *Vidi*
25. Land or sea follower
26. Now, in Málaga
27. Town NNW of Bismarck
28. Ecstasy's literary mate
29. Eager, plus
30. ___ Rock (Aussie landmark)
31. Trunk
32. Frequently
34. Oklahoma city
35. Openings
37. Tabloid tidbits
40. ___ Bator
41. Hose hue
44. Negotiated a check
45. Alice or Etta
46. 10%
47. Half a Samoan port
48. Bouquet
49. Director Fritz
50. Be foolish
51. Thespian Garr
52. "By gum!"
53. NCOs
56. Writer Hentoff

ANAGRAMS

ACROSS

1. Coin holder
5. Dungeness diggings
10. Salinger girl
14. Abhor
15. ___ Soleil, Louis XIV
16. Manhandle
17. Actress Morani
18. Viva voce
19. New England stopovers
20. GAINING COMMAND OF
22. Farm-school student
23. ___ Men
24. Charles, to Elizabeth
26. One ___ time
29. Seoul soldiers
31. Entice
35. Manon composer
37. High-card combo
38. Common contraction
39. Morse-code sound
41. Kiddie
42. Cubic meters
45. Withstood
48. Irenic
49. Cut in shop
50. Curve
51. Graceful horse
53. A Tilly
54. Icky to touch
57. FIXING A SHIP
63. Old Atlanta arena
64. Arctic-related
65. Garfield's foil
66. Soon

67. Michelangelo work
68. Radius neighbor
69. King ___
70. Winter forecast
71. Farewell-note blemish

DOWN

1. Ark passenger
2. Yuri's love
3. Lift man
4. Camp necessity
5. Medieval horn
6. Fixed a necklace
7. Elvis' middle name
8. "When the ___ breaks..."
9. Funny Caesar
10. VOLUNTARY EXILES
11. Told all
12. Pasteur player
13. Otherwise
21. Raison d'___
22. Yorkshire river
25. NYC clock adjustment
26. Off
27. Sample
28. Former SAG prez
30. Hubbubs
32. Ralph of "The Waltons"
33. Interior Secretary under FDR

34. Exigencies
36. TORRENTIAL
40. Co-player
43. Prof. 'iggins
44. Pelagic area
46. Cuss out
47. Gerund closers
52. Grill
54. Overcharge
55. K followers
56. Home ___, track
58. CSA's Robert
59. Be a puffer
60. Lazy Python?
61. Famous caravel
62. Equipment
64. Epistolary extra: abbr.

ACROSS

1. Button one's lip
7. Opt for
13. Paris' girl, in Paris
14. Bargain-priced, as flats go
16. Perturbation
17. Ran
19. Tiny surfers' delight?
21. Algonquian
22. Leather with nap
23. Reason's partner
24. Objective
27. Beatty of *Deliverance*
28. Yucatán native
30. Three, proverbially
32. Amorous
36. Muddle
37. Sales of comedy
39. Pixilated
40. Seductive
42. Legendary hero, ___ Bill
43. Make the engine hum
44. Haggard heroine
46. Mork's home
47. Was presumptuous
50. Composer Saint-___
52. Global cartel
53. Dover Beach blanket?
58. Legendary libertine
60. Cope after a snowfall
61. Rueful one
62. Opposed
63. Concert souvenir
64. Toadies

DOWN

1. Buddy
2. Filmmaker Riefenstahl
3. He played Obi-Wan
4. Indy winner Rick
5. Not hale
6. Little one
7. Garlic portion
8. Ambition
9. Pays with plastic
10. Hockey great
11. Coin of Neptune's realm?
12. Ingress
15. Abound
18. Actress Wallace
20. Recipe word
23. Carpet type
24. Heart throb?
25. Rasht land
26. Maximally much
28. Swab
29. Irving of film
31. Nurses' garb?
32. Throw follower
33. *Comida* option
34. Opera prince
35. Firkin, e.g.
37. Moral no-no
38. The same partner
41. Cow's chaw
42. Musing
44. Cheers owner
45. Prime time?
47. Neil Simon's nickname
48. On ___ with
49. VCR button
50. Chic
51. Wise guys
53. *Beloved* novelist Morrison
54. Cricket unit
55. Comic Crosby
56. Bernhardt's rival
57. British gun
59. US agcy.

SEEING SPOTS

ACROSS

1. Thunder unit
5. Kaplan of TV
9. Face value
12. Architect Saarinen
13. Tennessee town
14. Author Wister
16. Safecracker
17. Young and old followers
18. Kegler's milieu
19. Prompt
21. Zurbriggen or Street
22. Letters for Cayce
25. Shoe width
26. Jubilant
27. Smashes
30. Beckett absentee
31. Retail events
32. PR concern
34. Denali, et al.
37. Yemeni port
38. Lulus
39. Comical Betty
40. *Oui* or *ja*
41. Samantha of films
42. African loris
43. Overloving one
44. Held a grudge
46. Mortar mate
49. Navy cops, for short
50. Keats work
51. Mehitabel's friend
52. Financial gift
55. Underdone
56. Estevez's dad
57. Singer James
61. Thine, in Tours
62. Tonto's companion
63. Roentgenogram
64. GI wear
65. Seth's son
66. Mountain lake

DOWN

1. Shortstop Ron
2. Shaker mystic Ann
3. S.A. land
4. Kelly strip
5. Assemblage
6. Critic James
7. French sex kitten
8. Printer's measures
9. Fabric pattern
10. Anticipate
11. Actress Jeanmaire
13. First name in beauty
15. Twerp's kin
20. Jersey five
21. Blackthorn
22. Attempt
23. Parasol's provision
24. Loses ruddiness
26. Fabergé creations
28. KO count
29. Vilify
33. Cops, at times
34. Saw relative
35. Shlepped
36. Fine porcelain
38. Tyrannical boss, e.g.
39. Half a candy
41. Slippery
42. Mexican moola
43. Put on finishing touches
45. Echidnalike
46. Medic's intro
47. Muse of poetry
48. Back Bay entree
52. Alabama city
53. Of flight
54. Cashier's cry
56. That ship
58. Refrain start
59. Salt
60. Writer Rand

ACROSS

1. Liven (up)
5. Sandy's vocabulary
9. Fall bloomers
13. Duel tool
14. Cry from the bleachers
15. ___ noir (wine grape)
16. Settle (a dispute)
18. Occupied
19. MS accessory
20. Ice star Elaine
22. Early Hanks hit
25. Have a direct ___ (swing influence with)
28. In a true way
32. Dick or Jane
34. Punitive prefix?
35. Many summer babes
37. Fissile rock
38. Tough trip
39. Nancy's advice
41. One of Earth's seven
42. ___ of God
44. Feeling
45. Welsh emblem
46. Old explorer
48. Free-___ (slavery foes)
50. Can again
52. Bag leaves
53. Classic platter
55. Nearly never
59. Have ___ to grind
62. Okay to forgive
66. Blush wines
67. Start of two Gershwin titles
68. Squad
69. Oland role
70. Seine feeder
71. "Answer yes ___"

DOWN

1. A Clampett
2. Mimicry experts
3. Greek letter
4. Puzzle's center
5. Hand holder
6. Crowned *tête*?
7. Winkler role
8. Filch
9. Small cetacean
10. Former Burma VIP
11. Felonious styles: abbr.
12. Sacred mlle.
15. *Shine* props
17. Ms. McEntire
21. Shrill bark
23. Difficulties
24. Twinkle
26. Riddle
27. Hardy and North
28. Sequel to 22-Across?
29. Danish city
30. Plow pair
31. Sleepers, sometimes?
33. Rowboat woe
34. Afrikaner town
36. Proboscis
40. Garfield's pal
43. Fence traversers
47. RN's colleague
49. Land in 41-Across
51. Farm sounds?
54. Army vet
56. Noted alliance
57. Good buddy?
58. Exuberance
59. Bow
60. Honshu show
61. Simile center
63. Romaine
64. Rockies native
65. Comic Phillips

DIAGRAMLESS CROSSWORDS

To solve Diagramless Crosswords, use both the definitions and the definition numbers as aids in supplying the words and the black squares that go into the diagrams. As in a regular crossword puzzle, the pattern of black squares in each Diagramless is symmetrical: When you have discovered the correct placement of a black square, its mate can be inserted in a corresponding position on the opposite side of the diagram. The following example illustrates the concept of diagonal symmetry within Diagramless Crosswords.

Insert the corresponding number from the definition list with each starting letter of an Across or Down word. In addition, be sure to insert a black square at the end of every word. Continue to plot the black squares in the mirror-opposite portion of the diagram as you complete the top; as you make your way through the puzzle, its emerging design will reveal the length and placement of other words.

If you need help getting started, the box in which each puzzle begins is listed on the last page.

ACROSS

1. Muscular strength
6. Kicking's partner
7. Golfer's targets
8. Dry, to an oenologist
11. Prevents (disaster)
13. Exact duplicate
16. Theme song from *Mondo Cane*
18. Baltimore sluggers
20. Journalist Tarbell
21. Parenthesis alternative
24. Walk off the job
25. Headache cause
27. Graduate of Smith, e.g.
29. Advanced math
30. Leopold's codefendant
31. Addison's partner
33. Dignify
37. Aid a criminal
38. Bowling-lane button
40. Tire filler
41. John, for one
43. Run in panic
44. Square measurements
45. Embroidery yarn
49. Q–U link
50. Davy Crockett's last stand
51. Swedish port
52. Gracie or Woody

DOWN

1. Dry as a desert
2. "— Lucy"
3. World's longest river
4. At any time
5. It was often wild
8. Tech field: abbr.
9. Silver-tongued
10. Falk's detective
12. League: abbr.
14. German denial
15. "¿Cómo ___ usted?"
16. School near Harvard: abbr.
17. Keats creation
19. Old Spanish coins
21. Priests' caps
22. Agitate
23. Infuriates
26. More inclined
28. Lacking an escort
31. Caribbean resort island
32. Skier's transport
34. Party decoration
35. Pinocchio's nose lengthener
36. Before, in poesy
39. And so forth: abbr.
42. One who does: suffix
43. *Fatale* lead-in
46. Incarnation of Vishnu
47. Israeli airline
48. Former Berlin divider

DIAGRAMLESS NUMBER TWO

ACROSS

1. Arcing tennis shot
4. Pester relentlessly
7. Seeger of The Weavers
8. Mediocre
9. Michelangelo masterpiece
10. Statesman Root
11. Bearded spring bloom
12. "Good Times" star John
13. Venture
15. Poppycock
16. Women's magazine
20. During
21. Former governor of Algiers
22. Gobble up
23. Fragile and slender
24. Oleo daub
25. Saki composition
27. Model often seen in 30-Across
28. Thanksgiving staple
29. Lay out
30. Fashion magazine
33. Angel of the Battlefield Barton
34. Wheel shaft
35. Dutch dancer Mata
36. Seedy nightspot
38. Unworldly
40. Macho types
41. Floor square
42. Panache
43. Lanka lead-in
44. Wrestling victory

DOWN

1. One of Jacob's brood
2. *The Adventures of Milo & —*
3. Breakfast companion?
4. Ruckus
5. Cinder
6. Epicure's magazine
7. Skier's jacket
8. Skier's surface
9. Indoor jockey's prop
10. A Brontë
12. Gobi-like
14. Cold and slippery
15. Greek letter
17. Harridan Helmsley
18. Shortening
19. Where squealers are sent
20. Gusher
21. Restrain
23. *The Globe,* e.g.
24. Child-rearing magazine
25. Trunk item
26. Frequent talk-show guest Garr
28. Bald Brynner
29. Nat Turner, e.g.
31. Expert
32. Plow pullers
33. Cantina order
36. Place for pastrami
37. Mrs. Bowie
39. Atmosphere
40. With-it, to Dad

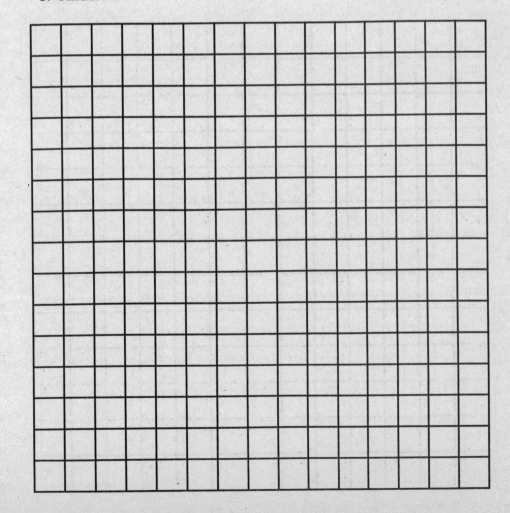

ACROSS

1. Roller-coaster segment
4. Cousteau's milieu
7. Supped
8. Drenched
9. Record of a ship's speed
10. Sings (out) forcefully
12. Buddy
14. Period of note
15. Possessive pronoun
17. Gift at a luau
19. *No* ___, Sartre play
20. Southeast Asian language
21. Create art with acid
23. Caboodle's partner
24. Vase with a base
25. Dead heat
26. Kazan of Hollywood
28. Create a trench
29. Colonial Quaker
30. Superlative suffix
31. Printer's measures
32. Work unit
33. Torrid
35. Hands over
37. Court divider
39. Pinch
40. Unit of maize
41. Dental anesthetic
42. Parched

DOWN

1. *East of Eden* youth
2. On the peak
3. Serve sumptuous delights
4. Perspire
5. Slippery swimmer
6. Posture
10. From Leeds, for example
11. Looking and looking
13. Epistles
14. Banish
16. Prison on the Hudson
18. Cake decoration
19. Just manage (with "out")
22. Barnyard matron
27. Made amends
29. Gazes at Godiva
34. Glum drop?
36. By means of
38. Rugby score

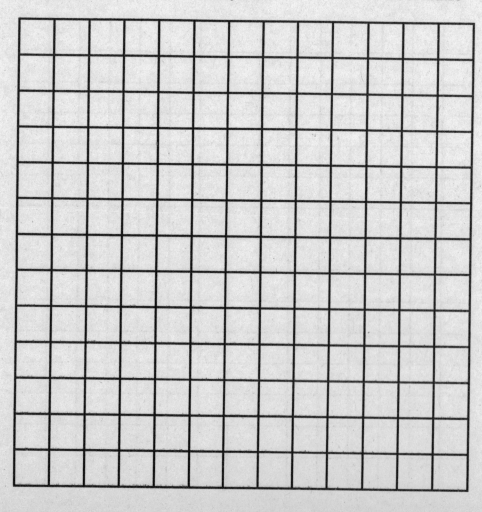

ACROSS

1. Arafat's group: abbr.
4. Earl or duke
5. Actor Gulager
8. March 17th event
10. The least amount
11. Space
12. Blushing
13. Tiller
14. On the briny
16. Passenger, for one
18. Boat propeller
21. Play, as a uke
23. Show sadness
24. Daughter of Oceanus
25. In need of a wash
27. In a very appropriate way
28. Frosty incrustation
29. Comfort
31. Place for a barbecue
34. Marsh wader
36. Matured
37. Nonflying bird
38. Move furtively
42. Old sailor
43. Short composition
45. Tooth part
46. Speak wildly
48. Narrow inlet
50. Mythical bird
51. Nasal woodwind
52. Misrepresentation
54. Legal matter
55. Rents
56. Presidential monogram

DOWN

1. According to
2. Shakespearean king
3. Law's partner
4. Theme, e.g.
5. Chastity's mom
6. Diamond ——
7. The nth degree
8. Bygone
9. Official proclamation
10. Curds' partner
11. Liquid fuel
15. Sound related
17. Home appliance
19. Be in poor health
20. Musician Charles
22. Not speaking
24. Mimic
26. Appears
27. In motion
28. Free (of)
30. Monogram of 56-Across' opponent
31. How to stand in poker
32. Muslim title
33. Total fear
35. Keep safe from harm
37. Spanish pronoun
39. Singer/actress Day
40. Spoils
41. Common abbreviation
43. Son of Seth
44. Give way
47. Jurist Fortas
49. Hit a perfect tennis serve
53. French season

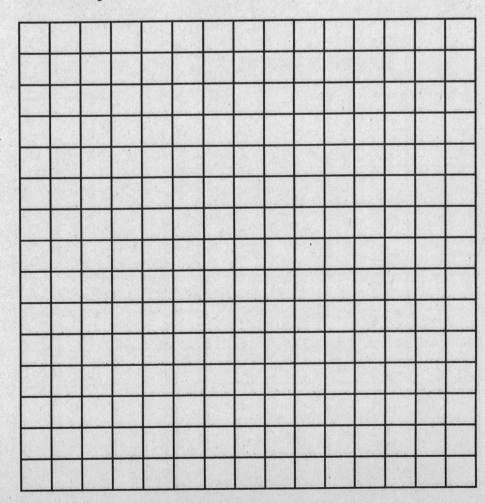

125

DIAGRAMLESS NUMBER FIVE

ACROSS

1. Bohemian dance
6. Ar chaser
9. Once more
10. Tuck's partner
11. Saline
12. Colorless and dull
14. Give for a while
15. Public spectacle
18. Lingerie item
21. Moses' sister
22. Like the Kalahari
23. Truthfulness
24. Oasis treat
25. Thrown
27. Typewriter key
29. Self-styled expert
30. Hawaiian tuber
31. Cope with
33. Finished
34. Scold vehemently
35. Beatnik's abode
36. Most ashen
37. Celebrity
39. Ticker-tape parade honoree
42. Sharp-tongued
43. Stocking mishap
44. Parson's residence
45. Notice
46. Category; class

DOWN

1. Infant's cereal
2. Fairy-tale heavies
3. Reclined
4. Group with common bonds
5. Random one or another
6. Terminus
7. Title for Elton
8. Positioning at intervals
13. Winged being
16. Out-of-control demonstration
17. Chewy candy
18. Stout-hearted
19. Confirmation, for one
20. South Yemen port
21. Wealthy family's estate
22. Maxim
23. Processed, as ham
25. Put a hold on
26. Mauna Loa output
28. Unclothed
29. Is important
32. Poet Ogden
34. Figaro, for one
36. Diagram sentences
37. Cicatrix
38. Lean (toward)
40. Feel sorry about
41. Folding change?
42. I love, to Brutus

ACROSS

1. Bounder
4. Poetic ring champ
7. Urgently eager
9. Plenty
11. South American capital
12. Has trouble with sibilants
14. Clerical storeroom
18. Affirmation
19. Starts with fright
20. Ski lift: hyph.
21. CIO cohort: abbr.
22. Actor Dullea
23. Want
27. Grooves
28. Affectionate acts
30. Boisterous
31. Practical; simple
32. Tease
33. Squid's screen
34. Elevated in pitch
35. Reporter's coup
38. Rhoda Morgenstern's mother
39. Assayed
41. Organic compound
44. Stepped (on)
46. Prefix with scope
47. Gymnast Korbut
48. Performed
49. Poetic nightfall

DOWN

1. Coolidge's nickname
2. Tel ___
3. Phone change, once
4. Every one
5. Paris legislation
6. Very small: hyph.
8. Sprint
10. Opera extras' props
13. Georgia or Latvia, formerly: abbr.
15. Coronet's cousin
16. Mention
17. *Couture* intials
20. Decimal component
22. Illustrator Rockwell
23. Disparaged
24. Tennyson's Arden
25. Pierre's state: abbr.
26. Suffix for cash
27. German article
29. Killer sharks
30. Surrounded by
33. Social follower
34. Hurry
36. Psychoanalyst Rank
37. Hostess Mesta
40. Former Venetian VIP
42. Inventor Whitney
43. Scarlet or cerise
45. A son of Jacob

ACROSS

1. Shoot-'em-up org.?
5. Augury
6. Embellish
10. Monarch's tenure
12. Pollen pantries
14. Temper (glass)
16. Disney version of a Barrie play
19. Red Muppet
20. Gobbled up
21. Ancient Iranian
22. Disney's Sleeping Beauty
24. Light's former costar
25. Gun gp.
26. Feline collective
27. Valuable violin
30. Extols
31. Has twinges
32. *Les Fleurs du* ___
33. Casting catch
34. Mills of many Disney flicks
37. Small particle
38. Virtue's downfall
39. Yoke sharers
41. Pinocchio's pop, animated by Disney
43. Connect
46. Vaccine
47. Awards for ads
48. Dramatist David
49. Festive nights before
50. Make over

DOWN

1. Ibsen heroine
2. Worship windup
3. Parisian flower?
4. Lansbury of Disney's *Bedknobs and Broomsticks*
6. Greek letter
7. Ceremony
8. Common contraction
9. Disney's Ariel, e.g.
11. Killer whale of film
13. Puts out
15. Luft and Doone
16. Legal beginner
17. Chopping tool
18. Pedagogic gp.
23. Nebraska town
24. Actress Joanne
26. Unhealthy color
27. Sherbet servings
28. Rabbit pal in Disney's *Bambi*
29. Soak (flax)
30. Dispense, as an egg
31. Comedian Johnson
32. Hispanic hand
33. Recess game
34. Casino request
35. White-collar type, for short
36. "Old" Disney dog
38. Pencil piece
40. Unworldly
42. Part of BCE
44. Nailed at a slant
45. Exxon in Argentina

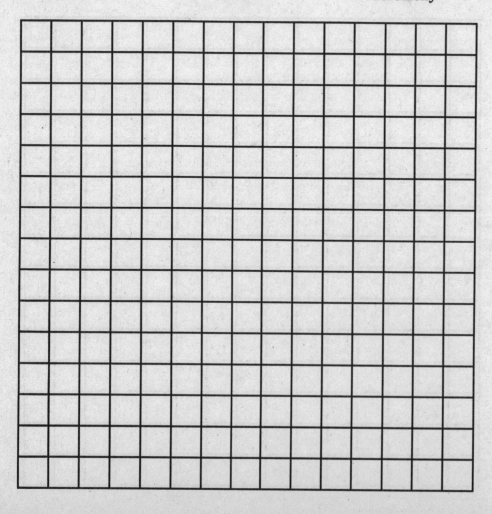

DIAGRAMLESS NUMBER EIGHT

ACROSS

1. Iraqi port
6. Man, for one
7. Put money aside at intervals
9. Sch. for youngsters
13. Tarzan transport
14. John Ritter's dad
15. Vincent Lopez theme
16. Pismire
17. Toothy display
18. *The Tin Drum* author
22. Stamp rolls
25. Exhilarate
27. National League East squad
31. Make effective use (of)
32. Kitchen emanation
33. Church recesses
35. King of primates
37. Marked the spot?
39. Mrs. Sundance
40. NOW cause
43. *Graf* ___
44. Usher's offer
45. Tubular pasta
47. Puccini creations
48. Chair or car

DOWN

1. Stripped to the skin
2. Qty.
3. Lovestruck, old style
4. Demolish
5. Trebek from Canada
6. National League East squad
7. An ex of Frank
8. Flash Gordon nemesis
9. Chang's twin
10. Spanish dramatist
11. Bede's creator
12. Envelope stock
19. Priestly robe
20. Poet Teasdale
21. Twinkler
23. Crater fluid
24. Cinch
26. Triggers
28. Poetic contraction
29. Indulge in histrionics
30. December deliverer
34. Spotted
36. It's found by frisking
38. "Agnus ___"
40. Piccadilly statue
41. Ready for picking
42. Grew hoarier
43. Laurel or Lee
46. Sky altar

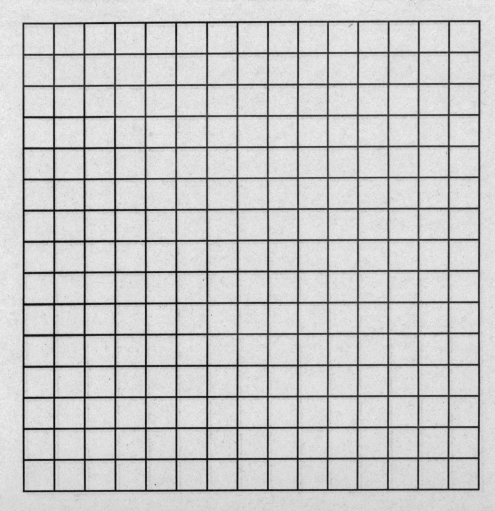

ACROSS

1. Resorts for the wealthy
5. Refrain syllable
8. Georgia or Virginia
9. Haggard novel
12. Start of a Wilder title
13. It may be his or hers
14. Triumphed
15. For each
16. Long time period
17. Correct text
19. Riled
21. It turns litmus paper red
22. Cringe abjectly
25. Some teen employees
28. Mississippi sight
29. Crowd count
30. Schedule abbreviation
32. Roman romantic poet
33. Avarice
34. Yellowstone herd animal
35. Wordplay
36. Cornered above ground
37. Stair part
38. Most hair-raising
40. Scuba users
41. Time periods
42. *Moonstruck* star
43. Ria
45. Place
46. Take from unlawfully
49. Oolong, e.g.
50. *Crème de la crème*
52. Company count
53. Piggery
54. Locales
55. Fasten with stitches
56. Rip

DOWN

1. Remained upright
2. Hock
3. Noshed
4. Chose
5. ___ *Hat* (Astaire hit)
6. Feel badly about
7. Achieved success
8. Epee material
9. Garbo, for one
10. Short endearment
11. Close
18. Teensy bit
20. Female ruff
21. Ventilated
22. Gooey stuff
23. Topical show
24. Sheepish?
25. Piece of paper
26. Pee Wee or Della
27. Take the wheel
29. Lock of hair
31. JFK abbreviations
33. *The ___ Story Ever Told*
34. Amuses
36. Inspire to yawn
37. Fix
39. Pass on (a message)
40. Palm products
42. More appealing
43. "___ a girl!"
44. Wimbledon barrier
45. Pocket bread
47. Be in debt
48. Respond to a curtain call
51. Stretch the truth

ACROSS

1. Short-range rocket: abbr.
4. Curve
7. Narrow blind piece
9. Boor
11. Othello, for one
12. Harass
14. Brit's potato snacks
18. Prufrock poet's monogram
19. Smidgens
20. Participate in a democracy
21. Table scrap
22. Arrived
23. State
27. Niçoise or Caesar
28. Common math term?
30. Circular Greek theater
31. Guard
32. *Out on a ___,* MacLaine opus
33. Handle brutishly
34. Adapts
35. Portal
38. Egg: prefix
39. Attack
41. Showy bloom
44. Pale meat
46. Old dagger
47. Paris pronoun
48. Sty denizen
49. Wedding dowry

DOWN

1. Gathering: abbr.
2. Political coalition
3. Native North Islander
4. Priestly garment
5. Caviar
6. Usual
8. Small combo
10. Tried
13. Pigskin holder
15. *The Eye of the ___* (White novel)
16. Side takers
17. JFK speedster
20. Courage
22. Early suffragist
23. Annexes
24. Gives the appearance of
25. Parvenu
26. Ages and ages and ages
27. Japanese honorific: suffix
29. Salamanders
30. Martini extras
33. Shooter ammo
34. Dandy
36. Favorable press
37. Cede
40. French composer
42. Modernist
43. Bow wood
45. Rent

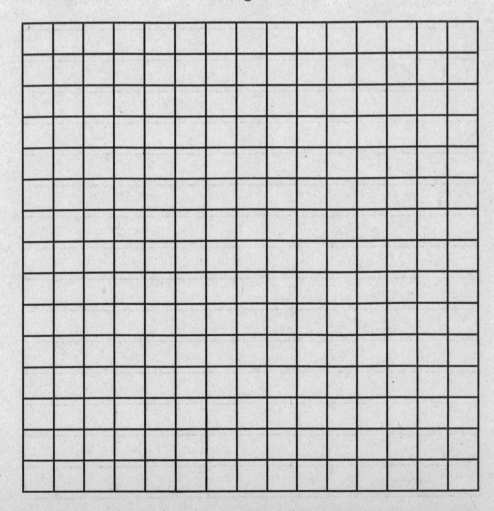

ACROSS

1. Belgian town
4. Remedy
6. Old World wild goat
7. Leppard of rock
10. Stat for a slugger: abbr.
13. Easy tasks
16. "No vacancy"
17. Small particle
19. In the thick of
20. Dictatorial and domineering
21. Adolescents
23. Launch
25. Weapon
27. Political cohort
28. Be in the red
29. Vinaigrette ingredient
30. Rice wine
32. Holiday season
37. Blow from beneath
39. Large sofa
40. Consecrate
41. Volume pumpers
43. French Sudan, today
44. Pride of a pride member
45. Condor's weapon
47. Actor Sparks
48. Neither Rep. nor Dem.
49. Erelong
51. New Haven campus
52. Donnybrook

DOWN

1. Biol. or Geol.
2. Taverns
3. Sphere of conflict
5. Scrutinize
7. Covered with grit
8. Otherwise
9. Emulate Peter Pan
10. Rudner of *Peter's Friends*
11. Dutch South African
12. List particular
14. Serving at 2-Down
15. Star Wars, initially
16. Paddock youngster
18. Collection of anecdotes
20. Charged for
22. Treats a ham
24. Caboose
26. Water jug
29. Perform better than
30. Disburse
31. Church niche
32. Arizona city
33. Youngest Cratchit
34. Beleaguered Boesky
35. Valley
36. Author Bagnold
37. ___ Bator
38. Ocelot, for one
40. ASCAP alternative
42. Detection device
46. Contendere header
50. Hot off the presses

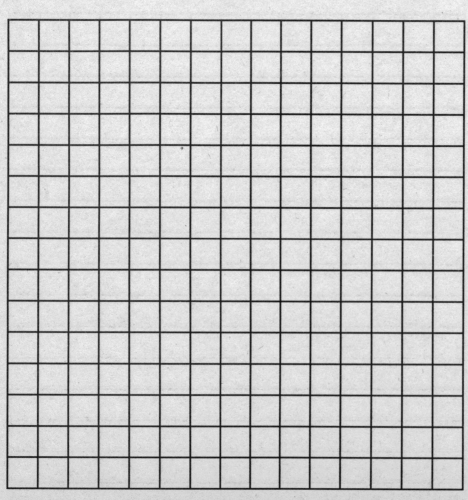

ACROSS

1. Indistinct
4. Barnyard bleat
7. Historical periods
9. Difficult problem
10. More sagacious
12. Country in central Africa, formerly
13. Former Met Rusty
15. Toast named for a diva
16. Pliny's paths
18. 10,000,000 ergs
19. Capitol pressure gp.
21. Zones
23. Eurasian waterway
25. Had a glass of water
26. Hops heater
30. Destiny
31. Courtesy title for an att.
32. Signals on stage
33. Feeder on Fido
34. One of the Alou brothers
36. Movie mutt
37. Flies back
39. Paving substance
40. Cager Thomas
42. At a future time
44. Sound of pain
45. Spanish court dance
47. Creature of Nordic folklore
48. Frozen
50. Actress Skye
51. Resort on the Riviera
52. Mousy
53. Alias, initially

DOWN

1. Morning moisture
2. Rainbow
3. Chew
4. Illegal gratuity
5. Invisible emanation
6. Fall River feller
8. Bench
9. Phone
11. Feels sorry
12. Son of Cronus and Rhea
14. Sired
15. Robin's sitcom role
17. High-pitched cry
18. Daffodil kin
19. Magic Dragon of song
20. Caspian neighbor
22. 16th-century Italian poet
24. Actress Thompson
26. Wood sorrel
27. Canberra's country
28. Bristle
29. Russian despot
34. Harlow
35. Challenge to a duel
37. Iranian monetary unit
38. Male caribou
40. Wit with a twist
41. Foot part
43. Tied
44. Actor David of "Rhoda"
46. Barbra's 1991 costar
47. "___ the season…"
49. Narcs' org.

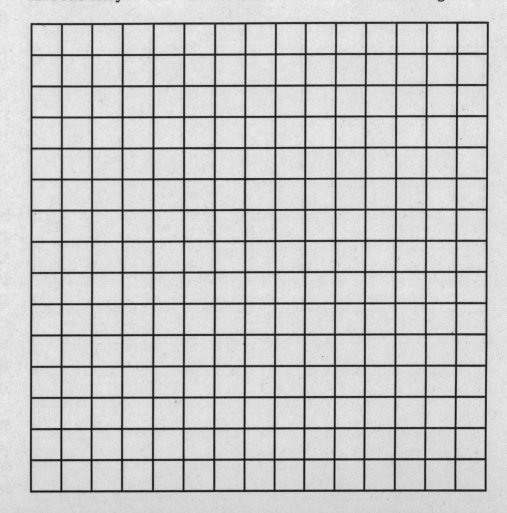

OSCAR LOSERS

ACROSS

1. Get a sense about
5. Horse urger
9. Beat around the bush
11. Desert stopover
13. Tropical grassland
14. *Shogun* author
17. Rush
18. ___-en-Provence, France
19. Katmandu's land
20. Exist
21. Vague suffix
24. Beach scramblers
25. Org. that abducted Patty Hearst
26. Nantes notion
27. Musical sense
28. Frank McCourt book
29. Asian sea
30. Lime quaff
33. Some
34. Stocking thread
36. Mad Hatter's brew
37. Oct. preceder
38. Cello kin
39. Compass dir.
40. Doctrine
43. Christian Science founder
44. Tyke
45. "___ man with seven…"
47. Vintage car
48. Dijon donkey
49. Georgia county
50. Wall St. Deal: abbr.
53. Saloon
54. Absolute
57. Hand-lotion ingredient
59. Musical bridge
60. Movie mutt, Old ___
61. Terrible test marks
62. Dark breads

DOWN

1. Best Picture nominee, 1970
2. Spanish queen
3. Sicilian spewer
4. O'Grady of "Eight Is Enough"
5. Pt. of "ASPCA"
6. Crony
7. Payment period
8. Artist Diego
9. Pate receder
10. Best Picture nominee, 1976
12. Best Picture nominee, 1958
13. Some daisies
15. Science room
16. Bean and Cool J
22. Vacation spot
23. Best Picture nominee, 1969
26. Fin follower
31. Urbane
32. Oriental
35. English town
41. Pelted
42. Cope
45. Little troublemaker
46. ___ *de mer*
51. Heavyweight champ Max
52. Best
55. Paris street
56. Uh-huh
58. *Corrida* cheer

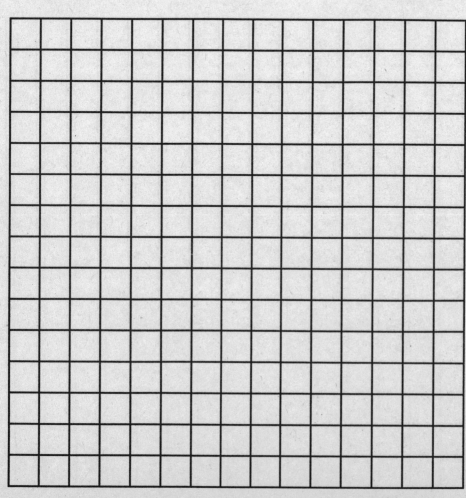

ACROSS

1. Guzzle
5. Blintz's cousin
6. Four-posters, for example
10. Tyne's former costar
11. Jai chaser
12. Two-time US Open champ
14. Essence
15. "Nevermore" speaker
16. Five-time Wimbledon winner
17. Cognizant
19. Paint container
20. With, to Watteau
21. ERA promoter
24. Lateral lead-in
25. Acid variety
26. Hippie digs
28. Blackbird
30. *Hair* composer MacDermot
31. Western lily
32. It puts the red in redheads
34. Soon, once
35. Say cheese
37. Poet Conrad
39. 1988 US Open champ
43. "... ___ saw Elba"

44. Hydrophobia
45. Aren't any longer
46. Valiant's love
47. ___ bene

DOWN

1. Manual art
2. Zeus' better half
3. Straddling
4. Hereditary factor
5. Mother of Chastity
6. Storybook pachyderm
7. Football team

8. *Where Eagles* ___
9. Ratify, in a way
10. Block a play
12. Belgrade's locale
13. Athenian tyrant
14. Baskerville brute
16. Heat meas.
17. City in central Spain
18. Departed
20. ___ *Called Horse*
22. First play of a hand

23. Kiddie cart
25. Veep who stepped down
27. Dress in
29. More bleached
31. Rice brews
33. Borden bovine
35. Small merganser
36. Adult filly
37. O'Day of jazz
38. Brainstorm
40. Qishm's land
41. French composer
42. Help a felon

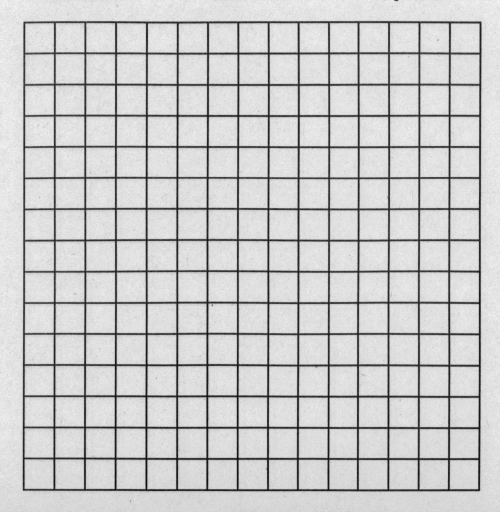

ACROSS

1. Jazzman Getz
5. New ones come out annually
9. Noted positive thinker
10. Takes in
11. Jane Curtin role
12. Singer Bonnie
13. '91 film based on a '50s novel
15. Iowa town
16. Hook's henchman
20. Overseas rep.
21. Caliban, for example
22. Naturalist William
25. Bet
26. '91 film based on a '60s sitcom
31. Siva follower
32. ___ *the Aisle*
33. Soviet cooperative
34. Wine cask
35. Light gas
36. Cinematographer Nykvist
38. '91 film sequel based on a '70s sci-fi series
44. Texas treat
45. More secret
46. Infant's ill
47. Medieval text, ___ *Plowman*
48. Put pedal to metal
49. Utopia

DOWN

1. Ward of *The Fugitive*
2. Chew the fat
3. Washington no-no
4. Requirement
5. Eddy of music
6. Sweeping stories
7. One of Alcott's quartet
8. *Concorde* initials
9. Roast in a review
10. Tattoo of sorts
14. Hebrew letter
16. Coup for Sharif
17. Starstruck sages?
18. First name in stunt cycling
19. Unearthly
20. Pop singer Paula
21. Proust hero
23. Luxury car letters
24. Abstruse
26. Comparison word
27. Take on
28. Within: prefix
29. Mideastern seaport
30. Source
36. Steps over a wall
37. Legitimate
38. Bargain hunt
39. Ready to pick
40. Oklahoma city
41. Low joint?
42. Dancer Castle, casually
43. 1040 collectors, for short
44. Dosage units: abbr.

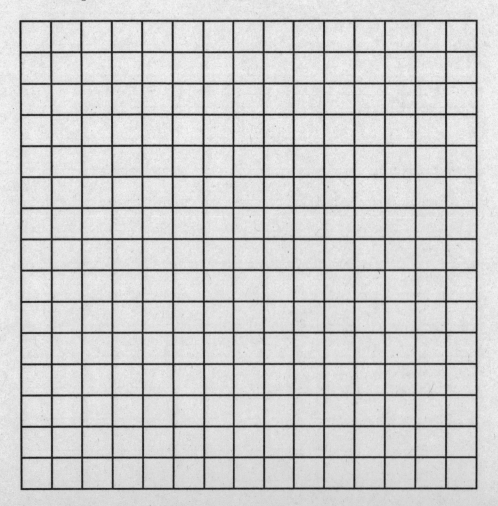

DIAGRAMLESS NUMBER SIXTEEN

CLASSIC SPORTS STARS

ACROSS

1. Bianca's sharp sister
5. Rigatoni or spaghetti
10. Norwegian royal
11. Coffeepot paper
12. Harvest-ready
13. Joe of 49er fame
14. Dinner-table staple
16. Job extra
17. Short cut
18. Pleasant path
19. Stout relative
20. It's held by a thole
21. Frolic
23. Famed reliever Rollie
27. Related through mom
29. List-ending abbr.
30. Taj follower
33. Racket wielder Ilie
35. Word with "land" or "made"
36. Formal address
37. *6 Rms __ Vu*
38. French troubadour Jacques
40. Vigoda of "Fish"
43. Legal eagle: abbr.
44. Elegant
46. Cager Charles
48. First of billions
49. Filled pastry
50. Pedestal part
51. Greek letter
52. Pt. of "USA"

DOWN

1. Moslem holy book
2. Showing similarities
3. Video ribbon
4. At any time
5. Possible nursery hue
6. Carol of high fashion
7. Try of sorts
8. __'clock scholar
9. Spirited steed
11. Heavyweight George
13. Casaba, for one
14. Smeltery dross
15. Seraglio
16. Whittle (down)
20. Fairy-tale opener
22. School grp.
23. FDR's repeated word
24. Possessive pronoun
25. Cheer syllable
26. More abbreviated
28. Elizabeth I's treasonous courtier
31. Friendliness
32. Enlist troops
34. Flooring piece
38. Lawn leaf
39. Tidbit of gossip
40. Sanction felonies
41. Master of the fugue
42. Perry's creator
43. *Inter* __
44. Arp's movement
45. Dutch export
47. Krazy __ (comic strip)

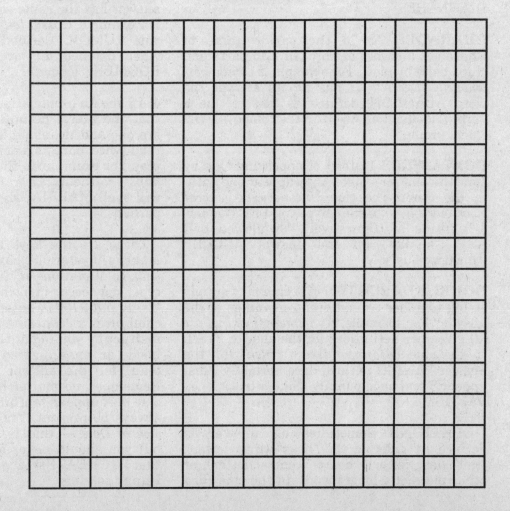

Cryptic crosswords are puzzles specially designed for lovers of wordplay. Each clue in a cryptic crossword is a miniature game of wits. To play, you need to know what's in the puzzlemaker's box of tricks. The keys to that box are given below, to get you started in the game.

The master key is knowing that every cryptic clue is like an equation with two parts: a normal definition of the answer, plus a second hint using wordplay. These two parts are strung together; figuring out where one part ends and the other begins is the challenge of the game. Seasoned solvers learn to look for the following types of wordplay:

ANAGRAMS The letters of the answer may be given in scrambled form in the clue, along with a figurative word or phrase to warn you. In the clue *Analyze San Diego wrongly (8)*, you are asked to find an 8-letter word meaning "analyze" that is an anagrammed (i.e., wrongly spelled) version of "San Diego." The answer? DIAGNOSE.

CHARADES As in the parlor game of Charades, answers are broken into parts and clued piece by piece. For example, *A combo performing "Desert" (7)* has for its answer the word ABANDON, defined as "desert" (as a verb) and clued as A + BAND ("combo") + ON ("performing").

CONTAINERS Instead of appearing side by side, the answer's pieces may appear one within the other. The clue *Unconscious general swallowed by snake (6)* gives you LEE ("general") inside of (figuratively, "swallowed by") ASP ("snake") for the answer ASLEEP ("unconscious").

DOUBLE DEFINITIONS A clue may simply string together two different meanings of the answer. For example, *Apartment lacking air (4)* gives two definitions for the answer FLAT. In the clue *Disappear like a truck? (6)*, the answer VANISH is clued once normally ("disappear") and once punnily ("like a truck," i.e., VAN-ISH).

DELETIONS Sometimes an answer is derived by deleting the "head" (first letter), "tail" (last letter), "heart" (central letter), or other piece of a longer word. In the clue *Bird dog loses its head (5)*, the answer EAGLE is derived when BEAGLE sheds its front letter.

HIDDEN WORDS On occasion, the answer may actually appear within the clue, camouflaged. In the clue *Santa's teddy bears sampled (6)*, the phrase "Santa's teddy" carries (i.e., "bears") the answer TASTED. Easy, when you know what to look for!

REVERSALS A clue may playfully hint that the answer spelled backward would create a new word. In the clue *Lucifer was returning (5)*, the answer DEVIL results when the word LIVED ("was") turns backward. In Down clues, which refer to vertical diagram entries, look for hints like "rising," "northward," "overturned," etc. For example, the Down clue *Jeans material is dug up (5)* gives the answer DENIM, which is MINED ("dug") when seen upside down.

HOMOPHONES A clue may tell you that the answer has the same sound as another word. For example, *Gossip lodger overheard (5)* gives you RUMOR (defined as "gossip"), which when listened to ("overheard") sounds like ROOMER ("lodger").

& LITS. An exclamation point will tip you off that the literal definition and the wordplay are one and the same. The entire clue can be read twice: once as a definition, once as wordplay. For example, in the clue *A grim era, perhaps! (8)*, the letters in AGRIMERA "perhaps" will spell MARRIAGE, which is "a grim era, perhaps!"

These are the keys that unlock the cluemaker's mysterious box. Be aware, however, that combinations of two or more wordplay types may occur in a single clue. For example, *Writer put $100 in battered portmanteau (6,6)* combines a container and an anagram, instructing you to put C (short for a $100 bill) inside an anagrammed version of "portmanteau" for the answer TRUMAN CAPOTE. Remember, no matter how weird or twisty a clue may appear, fair hints for its solution will always be present. You may get temporarily *sick of Dole* — that is, FOOLED (anagram), but you should never feel *Centigrade-hot* — that is, CHEATED (C + HEATED). Happy solving!

ACROSS

1. Hose got nicks at sea (8)

5. Sound of pursued virgin (6)

10. Opposed anti-gas amendment (7)

11. Part-time athlete breaking promise (7)

12. California town thug captures lowly bum (9)

13. Employers in American emergency room service (5)

14. Squatters enter disruptively, circling southern school (7)

16. Funny gags editor declined (6)

18. Police department, taking speed, chattered on and on (6)

21. Reversing routine, bites vegetables (7)

24. Two companies with a hot drink (5)

25. Lacking space somewhat, alternatively ran back to goal (9)

27. Turner's article in garbage hill (7)

28. Old resident of Nova Scotia in current notice by author Fleming (7)

29. Fool guy about train (6)

30. Experimental trial lot is Mexican food (8)

DOWN

1. Hiding evidence of smoking in vice squad operation (8)

2. Revelations: somehow so clear (7)

3. Bizarre kindergarten in Kentucky (5)

4. No note on small household items (7)

6. Chow Mom put back in her sandwich (9)

7. Best new perm accepted by Sue (7)

8. Foul stogie for selfish one (6)

9. A team's digressions (6)

15. Drew out person in a crowd scene, played without lead (9)

17. In regattas, then, I anticipate weakness (8)

19. Performance coming up later includes one Catholic (7)

20. Actor ironed shifts (2, 4)

21. Road not destroyed in big storm (7)

22. Conversely, Latin I has one beginning (7)

23. Cowardly charge in South Dakota (6)

26. Catch circle up in modern designs (2, 3)

ACROSS

1. Dough in small amount for gate-crasher? (9, 3)

8. Withdraw from former President, backing Democrat ultimately (7)

9. Start off Percival playing piano (7)

11. Pronounced chunks of ice in streams (5)

12. Walked in the morning with Bud, keeping behind schedule (9)

13. Serve one's time for lying (9)

15. Seabirds head away from backs of ships (5)

16. Author of *Dee Wilder* (5)

18. Fish submit to workman (9)

20. Governed by bishops sloshing Pepsi-Cola (9)

23. Go up average branch (5)

24. Crowded turf surrounding me (7)

25. Cast that won this and that (7)

26. Saint given rank after evil spirit showed (12)

DOWN

1. Fasteners save large loads (7)

2. Parson set off switch (9)

3. Complex tragedy involves nameless actor (5)

4. Egg container in Caribbean island garbage that's overturned (9)

5. Good bar is something much sought-after (5)

6. A large pot containing iodine alternative for flier (7)

7. Some peaceniks make a sketch of a Los Angeles team? (5, 7)

10. Communist ones praise deal again (12)

14. Adventures complicated Spade case (9)

15. Perceptive insect following furrow (9)

17. Fortune taking truck aboard ship (7)

19. Hotel in *The Damned* initially lost substance (7)

21. Arrived with ring for small role (5)

22. Let down cow? (5)

ACROSS

1. Ring fee (4)

3. Respectable ID bracelet is undone (10)

9. One medium, taking cover, drank (7)

11. Harsh profligate sour about gold card's debut (7)

12. Fellow returned an unearthly gift (5)

13. Drew, having consumed two fifths of vodka, solicited (7)

15. Sneaky old woman veils bad hairstyle (7)

16. Unusual street compass (7)

18. One's one mule ran out (7)

21. Toronto's starting rent fell (7)

23. A couple of judges finish off keg and hit record player? (7)

25. Give directions to ox (5)

27. Circulating fruit to the audience (7)

28. Teacher is home hiding treasure (7)

29. Copy ran: "Scene printed in *People*" (10)

30. Switch dog's feet around (4)

DOWN

1. Successful wrestling tip hurt man (10)

2. The French prohibit running Mideast nation (7)

4. Clearing delegate's lead in Canadian constituency (7)

5. Gets car trips around east (7)

6. Transport friar around Central America (5)

7. Widen thoroughfare maintained by Franklin (7)

8. Leaders of expedition are sure you like pie? (4)

10. Tenant outside at hearing (7)

14. Perish, tangled under heavy metal power structure? (10)

17. Stamp, rise wildly, and take legal action (7)

19. Music session uplifted monster on one island (7)

20. Toss all but the tail of stiff seafood (7)

21. It might drive you to overuse a Bic, perhaps (7)

22. Showing viper we shot (7)

24. Ships polished up (5)

26. Meaningless bits of jazz get lost (4)

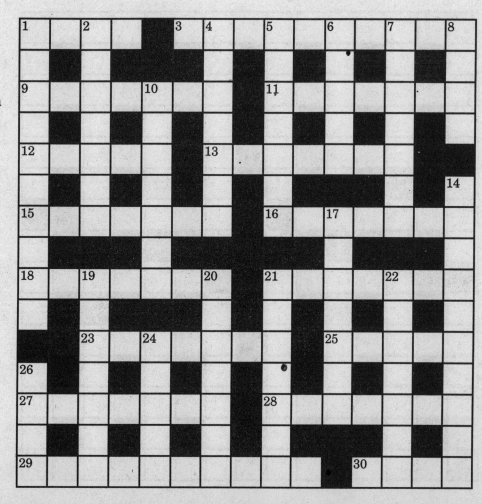

ACROSS

1. To become famous, drop a grade in school? (2, 4, 2, 7)

9. Idle realtors get their profits thus? (3, 2, 10)

10. I snared flying fish (7)

11. Ed provided ice for building (7)

12. Jazzy singer quit (6)

14. Types all but one of army chief's letters (6)

17. To pour rum takes pluck (6)

19. Ohio city, in addition, has been #1 (6)

23. Arbiter cooked up a cheese dish (7)

24. Ancient with wobbly sea-legs (7)

26. Removes shrubbery and is curtly dismissed? (4, 3, 5-3)

27. What a hammy performer does indicates herbivorousness? (5, 3, 7)

DOWN

1. Cooper has more expenses than income, making dictionary (8)

2. Discourage article (in German) about *E.T.* (5)

3. Fly around rear of ship, lightly moving in the wind (7)

4. Pressed counterfeit dinero (6)

5. Heavy-duty insulation for electrical unit is limited (8)

6. Nun almost gets into a certain chapel (7)

7. Partner of either one eating stew, to start (9)

8. Selection from Alfred Noyes is up there (6)

13. Rube involved in awful set-to with coquette (9)

15. Marriage breaks off for Ruby's anniversary? (8)

16. Fleshy or floppy type of pest (8)

18. Money-back deals wherein fortuneteller grabs the check and returns (7)

20. Examine poem in Old English (7)

21. Unfortunate soldier riding northbound carriage (6)

22. Mother and doctor like a city in India (6)

25. Lacking leadership, wild people run away (5)

ACROSS

1. For a hand, decent doctor ad-libbed (8)

5. Spots listener's eyeglasses (6)

9. Returned painting, poem and cross (8)

10. Cabbie's passengers carrying piece of luggage and torches (6)

11. Around 10, changing score, I'm getting dispirited? (8)

12. Audited *Country* and Travolta movie (6)

14. Date of Don's revue changed with receipt of last letter (10)

18. Chimp rode buggy, carrying club and needle (10)

22. Pretend to be Buchanan, penning ballad (4, 2)

23. Salt found in tree top (8)

24. Cinema clowns ineffective (6)

25. Small fork in grating (8)

26. Refusal at London gallery to score (6)

27. Neophyte groupie grabs poor Sherm (8)

DOWN

1. Spread for poker? (6)

2. Keep pulling fiery serpent (6)

3. Section of Ragtag Encyclopedia Company (6)

4. Gets discouraged as the roles changed (5, 5)

6. Split jackpot with leaders of Ohio Lottery Association (8)

7. Herb has to request ID from one parent? (8)

8. American prisoner's first beset by feeling—an uncertain feeling (8)

13. Be in charge of trade-ins I'm modifying (10)

15. Pastor fellow reclined (8)

16. Open with a soft pop? (8)

17. I trade; it's wrong for philosopher (8)

19. Against heartless class pranks (6)

20. "Beat It" contains excellent shout (6)

21. Scientist running after salamander (6)

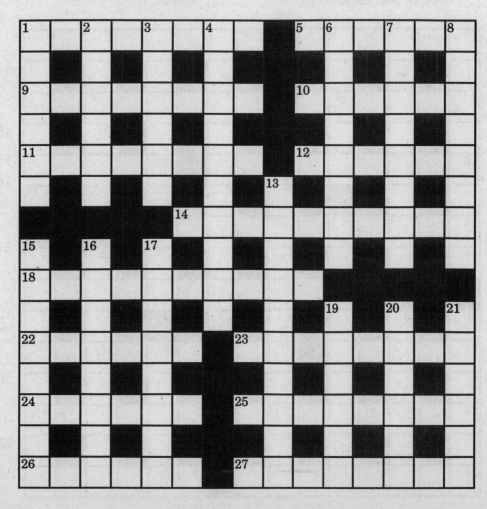

ACROSS

1. Many a cut of fish is left out (6)

4. Soldiers amid long day in a rural spot (8)

9. Revolutionary who rode for honor (6)

10. Hot dinner's beginning during mountaineering (8)

12. Walked into a remarkable stadium in Houston (9)

13. Gold coin—one lodged in pipe (5)

14. Actor makes painting in wood in two minutes (6, 6)

18. What New Jersey basketball fans yell back to criticize the female figure in court (12)

21. Albert endlessly exercises to get more fit (5)

22. Workers together temporarily during breakfast ask for cereal (4, 5)

24. Composer reversed part for soloist? (8)

25. Apparel used by Eskimo, normally (6)

26. Exam for grads—an exam that's best (8)

27. Britain's capital endures explosions (6)

DOWN

1. Some corn protected by company's guns (8)

2. John, conservative, follows hot rock (8)

3. Roots all around trunk (5)

5. Scientist got oil search reorganized (12)

6. Mom embraces the Spanish "love doctor" in play (9)

7. Each pastry gets eaten by pilot (6)

8. Understand the thing's figures (6)

11. Search is restricting country's alliances (12)

15. Meet in brief court (9)

16. Has a conversation about Brazilian resort vehicles (8)

17. In sport, tee up in some woody greenery (8)

19. Blabbermouth from Georgia idly speaks up (6)

20. Chewed chicle with a jaded expression (6)

23. Unnecessary decoration makes pair of Frenchmen sick (5)

ACROSS

1. Stole two sleeping accommodations (7)

5. Party in Canada proposed Constitutional amendment in new bill (7)

9. Clean hit, then hit followed by error (5)

10. Union man getting cut 'round end of July (9)

11. English bloke rejected title (4)

12. To become hardened about Jack is wrong (6)

16. Blessing, to get free of debts? (8)

17. Hammer hosts leader of Rolling Stones (6)

19. Navigational aid with front missing, yet to be found (6)

20. Playing polo, man straddles one pony (8)

22. Walk like a bear in the wood? (6)

23. Club car turned risqué (4)

27. Eccentric crab's, well,...eccentric (9)

28. About 100 came afresh to Middle eastern city (5)

29. Unusual red item with black mark (7)

30. Many set free! (7)

DOWN

1. Taxi in the middle of traffic always produces claustrophobic feeling (5, 5)

2. I'd invested in friend's cow (10)

3. Cultivated so-called wheat product (4)

4. Major piece of wisdom in anthology (8)

5. Engineer must lie endlessly in scientific paper (6)

6. He takes vows to solicit alms, accepting free quarters (10)

7. In revolving door, get cross (4)

8. Places garlands on the ears (4)

13. Bad winter impedes movement of water for plant (10)

14. Muffling Quayle, a spokesman's repeated stonewalling (10)

15. Old army boy mixed a drink (6, 4)

18. Bush attended to rising American problem (8)

21. I'm getting bargain, in effect (6)

24. Consumed cactus, edible when peeled (4)

25. Bring up dirt about Cher's last tattoo (4)

26. Sign submarine captain up (4)

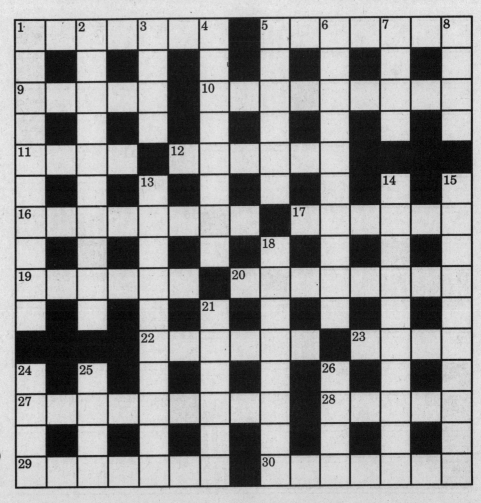

CRYPTIC CROSSWORD EIGHT

ACROSS

1. Vice President's bizarre clairvoyance (14)

8. Right chaps in advertisement (5)

9. I say bad things about Crusoe? (8)

10. Emissary admits it—I'm right (10)

11. Help Mr. Lincoln before start of term (4)

14. Sparkling $1,000 gem—in L.A., maybe (8)

15. Eddy gets "X"—voter mistaken (6)

17. Take to the ground during playground game, setting a record? (6)

19. Made clothing—black lame (8)

22. Attempt to infiltrate press table (4)

23. Animal causing havoc in mid-auction (10)

25. Note: call errant knight (8)

26. Explorer's duck (5)

27. Not essential to have nonsense poem ad-libbed (14)

DOWN

1. Stage player can make grand, final entrance (6, 5)

2. Record-breaking green centerpiece (7)

3. Written composition of criminal charge announced (10)

4. B-1 seized by 29th—I am in Europe (8)

5. Virginia allows servants (6)

6. Number belted by Peron in *Evita* (4)

7. Dessert gel includes seasoning (7)

12. Hacks with tip of the hatchet I had, topping flowers (4, 7)

13. Islamic man, describing love, overacted (10)

16. Czar's d*** Riot Act misapplied (8)

18. Group of troops encoded "Alpha"—name unknown (7)

20. Goolagong, dropping first two, faulted some time back (4, 3)

21. Small amount, half-dollar, cut off (6)

24. Top came off (4)

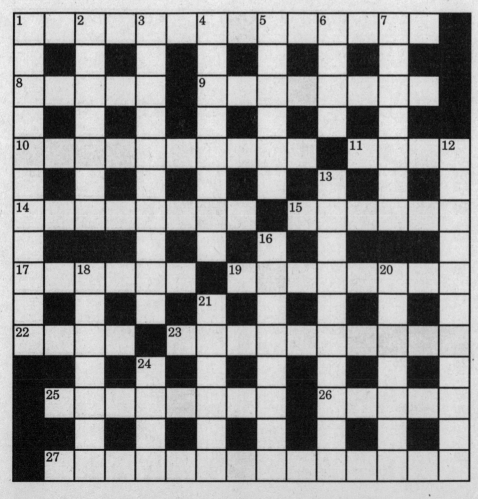

CROSSWORD 1

```
F O G G . A L U M . U M B E L
O L O R . F A R O . M A I N E
A L B A T R O S S . A N G S T
M A I T A I . A H S . A B U T
. . I N C A . E M I G R E S .
S E L F S A M E . O L E O . .
T R A Y . B L O C S . T E L .
E I S . P A L O O K A . H A E
P E T . O N E P M . M E S S .
. H A L T . E P I C U R E S .
B O U D O I R . H A H S . . .
W A R M . C O W . M U K L U K
A T R I A . S H A N G R I L A
N E A R S . E U R O . A N N E
A S H E S . S P A T . T E A L
```

CROSSWORD 2

```
A L A S . T E M P . S R A
R O S H . I G L U . H E R
M A K E A C O I N . E R A
. . K I S S . J U G U M .
A R C E D . A A R O N . .
P U L L A R A B B I T . .
E T E . I L E . T D S . .
. O U T O F T H E H A T .
S P R I T . E L E G Y . .
S H A N E . O S L O . . .
P O T . D I S A P P E A R
E R R . U R S A . E R G O
E T A . P E A R . D E E D
```

CROSSWORD 3

```
A B C S . P R I M . U L A
M O A T . R O N A . N I B
S O S O . U S E R . S E E
. T H U N D E R C L O U D
. . T O E . T H O U . . .
R O W . A R E . O G L E .
S T O R M Y W E A T H E R
T O R E . E R R . T E A .
. D A B S . A C T . . . .
G U L L Y W A S H E R S .
O N E . L I M E . X I I I
A D S . A P E R . A D D S
L O S . W E N S . S E E M
```

CROSSWORD 4

```
A L A . M E G A . S M E W
D O T . O A R S . T E L E
O W L . T R E K . I D L E
. A R E N A . D R I E D .
B A N E S . T R U S T . .
L O T S . A S I A . E W E
U N I . S M A L L . R E D
E E C . H O L E . T R I G
. O V E R T . S H A R E .
L A C E D . L I K E N . .
A X E L . S A R I . E A T
G L A D . A K I N . A G E
S E N T . L E S S . N O N
```

CROSSWORD 5

```
P E A R . T E S T S . E L M S
A C R E . A T T I C . S E E S
C H E V Y C H A S E . T E N T
K O S . E K E S . N E H R U .
. B A L L . S A S E . . . .
E R A S E . P O R T R A I T
A F A R . G I G I . R I D E
C R I B . L I N G O . O M E N
M E S A . O R G Y . L E A D
E M E R A L D S . W E L D S .
. A I L S . P A T E . . . .
H A R D Y . I A G O . D A S
S U L U . G O R D O N J U M P
A G E S . A D O R N . A P I E
M E S H . G E N E S . R E E D
```

CROSSWORD 6

```
. M A C S . W A S . F A Y
D I N A H . A L E . R O E
A N K L E . C A N . O N S
S T A L L F O R T I M E .
. . A T E . M A R . . .
A F T . E T A . O H I O .
P R O C R A S T I N A T E
R I T A . H U D . T A R .
. R I O . R E A . . . .
. F I D D L E F A D D L E
C O D . O L D . T O R U S
O I L . L I N . E R A S E
O L E . S E A . D E B T .
```

CROSSWORD 7

```
T A B S . P R O F . C A D .
A C I D . L A P I S . M A N I
C H R I S E V E R T . O T T O
T E D . E B E N . R A S H E R
. O V E N . P A S T Y . . .
B A S T E S . C E N T . R O B
A V O I R . B R A G A . I V A
S I N S . A R U L E . A G O D
R A J . O B E S E . A M B L E
A N A . M I N T . C R A Y O N
. H E A L S . R A T S . . .
S T E R N E . G E N E . A R C
W A N T . N A N C Y L O P E Z
I L I E . E R A T O . N I N A
G E E . A T O N . O N O R .
```

CROSSWORD 8

```
G A S . A L A I . P A C T
A X E . B O R N . A R L O
R E P . B U T T E R C U P
B L A M E D . R A I S E S
. R A Y . S E T S . . .
E R A S . P O P E . S E A
B U T T E R F I N G E R S
B E E . L O A D . O N E S
. M O P S . B E A . . .
T R O U P E . B A S T E D
B U T T E R F L Y . O L E
A L O E . T R U E . R I B
R E E D . Y A R D . S A T
```

CROSSWORD 9

```
R A Z Z . S O L D . S C E N T
O J A I . A P E R . T O P A Z
T A N G E R I N E . A R I S E
C R E S C E N T W R E N C H .
. . U K E . U L E . . . .
L O S T . S T E M . T R I O
O C C A M S . R E A L . E L L
T H E N E W Y O R K T I M E S
T E N . G A E L . I D O I D O
O R E O . Y A L E . O X E N
. N E Z . N B A . . . .
F U L L E R B R U S H M A N .
B A S I L . I R O N H O R S E
I R E N E . J I L T . P E T E
L O R E N . N E S S . I D I D
```

CROSSWORD 10

```
M A I D . A S K . A L D A
A C N E . P I E . R A I N
K E R N S E R N . O M A N
E R O S E . S T U M B L E
. . I T S . P A S . . .
D I C T A T O R S . D I P
X R A Y . I D O . C A K E
V E T . F R E N C H M E N
. T A I . A L A . . . .
I N S T E A D . U S I N G
R E B A . L O W E S D O E
O R A L . I R R . I L L S
N O T E . A M Y . S E A T
```

CROSSWORD 11

```
H O R S E . J A M B . A D O
U N I T A S . E L A L . L U X
M E D U S A . S I T U . I K E
. M Y B L U E H E A V E N .
S L A B . R E I N . H I E S
H E L L B E N T . R A M . .
Y O D E L . A S K E W . S I P
E N E . U M P . I D A . L O U
R A N . E X E R T . I C O N S
. O V I . E T H I O P I A .
S E R E . C L E A . L E A N
T H E B L U E A N G E L . .
O A R . V E N T . U N I T E D
A M I . E L S E . E D D I E D
D E E . T E E D . S E E K S
```

CROSSWORD 12

```
F L A G . B I N . C H E F
L A M A . R T E . H O L E
A P P L A U S E . E R L E
. A R T . P E N A L . .
S P A . C E N T E R . .
H A T C H . A R T I S A N
O P A L . E V A . N O N E
P A N A C E A . A G A T E
. P E G L E G . K I D .
D R A P E . M E G . . .
Y E T I . A P P R O V A L
E B O N . W E T . L E V I
S A N G . L A Y . D E E P
```

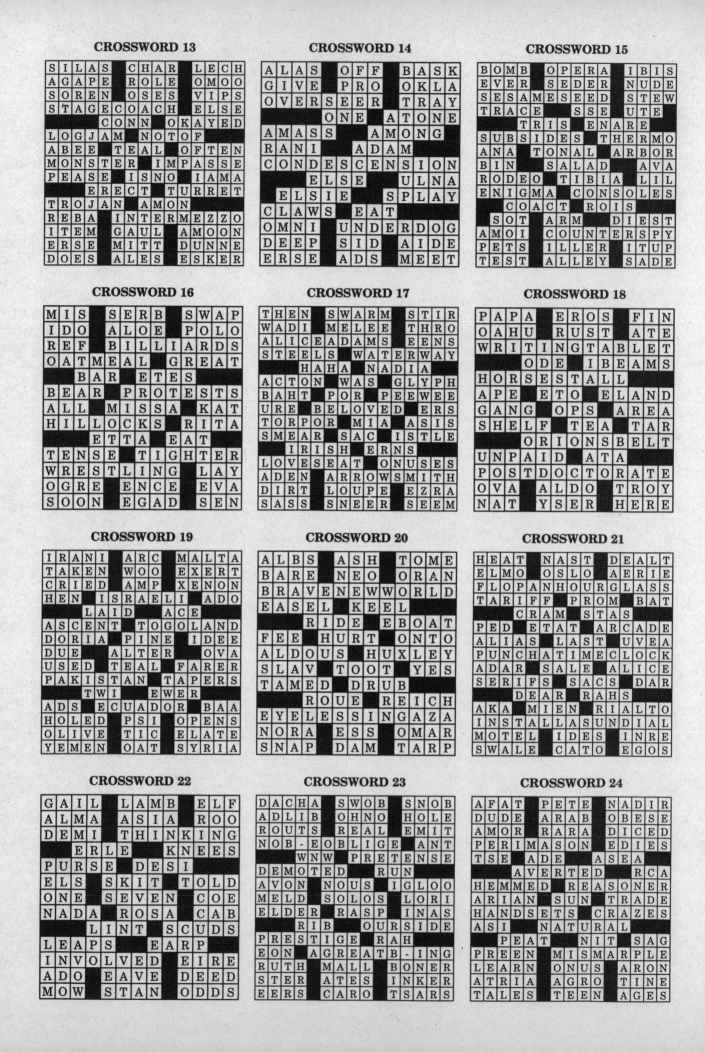

CROSSWORD 13   CROSSWORD 14   CROSSWORD 15
CROSSWORD 16   CROSSWORD 17   CROSSWORD 18
CROSSWORD 19   CROSSWORD 20   CROSSWORD 21
CROSSWORD 22   CROSSWORD 23   CROSSWORD 24

CROSSWORD 25

```
U S E S | B R I E | R O S I E
P A R T | R O T A | A N E R A
S L E A Z Y B A R | N E W E R
    N A C E L L E | M I N E
T A R D I E S | L O A N E D
I C I E R | L A D I N G
L E V E E | N O B E L | G T E
L I E S | S O R E R | S R A S
S N R | P A T E S | G L O S S
    B E R L I N | R O U S E
A P O G E E | S T E E P E N
P U R R | M E D I A T E
A R D E N | T E L L A Y A R N
R E E S E | A L O E | E L I A
T E R S E | T A S S | D E N T
```

CROSSWORD 26

```
  S A B A | D R A B | C A D S
R E L I C | A E R O | A D U E
E G E S T | W A N G | B O E R
F O G H O R N L E G H O R N
      O R E S | L E O N A
E L A P S E | B L E N D
T E D | S A L E | C L A N G
C H I C K E N O F T H E S E A
S I T O N | N O T A | T E M
    R E C A P | N O B O D Y
  T Y P E A | A G R O
R O O S T E R C O G B U R N
T O U R | H A I R | I B S E N
H O R A | E S S E | E L O P E
O P E L | R Y E S | S E S S
```

CROSSWORD 27

```
O S H A | A L A S |   A R A S
R A E S | N I C E |   D O L E
T R I T E | T R E E | O M I T
  A R I V A L A S P I R A N T
A F L | E R E | R E N E E
R I O | C R E O L E | O D E
K N O B |   G R U N T
  A M B R O S E B I E R C E
  C H A P S |   Y A M S
E A R | O R A T O R | N E E
S P A S M | T O O | A R E
T O P U B L I C H O N O R S
E L I A | A C H E | E L I O T
E L E V | R O A R | G E N E
M O R E | A N T S | A S S N
```

CROSSWORD 28

```
S H E S | A D A M | W H O L E
P E S T | T O G A | A U R A S
L A K E W O B E G O N D A Y S
U T I L I Z E | N O D | T E A
R E M E T | R H E O | C O T Y
G R O S | O M I T | P A R T S
E S S | C H A D | T E V Y E
    M I N N E S O T A
B L U T O | O P T S | P E R
L E A R Y | P U R E | D O L E
A L T E | C A T O | F O O L S
A D E | L O G | C B R A D I O
G A R R I S O N K E I L L O R
E M A I L | D I E D | L E T T
R E L A Y | A N T E | S S T S
```

CROSSWORD 29

```
L A D S | E R R I S | T S A R
A V O W | S A I N T | A H O Y
V I P E R P I P E R | L E N A
A D E L A I D E | E I L E E N
      T I E S | P A W E R
A P P E N D | D E M A R C H E
C H A R S | P A T E S | H A L
T I P S | M O W E R | T E L L
O L E | R O W E R | B R E V E
F E R R U L E S | G L A R E S
  C E D A R | S E A N
C R A V E S | S P O N S O R S
H O P E | S U P E R D U P E R
O V E R | E K I N G | D U S T
P E R T | S E T T E | E S T A
```

CROSSWORD 30

```
W A L T | S T A F F | E S P Y
I G O R | H O V E R | S E R A
M A C A D A M I Z E | T R A P
P R O V O K E D | A D A P T S
      E R O S | S K A T E
T H E S I S | E M I N E N C E
H E A T S | C L O S E | T A B
I T S Y | C O U T H | S I N E
N U T | S H A D E | S A N E R
S P O L I A T E | F O R E S T
    F I N I S | L I L A
B R E T O N | M A N I T O B A
L E D A | S T E V E D O R E S
O P E N | A U G E R | G E E K
T O N Y | W E A R Y | A L P S
```

CROSSWORD 31

```
A G O G | O M E G A |   S E T
L I R A | H U L A S | E L S E
L O I S | A D M I T | L A T E
I T S H A R D O N A F A C E
E T O | G A Y |   I N K E D
S O N A R | R A B E | E M U
    T E A T I M E | O R S O
  F R E S H V O I C E S
S H A Y | T R E N T O N
R O C | T O U R | N O M E N
A S T A R | D E C | O D A
  T O G E T L A U G H E D I N
S A T E | S E I N E | R U S T
A G U E | A N D E S | A L O E
G E M | R O A S T | T E N S
```

CROSSWORD 32

```
F R O S H | S L I D | S T U D
R E V U E | T I N E | L O N E
A L I B I | A D A M | A N D S
    A S T R O N O M Y I O I
S H U T T E R | L U S T E R
K E T O S E | G R I S | E S E
I M A M | A L A S K A
P H I L O S O P H Y I O I
    C A R E S S | R I S E
O R G | R N A S | H A M L E T
B E L U G A | F O R A Y E D
E C O N O M I C S I O I
Y E R S | E T A T | U L T R A
E D I E | N O V O | S E R U M
D E A R | T R A P | E D I T S
```

CROSSWORD 33

```
T A N G O | C A S S | J A M B
A B O U T | A S H E | O M A R
T O N I T O N Y A N T H O N Y
S U E D | N Y E | S E A S O N
    A U T O | B U R N
  A N N A N N E A N N I E
M A D C A P | I L L | D N A
E P E E S | A C T | T A L O N
T I A | A S H | L O N E L Y
  E L I E L I E E L I A S
    N A B S | G A L L
P L A T T E | A R M | Y O R E
A R T E A R T I E A R T H U R
C O N N | T O R T | L I N E N
K N O T | A M Y S | S C O R E
```

CROSSWORD 34

```
F A R M | S U R A T | K I N G
E Q U I | P H A S E | E S A U
N U N N | O U S T S | W E B S
D A G U E R R E O T Y P E S
    T A T U |   T A I
S T A I R S | U K U L E L E
T I D A L | T A B U | O N T
O B I | F L U T E | T S E
P I E | B E E R | E Q U U S
  A U D U B O N | P L U S E S
    E R R |   S I L O
S E P T U A G E N A R I A N
E U R O | A R E N T | U L N A
A L A S | R E E S E | M E N U
R U S E | Y O K E R | S T E T
```

CROSSWORD 35

```
C L O D | V I C E | B E R G S
R A R A | I D O L | O C A L A
I R A N | L E N S | V O C A L
B A L A C L A V A | I N E R T
      H A L E | N O S E Y
R A B B I | S Y S T E M
O C E A N S | S A O | I C E D
O R E G A N O | P I C C O L O
M E S A | A D O | L L A M A S
  T I G E R S | A L O N E
A R D E N | D I M S
D I A L S | L E G I S L A T E
A G I L E | U R N S | O B E Y
P O S E R | B E E T | P E A R
T R Y S T | E D D Y | E L L E
```

CROSSWORD 36

```
A M A H | M O R S E | G L U T
T I T I | A L E U T | R O S A
O N O S | R E A C H | A G E R
Z I P P O C I P H E R Z E R O
    A V E C |   R E E
R E G N A L | A L E F | L A T
A L A I | L E A R | E U R
Z I L C H D I D D L Y N A D A
E T E | O I S E | E R I C
D E S | I V A N | D A I N T Y
    S S E | B E R G
S Q U A T S C R A T C H N I X
M U L L | T H E S E | B O R E
E I N E | E A T E R | O M A N
E D A M | D R E S S | R E N O
```

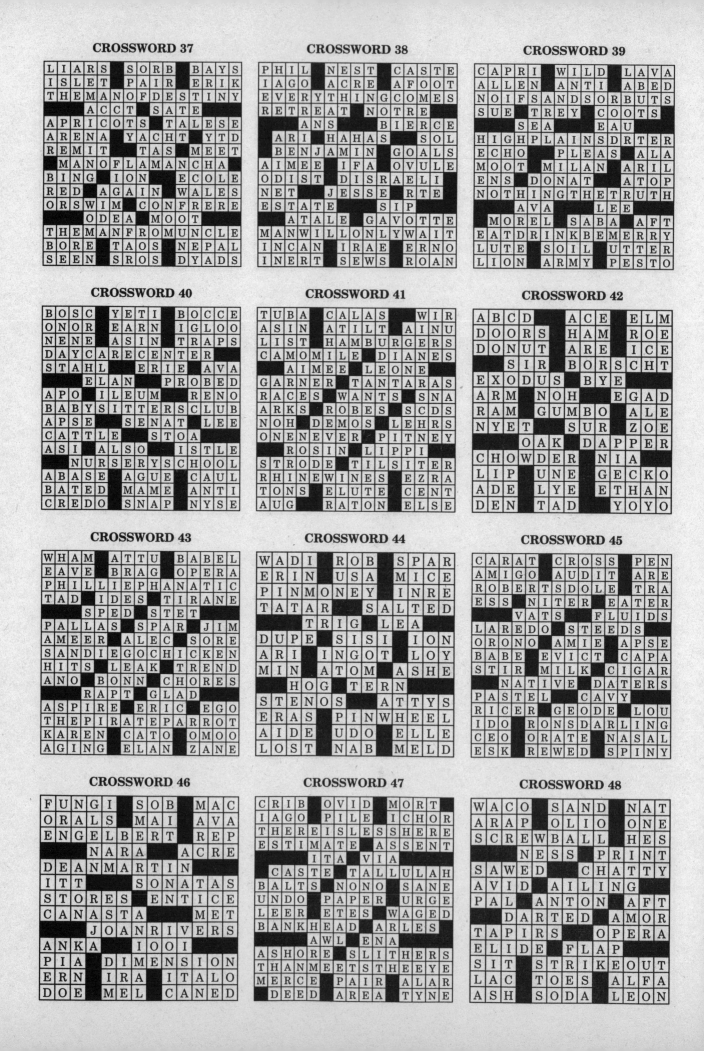

CROSSWORD 37

L	I	A	R	S		S	O	R	B		B	A	Y	S
I	S	L	E	T		P	A	I	R		E	R	I	K
T	H	E	M	A	N	O	F	D	E	S	T	I	N	Y
			A	C	C	T			S	A	T	E		
A	P	R	I	C	O	T	S		T	A	L	E	S	E
A	R	E	N	A		Y	A	C	H	T		Y	T	D
R	E	M	I	T			T	A	S		M	E	E	T
	M	A	N	O	F	L	A	M	A	N	C	H	A	
B	I	N	G		I	O	N			E	C	O	L	E
R	E	D		A	G	A	I	N		W	A	L	E	S
O	R	S	W	I	M		C	O	N	F	R	E	R	E
			O	D	E	A		M	O	O	T			
T	H	E	M	A	N	F	R	O	M	U	N	C	L	E
B	O	R	E		T	A	O	S		N	E	P	A	L
S	E	E	N		S	R	O	S		D	Y	A	D	S

CROSSWORD 38

P	H	I	L		N	E	S	T		C	A	S	T	E
I	A	G	O		A	C	R	E		A	F	O	O	T
E	V	E	R	Y	T	H	I	N	G	C	O	M	E	S
R	E	T	R	E	A	T		N	O	T	R	E		
			A	N	S			B	I	E	R	C	E	
	A	R	I		H	A	H	A	S			S	O	L
	B	E	N	J	A	M	I	N		G	O	A	L	S
A	I	M	E	E		I	F	A		O	V	U	L	E
O	D	I	S	T		D	I	S	R	A	E	L	I	
N	E	T		J	E	S	S	E		R	T	E		
E	S	T	A	T	E			S	I	P				
		A	T	A	L	E		G	A	V	O	T	T	E
M	A	N	W	I	L	L	O	N	L	Y	W	A	I	T
I	N	C	A	N		I	R	A	E		E	R	N	O
I	N	E	R	T		S	E	W	S		R	O	A	N

CROSSWORD 39

C	A	P	R	I		W	I	L	D		L	A	V	A
A	L	L	E	N		A	N	T	I		A	B	E	D
N	O	I	F	S	A	N	D	S	O	R	B	U	T	S
S	U	E		T	R	E	Y		C	O	O	T	S	
			S	E	A					E	A	U		
H	I	G	H	P	L	A	I	N	S	D	R	T	E	R
E	C	H	O		P	L	E	A	S			A	L	A
M	O	O	T		M	I	L	A	N		A	R	I	L
E	N	S		D	O	N	A	T		A	T	O	P	
N	O	T	H	I	N	G	T	H	E	T	R	U	T	H
			A	V	A				L	E	E			
	M	O	R	E	L		S	A	B	A		A	F	T
E	A	T	D	R	I	N	K	B	E	M	E	R	R	Y
L	U	T	E		S	O	I	L		U	T	T	E	R
L	I	O	N		A	R	M	Y		P	E	S	T	O

CROSSWORD 40

B	O	S	C		Y	E	T	I		B	O	C	C	E
O	N	O	R		E	A	R	N		I	G	L	O	O
N	E	N	E		A	S	I	N		T	R	A	P	S
D	A	Y	C	A	R	E	C	E	N	T	E	R		
S	T	A	H	L		E	R	I	E		A	V	A	
			E	L	A	N		P	R	O	B	E	D	
A	P	O		I	L	E	U	M		R	E	N	O	
B	A	B	Y	S	I	T	T	E	R	S	C	L	U	B
A	P	S	E		S	E	N	A	T		L	E	E	
C	A	T	T	L	E		S	T	O	A				
A	S	I		A	L	S	O		I	S	T	L	E	
		N	U	R	S	E	R	Y	S	C	H	O	O	L
A	B	A	S	E		A	G	U	E		C	A	U	L
B	A	T	E	D		M	A	M	E		A	N	T	I
C	R	E	D	O		S	N	A	P		N	Y	S	E

CROSSWORD 41

T	U	B	A		C	A	L	A	S			W	I	R
A	S	I	N		A	T	I	L	T		A	I	N	U
L	I	S	T		H	A	M	B	U	R	G	E	R	S
C	A	M	O	M	I	L	E		D	I	A	N	E	S
			A	I	M	E	E		L	E	O	N	E	
G	A	R	N	E	R		T	A	N	T	A	R	A	S
R	A	C	E	S		W	A	N	T	S		S	N	A
A	R	K	S		R	O	B	E	S		S	C	D	S
N	O	H		D	E	M	O	S		L	E	H	R	S
O	N	E	N	E	V	E	R		P	I	T	N	E	Y
			R	O	S	I	N		L	I	P	P	I	
S	T	R	O	D	E		T	I	L	S	I	T	E	R
R	H	I	N	E	W	I	N	E	S		E	Z	R	A
T	O	N	S		E	L	U	T	E			C	E	N	T
A	U	G			R	A	T	O	N			E	L	S	E

CROSSWORD 42

A	B	C	D			A	C	E			E	L	M
D	O	O	R	S		H	A	M			R	O	E
D	O	N	U	T		A	R	E			I	C	E
			S	I	R		B	O	R	S	C	H	T
E	X	O	D	U	S		B	Y	E				
A	R	M		N	O	H			E	G	A	D	
R	A	M		G	U	M	B	O		A	L	E	
N	Y	E	T		S	U	R			Z	O	E	
			O	A	K		D	A	P	P	E	R	
C	H	O	W	D	E	R		N	I	A			
L	I	P		U	N	E		G	E	C	K	O	
A	D	E		L	Y	E		E	T	H	A	N	
D	E	N		T	A	D		Y	O	Y	O		

CROSSWORD 43

W	H	A	M		A	T	T	U		B	A	B	E	L
E	A	V	E		B	R	A	G		O	P	E	R	A
P	H	I	L	L	I	E	P	H	A	N	A	T	I	C
T	A	D		I	D	E	S		T	I	R	A	N	E
			S	P	E	D		S	T	E	T			
P	A	L	L	A	S		S	P	A	R		J	I	M
A	M	E	E	R		A	L	E	C		S	O	R	E
S	A	N	D	I	E	G	O	C	H	I	C	K	E	N
H	I	T	S		L	E	A	K		T	R	E	N	D
A	N	O		B	O	N	N		C	H	O	R	E	S
			R	A	P	T		G	L	A	D			
A	S	P	I	R	E		E	R	I	C		E	G	O
T	H	E	P	I	R	A	T	E	P	A	R	R	O	T
K	A	R	E	N		C	A	T	O		O	M	O	O
A	G	I	N	G		E	L	A	N		Z	A	N	E

CROSSWORD 44

W	A	D	I		R	O	B		S	P	A	R
E	R	I	N		U	S	A		M	I	C	E
P	I	N	M	O	N	E	Y		I	N	R	E
T	A	T	A	R			S	A	L	T	E	D
			T	R	I	G		L	E	A		
D	U	P	E		S	I	S	I		I	O	N
A	R	I		I	N	G	O	T		L	O	Y
M	I	N		A	T	O	M		A	S	H	E
		H	O	G		T	E	R	N			
S	T	E	N	O	S			A	T	T	Y	S
E	R	A	S		P	I	N	W	H	E	E	L
A	I	D	E		U	D	O		E	L	L	E
L	O	S	T		N	A	B		M	E	L	D

CROSSWORD 45

C	A	R	A	T		C	R	O	S	S		P	E	N
A	M	I	G	O		A	U	D	I	T		A	R	E
R	O	B	E	R	T	S	D	O	L	E		T	R	A
E	S	S		N	I	T	E	R		E	A	T	E	R
			V	A	T	S			F	L	U	I	D	S
L	A	R	E	D	O		S	T	E	E	D	S		
O	R	O	N	O		A	M	I	E		A	P	S	E
B	A	B	E		E	V	I	C	T		C	A	P	A
S	T	I	R		M	I	L	K		C	I	G	A	R
			N	A	T	I	V	E		D	A	T	E	R	S
P	A	S	T	E	L			C	A	V	Y			
R	I	C	E	R		G	E	O	D	E		L	O	U
I	D	O		R	O	N	S	D	A	R	L	I	N	G
C	E	O		O	R	A	T	E		N	A	S	A	L
E	S	K		R	E	W	E	D		S	P	I	N	Y

CROSSWORD 46

F	U	N	G	I		S	O	B			M	A	C
O	R	A	L	S		M	A	I			A	V	A
E	N	G	E	L	B	E	R	T			R	E	P
			N	A	R	A			A	C	R	E	
D	E	A	N	M	A	R	T	I	N				
I	T	T			S	O	N	A	T	A	S		
S	T	O	R	E	S		E	N	T	I	C	E	
C	A	N	A	S	T	A				M	E	T	
			J	O	A	N	R	I	V	E	R	S	
A	N	K	A			I	O	O	I				
P	I	A		D	I	M	E	N	S	I	O	N	
E	R	N		I	R	A		I	T	A	L	O	
D	O	E		M	E	L		C	A	N	E	D	

CROSSWORD 47

C	R	I	B		O	V	I	D		M	O	R	T	
I	A	G	O		P	I	L	E		I	C	H	O	R
T	H	E	R	E	I	S	L	E	S	S	H	E	R	E
E	S	T	I	M	A	T	E		A	S	S	E	N	T
			I	T	A		V	I	A					
	C	A	S	T	E		T	A	L	L	U	L	A	H
B	A	L	T	S		N	O	N	O		S	A	N	E
U	N	D	O		P	A	P	E	R		U	R	G	E
L	E	E	R		E	T	E	S		W	A	G	E	D
B	A	N	K	H	E	A	D		A	R	L	E	S	
			A	W	L		E	N	A					
A	S	H	O	R	E		S	L	I	T	H	E	R	S
T	H	A	N	M	E	E	T	S	T	H	E	E	Y	E
M	E	R	C	E		P	A	I	R		A	L	A	R
	D	E	E	D		A	R	E	A		T	Y	N	E

CROSSWORD 48

W	A	C	O		S	A	N	D		N	A	T
A	R	A	P		O	L	I	O		O	N	E
S	C	R	E	W	B	A	L	L		H	E	S
			N	E	S	S		P	R	I	N	T
S	A	W	E	D			C	H	A	T	T	Y
A	V	I	D		A	I	L	I	N	G		
P	A	L		A	N	T	O	N		A	F	T
		D	A	R	T	E	D		A	M	O	R
T	A	P	I	R	S			O	P	E	R	A
E	L	I	D	E		F	L	A	P			
S	I	T		S	T	R	I	K	E	O	U	T
L	A	C		T	O	E	S		A	L	F	A
A	S	H		S	O	D	A		L	E	O	N

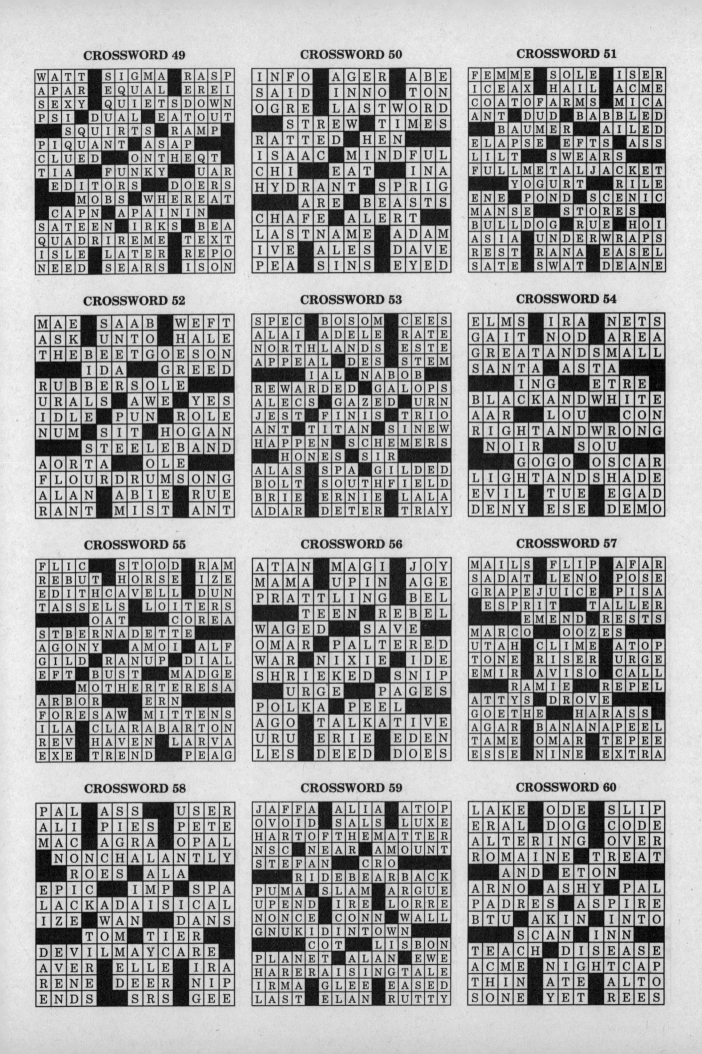

CROSSWORD 49 CROSSWORD 50 CROSSWORD 51

CROSSWORD 52 CROSSWORD 53 CROSSWORD 54

CROSSWORD 55 CROSSWORD 56 CROSSWORD 57

CROSSWORD 58 CROSSWORD 59 CROSSWORD 60

CROSSWORD 61

```
P A S C A L   C A F E   O P S
A G O U T I   O T O S   H A T
R O U R K E   S T U P I D L Y
    S I D E B A R   N E A L
F L U E N T L Y   S E D A T E
L O B   S O L   H O V E R E D
U S E D   I M A M A N
  T R A N S P A R E N T L Y
    Y E A S T S   S E A R
S E A T T L E   H E S   A W E
U P R I S E   H E A T E D L Y
P O E M   S C A R R E D
I N T E N T L Y   N E W A G E
N Y E   G A U D   E L I D E S
E M S   O X E N   D Y N A M O
```

CROSSWORD 62

```
O L D   E N O S   A B L E
W O O   T O J O   C R E E
L U N C H E O N   R E A L
    H A L S   D E A N S
A T H E N S   R I S K
L E A S   C O S   F R O
F A S T F O O D C H A I N
A S H   I N N   I S L E
    H A L O   C E N T E R
A R O S E   R U N G
P O U T   F A T T E N U P
E L S E   O K I E   U S A
D E E R   P E E R   N E W
```

CROSSWORD 63

```
C L A M   V I L A S   B L A B
O O N A   I C A N T   O I L Y
P O N Y   C H I N E   N E A T
S N O O Z E   C U M L A U D E
    D R I V E   A S I F
B R O   N E V I L   M I T E
A I M   G R I N   P E D A L S
S P I N   S L A D E   E B O N
S E N O R A   L O R E   U P A
  N I T A   E L E C T   L E G
    A R A M   S A N T A
V E R B A T I M   P A I R E D
E R I E   A L I B I   D A R E
E G O N   L I C I T   A S O F
R O T E   K O A L A   L A S T
```

CROSSWORD 64

```
A M O Y   F A R   W E A K
N O V A   A H A   I R M A
K R E K E R O H A N I A N
H E R   D E Y   G E N T S
    L C D   B A Y
S F A X   S H O P   R I A
E U N I C E Q U E D E N S
A N D   L E S T   O A K S
    T A M   S T S
J O K E R   E A T   S A T
A L E X A N D R A Z U C K
G E N A   A G O   A R N O
S O O N   P E W   G E E S
```

CROSSWORD 65

```
C L A Y   T R A D E   F O G G
L E N O   R A C E S   A G R A
A S T U D Y I N S C A R L E T
W E S   A O N E   A L L E G E
    G N U S   T R E S
  S T R U T   T A G S   M T V
C A R O B   S I L O   S U R E
I H A V E N T G O T A C L U E
R I P E   E A R N   N O T E S
C B S   P E T E   D O R I S
    H I D E   A A R E
A R G Y L L   A N N A   B O O
C A N D L E S T I C K P A R K
T S A R   S P A C E   A R E A
S E T A   S A N E R   R E L Y
```

CROSSWORD 66

```
P U M P   E N C   T A L C
O H I O   L O O   O L E O
R O L L   T O W   O V E R
T H E L I O N S S H A R E
    E O N   L E O
H I N D U   W I N T E R S
O R E   C A P   G U T
C R E A T O R   B A G G Y
    N I P   T A M
M O N K E Y S A R O U N D
E V I L   C O X   E R I E
S A N E   A L E   B I L L
A L A S   T D S   A S E A
```

CROSSWORD 67

```
T R I P   S T E R N   R A M S
A I D E   T A R O T   E R I E
C L E A N A S A W H I S T L E
T E A   A C T S   N E E D S
    P I K E   B A T T
C A M E L S   E R L E   C P O
A L E E   O N A I R   L I L
R O A R I N G T W E N T I E S
R U N   S I R E N   O N C E
Y D S   A C E R   S P O K E N
    A B E S   M E E T
E A G L E   T E A R   S R O
D R I L L I N S T R U C T O R
G I N A   S N A R E   E A V E
E A S Y   H E R O D   E Y E S
```

CROSSWORD 68

```
A L E C   A L I   T H U G
L I R A   B E N   O I S E
B E A N T O W N   W R E N
    S E R   E R N E S T
M O D   S T A R E S
E N A C T E D   T H O N G
L E N A   D O R   I D O L
T R A M P   R E S P I R E
    P A L E S T   N A N
N E S T L E   O A S
O S L O   T O W N L I N E
S T E W   O R E   O V E N
H E W N   N O D   B Y T E
```

CROSSWORD 69

```
L E A S T   T O N G   S K I P
O P R A H   I T E R   H A N A
S O C L E   R I C A   E R R S
  S H E R L O C K H O L M E S
    M A O   S A D   A D E
E S E   P U R E   M D S
C O C O   P U M A   L O D G E
H U C K L E B E R R Y F I N N
O P E R A   E R G O   A C A D
  A D O   Y O G I   E T S
A L A   E B B   E G O
R O B I N S O N C R U S O E
D I O R   E R I E   A C C R A
E R D A   S I N N   N A T A L
B E E N   S C A T   A R O S E
```

CROSSWORD 70

```
O A K   J E F F   S H E D
A R E   A X E L   H A L E
F I R   M U L E   A R L O
  D R G I L L E S P I E
    N E T   I L E
A T T A   O N O   S O Y
D R S T R A N G E L O V E
S A P   A C E   A L A N
    A S H   A D D
  D O C H O L L I D A Y
R A P T   R U I N   L O T
O L I O   U R G E   A G E
D E E R   S E N D   S I D
```

CROSSWORD 71

```
A M A Z E   I T S A   P S I
P A C E D   I C I O N   L U V
P L U S O R M I N U S   U R E
L E T T   A P E A R   A S P S
E S E   S P A R S E   N F L
    D I T S   S A T O U T
P N O M   S E C T S   U S E
S L O M O   E X O   T I R E D
R U N   N E S T S   R O S S
O S P R E Y   T H O U
  S L Y   E L O P E S   C A L
P I U S   L U L L S   S O R E
L G S   N E P L U S U L T R A
U N E   E T U I S   F A T E S
S S S   E S S E   O V A T E
```

CROSSWORD 72

```
F A C T   P E S T   H E Y
I G O R   O G R E   I R E
N E M O   E G O M A N I A
  M O A T S   P I T C H
C H A P S   G O D
R A N   P O L E   E R G O
A L D A   M A N   S O O N
B O O M   I O T A   M A L
  A C T   S H A D Y
D I A N A   S U S A N
A L M A N A C K   S T I R
T A O   A L O E   P I N E
A Y S   L A W S   S C A M
```

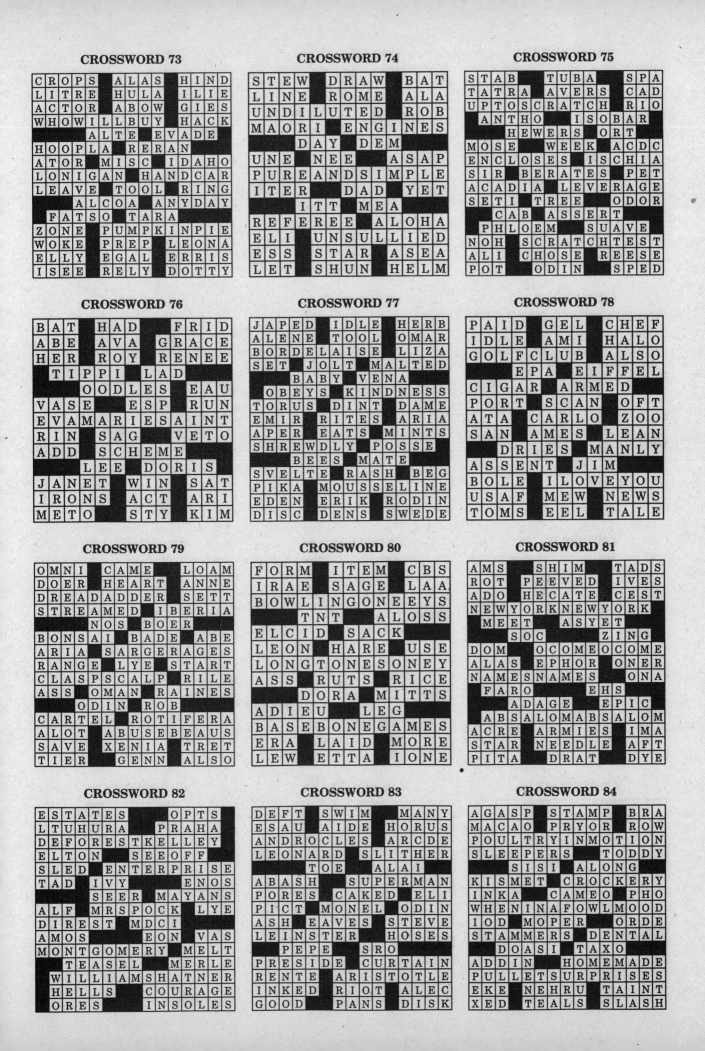

CROSSWORD 73

```
CROPS ALAS HIND
LITRE HULA ILIE
ACTOR ABOW GIES
WHOWILLBUY HACK
      ALTE EVADE
HOOPLA  RERAN
ATOR MISC  IDAHO
LONIGAN  HANDCAR
LEAVE  TOOL  RING
    ALCOA ANYDAY
   FATSO  TARA
ZONE  PUMPKINPIE
WOKE  PREP  LEONA
ELLY  EGAL  ERRIS
ISEE  RELY  DOTTY
```

CROSSWORD 74

```
STEW  DRAW  BAT
LINE  ROME  ALA
UNDILUTED  ROB
MAORI  ENGINES
    DAY  DEM
UNE  NEE  ASAP
PUREANDSIMPLE
ITER  DAD  YET
    ITT  MEA
REFEREE  ALOHA
ELI  UNSULLIED
ESS  STAR  ASEA
LET  SHUN  HELM
```

CROSSWORD 75

```
STAB  TUBA  SPA
TATRA AVERS CAD
UPTOSCRATCH RIO
 ANTHO   ISOBAR
   HEWERS  ORT
MOSE  WEEK  ACDC
ENCLOSES  ISCHIA
SIR  BERATES  PET
ACADIA  LEVERAGE
SETI  TREE  ODOR
   CAB  ASSERT
 PHLOEM   SUAVE
NOH  SCRATCHTEST
ALI  CHOSE  REESE
POT  ODIN  SPED
```

CROSSWORD 76

```
BAT  HAD  FRID
ABE  AVA  GRACE
HER  ROY  RENEE
 TIPPI  LAD
  OODLES  EAU
VASE  ESP  RUN
EVAMARIESAINT
RIN  SAG  VETO
ADD  SCHEME
  LEE  DORIS
JANET  WIN  SAT
IRONS  ACT  ARI
METO  STY  KIM
```

CROSSWORD 77

```
JAPED  IDLE  HERB
ALENE  TOOL  OMAR
BORDELAISE  LIZA
SET  JOLT  MALTED
  BABY  VENA
 OBEYS  KINDNESS
TORUS  DINT  DAME
EMIR  RITES  ARIA
APER  EATS  MINTS
SHREWDLY  POSSE
  BEES  MATE
SVELTE  RASH  BEG
PIKA  MOUSSELINE
EDEN  ERIK  RODIN
DISC  DENS  SWEDE
```

CROSSWORD 78

```
PAID  GEL  CHEF
IDLE  AMI  HALO
GOLFCLUB  ALSO
   EPA  EIFFEL
CIGAR  ARMED
PORT  SCAN  OFT
ATA  CARLO  ZOO
SAN  AMES  LEAN
  DRIES  MANLY
ASSENT  JIM
BOLE  ILOVEYOU
USAF  MEW  NEWS
TOMS  EEL  TALE
```

CROSSWORD 79

```
OMNI  CAME  LOAM
DOER  HEART  ANNE
DREADADDER  SETT
STREAMED  IBERIA
  NOS  BOER
BONSAI  BADE  ABE
ARIA  SARGERAGES
RANGE  LYE  START
CLASPSCALP  RILE
ASS  OMAN  RAINES
  ODIN  ROB
CARTEL  ROTIFERA
ALOT  ABUSEBEAUS
SAVE  XENIA  TRET
TIER  GENN  ALSO
```

CROSSWORD 80

```
FORM  ITEM  CBS
IRAE  SAGE  LAA
BOWLINGONEEYS
   TNT  ALOSS
ELCID  SACK
LEON  HARE  USE
LONGTONESONEY
ASS  RUTS  RICE
  DORA  MITTS
ADIEU  LEG
BASEBONEGAMES
ERA  LAID  MORE
LEW  ETTA  IONE
```

CROSSWORD 81

```
AMS  SHIM  TADS
ROT  PEEVED  IVES
ADO  HECATE  CEST
NEWYORKNEWYORK
 MEET  ASYET
  SOC  ZING
DOM  OCOMEOCOME
ALAS  EPHOR  ONER
NAMESNAMES  ONA
 FARO  EHS
  ADAGE  EPIC
ABSALOMABSALOM
ACRE  ARMIES  IMA
STAR  NEEDLE  AFT
PITA  DRAT  DYE
```

CROSSWORD 82

```
ESTATES  OPTS
LTUHURA  PRAHA
DEFORESTKELLEY
ELTON  SEEOFF
SLED  ENTERPRISE
TAD  IVY  ENOS
  SEER  MAYANS
ALF  MRSPOCK  LYE
DIREST  MDCI
AMOS  EON  VAS
MONTGOMERY  MELT
 TEASEL  MERLE
 WILLIAMSHATNER
HELLS  COURAGE
ORES  INSOLES
```

CROSSWORD 83

```
DEFT  SWIM  MANY
ESAU  AIDE  HORUS
ANDROCLES  ARCDE
LEONARD  SLITHER
  TOE  ALAI
ABASH  SUPERMAN
PORES  CAKED  ELI
PICT  MONEL  ODIN
ASH  EAVES  STEVE
LEINSTER  HOSES
  PEPE  SRO
PRESIDE  CURTAIN
RENTE  ARISTOTLE
INKED  RIOT  ALEC
GOOD  PANS  DISK
```

CROSSWORD 84

```
AGASP  STAMP  BRA
MACAO  PRYOR  ROW
POULTRYINMOTION
SLEEPERS  TODDY
  SISI  ALONG
KISMET  CROCKERY
INKA  CAMEO  PHO
WHENINAFOWLMOOD
IOD  MOPER  ORDE
STAMMERS  DENTAL
  DOASI  TAXO
ADDIN  HOMEMADE
PULLETSURPRISES
EKE  NEHRU  TAINT
XED  TEALS  SLASH
```

CROSSWORD 85

```
PENCE  LAPP  BAAL
INCAS  ECHO  ERLE
SCALP  VERMILION
ALAMODE  PRUDES
    NUDE  HAAG
SHYEST  MONTAGES
HOUSE  CANOE  NAP
ASKS  SOCKS  MAGI
CEO  LUCAS  TITLE
KANGAROO  HISSED
    LUNA  OILS
FEDORA  DELILAH
ORESAMPLE  AVILA
AGES  ESAU  GENTS
LORY  STEM  ESTOP
```

CROSSWORD 86

```
SCRAPE  ALEPHS
PHOENIX  RESEATS
LEAPSUP  ASPWREN
AIL  LIMEY  TEE
SLED  POLA  ABRA
HARERAISIN  LEAK
   FEST  COLLEGE
AMBUSH  JESTER
FIESTAS  POET
FREE  STORKRAVEN
LAWS  ISEE  REPO
ICH  ERRED  NIB
CLAMBUR  AVARICE
TELLONE  TOPICAL
SEINED  ENAMEL
```

CROSSWORD 87

```
CARP  OHARA  SRAS
ODER  SAGAN  TIRO
NANO  WREST  ACES
MOVIEVEHICLES
    EDGE  POE
BORNEO  TROY  RAT
ARICA  COED  CASE
LEGALCONVEYANCE
SAIL  ODES  ARGON
ADD  ONES  SHEETS
    TIN  SOOT
ATHLETICCOACH
ILIE  CROAK  KEYS
STEM  TULLE  EDDA
TORE  SKEET  REEL
```

CROSSWORD 88

```
TAPS  PIP  ANCE
ONEOCLOCK  IDOLS
NETLOSSES  ROMES
ILE  UTES  ORNATE
CESAR  RUGA  ATEN
    STY  PATRIC
LIBIDOS  SMASHES
IDA  ADA  TEC  ELA
LOBSTER  RAKESIN
   YIELDS  LEG
CELL  ESTH  TOTEM
ALOVER  RACE  ODE
ROVER  CALLEDOUT
OPERA  INFERENCE
BESS  ODA  BEES
```

CROSSWORD 89

```
ABLE  LEADA  MAIL
TOOT  ATLAS  ACRE
EATHIGHONTHEHOG
ESTERS  HIRE  ENS
   TORE  TATARS
    FAR  ELAPSED
THEMUSIC  OLGA
MIDDLEOFTHEROAD
ALEC  MOISTENS
NONCOMS  REC
    INAPET  OPUS
APE  TRIM  ERASER
LOWCOSTMORTGAGE
PLEA  HEADS  EGOS
SORT  ASSET  TEST
```

CROSSWORD 90

```
SLAG  ENID  SCAR
TACH  MINE  ACORN
OREO  CEDE  SIMMS
LASSIECOMEHOME
    TREE  LENO
SALAD  MEIN  DAH
SPRIT  ISH  DORA
ROCKETJSQUIRREL
ITHE  AFT  MEETS
SSE  IRKS  PASSE
    TANS  AILS
MYFRIENDFLICKA
EAPOE  REEF  NOAH
SNERD  MALL  GONE
SASE  ATEE  STEM
```

CROSSWORD 91

```
SHOD  ABAS  FETE
POUR  ELLE  ERNIE
ANTI  NEAR  TATER
REDBREASTBONE
SOBEIT  ENTRE
   LAD  BAD  ITAL
CAMEL  CARIBCAGE
OBI  TWOSOME  ILO
REDEYELID  ANNES
NASA  MEN  ETO
   MUSEE  ALLOWS
   MISTLETOENAIL
ARMES  ATOP  DINA
MEESE  MULE  AVES
PORT  AILS  YEWS
```

CROSSWORD 92

```
VAMP  SALAD  DOLL
CHAR  AMOLE  EXIT
RANI  DINER  BEND
BUNTINGGROUND
    TREE  IBN
FAMOUS  SHEIKDOM
ILIUM  SEAR  URI
LASTPITCHEFFORT
LIT  NOTA  RAMIE
SNOWCAPS  COLONS
    ARF  RAND
FAMILYBATTERS
SOUP  AURIC  REPO
TUTU  SMASH  ADIN
PROM  HANEY  LOVE
```

CROSSWORD 93

```
COALCAR  CURABLE
ATLARGE  OPENAIR
STATEOFTHEONION
HOSED  SWAN  AONE
    ROB  INDY
HIM  SEAN  SATUP
ODES  TREE  LOTUS
RADISHINGBEAUTY
SHANE  AGAR  TRON
OLORD  IDES  NNE
    BORN  DOG
TRIP  TEED  PROAM
GIVEPEASACHANCE
ICECOLD  RAIDERS
FOSSILS  CLASSES
```

CROSSWORD 94

```
OLE  GISMO  FLIP
KOCH  ASPEN  RUDI
ACRE  NOISE  ELON
YOUMIGHTASWELL
    SLOE  HAL
FALLFLATONYOUR
WADES  MITT  NNE
ACHY  HOPES  GIDE
ITO  HOWL  DINED
FACEASLEANOVER
    BLT  DICE
TOOFARBACKWARD
COMA  GOUGE  AJAR
ABET  EMMET  YOYO
PENS  SASSY  YEP
```

CROSSWORD 95

```
SWIFT  BARB  NAME
ARDOR  REAR  OPAL
PALMA  ARIA  NICK
SPEEDYGONZALES
    NEA  YORE
DAFT  WAS  SIGMAS
EMU  GENTS  SAUCE
FASTEDDIEFELSON
ATEAM  ANTON  IRS
TIDBIT  GAI  ACNE
   BNAI  SAD
FLYINGDUTCHMAN
FLIC  NOOK  TEASE
AURA  ETTE  ERATO
ABET  DOES  DEMON
```

CROSSWORD 96

```
BASTE  MEAT  EBB
UNTIL  ERIE  OGLE
GNATIONALLEAGUE
OUTLETS  LATTER
FLOE  SAWS  SHINY
FIRST  EPEE  MOS
   HASSLES  RES
GNOMENCLATURE
RAT  LAOTIAN
RIM  SLIM  RSVPS
ADELE  LEAN  CARP
MISERS  SOMALIA
BRAVEGNUWHIRLED
LOKI  TAPA  REESE
ENE  SWAN  ODETS
```

CROSSWORD 97

```
DEBRA   SLAB   GREW
ELLAS   AERO   LARA
BUOYSFROMBRAZIL
ADO   IRAN   BEDECK
REPOSE       LID
    CITIZENCAINE
MOOT   SNAG   ASTER
ATLAS   SIR   PLAIN
GHANA   AREA   ELLE
IOFTHENEEDLE
      AXE   ZIPPED
PIERRE   BEET   AAR
LOVEATFIRSTBYTE
OTIS   EARL   LANES
WALT   RODE   EDENS
```

CROSSWORD 98

```
RAN   UTE   OLGA
PIVOT   PAST   AULD
EVERYWHICH   FLUE
KARACHI   HELIUM
ELY   OIL   EWES
   WORLDWITHOUT
WARN   EER   PRO
DENY   BLADE   SAGE
AGE   EAT   COLE
DOWNONTHEJOB
   ANNE   NIL   HOT
SPREES   AVOCADO
TIER   THEMERRIER
INTO   TOTO   SALON
SKEW   WAR   BEN
```

CROSSWORD 99

```
AMID   PEEK   BBB
PALES   DANTE   LOA
BILLYMONDAY   URI
   SINGS   CEIL
CASTLES   BLOTS
CONCEDE   AEIOU
GOYIM   TITTLES
SET   COEDS   SAP
RHOMBIC   HIDES
   URIEL   BHUTANI
ARBOR   ROONEYS
BOSS   PILOT
ORD   JOESATURDAY
ITA   ANNES   PEETE
LAY   MEAN   DYAN
```

CROSSWORD 100

```
   DSC   ACT   PEEL
RECAP   CHIC   ROTE
SLAVE   HEAR   ENOS
TERISBERRIES
SEATO   AMUSIVE
ROONESPRUNES
WED   STAR   SERIES
ACES   PAL   ETRE
GOATEE   SIPS   SYS
ELLENSMELONS
DETENTE   LAPSE
PEEWEESKIWIS
ROPE   ELLA   ERODE
APES   MESS   SIREN
TENT   DAY   TER
```

CROSSWORD 101

```
SPECS   CAMP   CAPE
PEARL   EVEL   ASEA
ATRIA   TELE   BARS
   MYPARENTSPUT
CAREER   TEAR
ARI   ROT   REACT
PEND   WOODYALLEN
ROGET   NRA   TEASE
ALIVETEDDY   ENTS
   ANIMA   SET   GET
PRAT   ARISES
BEARINMYCRIB
ELLA   IPSO   ASSET
LIST   SLOW   LEERS
TAOS   HENS   SNARE
```

CROSSWORD 102

```
GARR   SCAM   BEGAN
IRAE   CAME   IGAVE
LEIA   ALOT   DORIA
DANGERFIELD   DDT
ASSAY   REESE
   NESTS   ORANGE
SAR   DARIEN   DIAL
ONIT   VILLA   ANTE
ATOY   ASTERN   GEM
PIGPEN   SEDAN
   ROANS   DOING
SPA   TAKEAGANDER
HANSE   ANDI   ALVA
ARDOR   TOED   GEES
WEEPY   ESNE   ERRS
```

CROSSWORD 103

```
PILAF   FROG   SEER
AMIEL   ROLE   EYRE
SPACECADET   READ
SSR   ELI   LAIC
   COLDCOMFORT
MICKEY   ERSE   NEE
AGEES   ABETS   TAR
DULY   LAS   GAPE
CAL   SCOTT   RACES
ANA   LONE   ROSTRA
PARTINGSHOT
TOPI   OSU   ACE
MEEK   FLYBYNIGHT
AWAY   EERO   DARER
NEMO   ROSS   ALATE
```

CROSSWORD 104

```
MAID   ATTIC   BLY
ADDED   MEARA   LEE
YELLOWPAGES   UAW
ELI   LAST   NEWER
RANCOR   IBIDEM
GARB   MAC   NOAH
PELLET   OUI
FORESEE   HIJINKS
IRE   TREMOR
TODD   HOE   PHIL
LOMOND   INSEAM
VIZIR   ROSS   AVA
WAG   GREENHORNET
ASH   HORSE   NOTRE
YET   TRESS   BOSS
```

CROSSWORD 105

```
POD   OBESE   DRAG
URI   NEVIL   RARER
BAD   SHALLRETURN
LITHE   ENIGMA
STROLL   WACO
MARDI   ACH   HEP
CLYDE   KENT   DAYO
HOWE   FEATS   EVEN
AGAR   AIRY   SEEDS
TOY   ARK   OUIJA
ACRE   UNMADE
FIASCO   SPYRI
AMTHEWALRUS   EGG
TIRED   PIANO   AHA
TYNE   REIGN   MTS
```

CROSSWORD 106

```
HAHA   GOODS   FEDS
IRIS   ULTRA   OLIO
FIVEANDTEN   USER
IDEAL   SATURATE
TAD   DAMP
OCTOBER   POEMS
SHOW   ALECS   SLIP
TARO   START   TUNA
ARAB   EADIE   EDEN
GALAS   SEVERED
SIPS   SER
MODERATE   GLAZE
UTAH   SIXSHOOTER
TONI   SLATE   NEAR
TEST   ELMAN   GELS
```

CROSSWORD 107

```
BING   MUFTI   SATE
ODOR   ANEAR   TRON
NORA   SWEDEHEART
EASYDOES   LEANTO
ELAND   MAIM
BASINS   PENNYFOR
ORANG   GRADE   INE
AMIE   SOILS   ANDY
RED   SHADY   ERNIE
DEEPPILE   FLOUTS
REPS   GASUP
ONAIRS   TRIANGLE
DANEMOTHER   DIET
IVES   URIEL   MRED
NEWT   TASTY   ELKS
```

CROSSWORD 108

```
BOSC   BEEP   PUFF
BALA   CENSE   ESAU
CHUMSANDQUAKERS
UMPIRES   DORMS
SOOT   DAZE
DATUM   LODE   COB
COCOA   BONE   PAGE
OTHONEROANDOVID
REEL   LUST   ILIVE
ADD   OBIE   AGILE
CLAN   FLIT
ALBEE   GRATING
FELLOWAMERICANS
ANET   ANARM   ADAM
ROWS   DINE   LARA
```

CROSSWORD 109

```
P A S T A   M A C E S   E R R
U S U A L   A V A S T   M O E
T H E M I R R O R Q U A C K D
T E D   A N N O     N E E D
      P E R E   L E A D E R
M O O O V E R M I A M I
A D A G E   A N T I   M O B
T I T O   L A N E S   P A V E
E N S   M O R O   R E G A N
    C A W O F T H E W I L D
  E G O I S M   O O P S
A V E R     A S T O   B E D
B A R K T O T H E F U T U R E
E N E   I D I O M   S E N S E
E S S   S E C T S   E N T E R
```

CROSSWORD 110

```
V I O L   C R E M E   V A M P
O N T O   A U D I E   A S E A
W R I G H T S D E L I G H T S
S O S   E T H A N   G U E S T
      A L L     C U E
C H A R M E D   B O A R D E R
A O N E   U T U R N   O R E
G L E A S O N S R E A S O N S
E L A   T W E E N   A N E T
S Y R I A N S   T O P L E S S
R L S       R E T
S A M O A   B E E N E   G U Y
G R A N G E R S D A N G E R S
T I L E   T E N E T   I N G E
S L E D   A L E N E   B E E R
```

CROSSWORD 111

```
I S L A M   S P A M   A C T
S T E L E   P U M A   T H A I
M A F I A   U P P E R H A N D
S G T   N E D S     E L I T E
    F I D O S   R E V E R E S
S M I L E S   M O N E T
E M E E R   M I D D L E R O W
A I L   M I D I S   I R A
M I D D L E M A N   L A G E R
    E A M E S   S I P H O N
A R R A Y E D   R O G E T
G E O D E   S I G H   S A S
U N D E R H A N D   T A I N T
A T E N   O R I G   E D D I E
  S O D   G A P E   R E E L S
```

CROSSWORD 112

```
S C A T   A C T E D   A D A R
L A M E   M A R G E   D I N E
A B E R R A T I O N   E S T E
D I S P U T E S   T E A M E D
E N S   S E R   A L L A
    P E U   S E L L   N B A
P E S O   R A P T   E N T E R
A M U S E   R O T   N O L T E
T I M E D   O R E S   S E E D
E L M   D E N T   H H H
    A S I N   S E E   T I S
G A R T E R   A L A R M I S T
E L I A   A F F O R D A B L E
M I S T   G O A P E   T I E R
S A T E   E R R E D   T A S S
```

CROSSWORD 113

```
I N D   B A B A   S T R A P
F O R D   E N O W   H A I T I
E V E R   A T T A   A R D E N
E A S Y W R I T I N G
L E S S E E   S T A G   A S P
    I R A   O Y S T E R
M A K E S   S H A M   A O N E
E R N E S T H E M I N G W A Y
S E A N   H E R O   D E N T S
S A R T R E   S A O
Y R S   E D D A   P L E D G E
      H A R D R E A D I N G
D O R I A   A L U M   A G O G
E W E R S   T A N A   M I M E
F L E S H   S I G N   T E R
```

CROSSWORD 114

```
C H I N   R A Z O R   A S W E
R O D E   A D E L E   T O A D
A W O L   N O S E A R O U N D
B E L L Y U P T O   E M P T Y
      O P T   A L I
    S C O W   P A N I C K E D
C U L L   B O A S T S   I C I
H E A D F O R T H E H I L L S
A D S   I N N E E D   N O A H
D E P E N D O N   C A S T
    D I S   I I I
A N T I S   B O T T O M O U T
T O E T H E L I N E   A R C H
U N T O   B O S O M   T A L E
B E E R   S T E W S   A L A N
```

CROSSWORD 115

```
A G A T E   E S T E S   I C E
B E L I E   S L I D E   R A G
E L L E R Y Q U E E N   E T A
    P I E   M I M E   N E D
A M B I E N T   N A G G E R S
L E O N S   A N S   A R C
A L B   T O R Y   P L E A S E
C E B U   S A L V O   Y S E R
K E Y N E S   O O P S   T V A
    K I T   A N T   W A L E S
C O N T E M N   E P I C E N E
O B I   R I I S   A N A
L E G   N A T K I N G C O L E
A S H   A M A I N   E I D E R
S E T   L I S P S   R A D O N
```

CROSSWORD 116

```
P O D S   A F R I C   G R A M
A T I C   N E U R O   R E N O
T H E H E N I S A N   A S T O
H O M E R U N S   T I N T E D
    D R A T   R S T
S A M U E L   A A A A   A T O
C H I L D   E G G S W A Y O F
A O N E   S N O O T   P E R T
P R O D U C I N G   T E R S E
E A T   L A D Y   C A R S O N
    J A N   T A U T
P O L A N D   D I S P U T E S
A D A M   A N O T H E R E G G
G O N E   L A T H E   E R A T
O R G S   S T E E D   S I D S
```

CROSSWORD 117

```
S L O T   C R A B S   E S M E
H A T E   L E R O I   M A U L
E R I N   A L O U D   I N N S
M A S T E R I N G   A G G I E
      T I N   H E I R
A T A   R O K S   D R A W I N
M A S S E N E T   T E N A C E
I S N T   D I T   T I K E
S T E R E S   R E S I S T E D
S E R E N E   S A W N   E S S
    A R A B   M E G
S L I M Y   R E M A S T I N G
O M N I   P O L A R   O D I E
A N O N   P I E T A   U L N A
K O N G   S L E E T   T E A R
```

CROSSWORD 118

```
C L A M U P   C H O O S E
H E L E N E   L O W R E N T
U N E A S E   O P E R A T E D
M I C R O W A V E S   C R E E
    S U E D E   R H Y M E
A I M   N E D   M A Y A
C R O W D   R O M A N T I C
H A S H   S O U P Y   G A G A
E N T I C I N G   P E C O S
    T U N E   S H E   O R K
D A R E D   S A E N S
O P E C   T O M M Y S A N D S
C A S A N O V A   D I G O U T
  R E P I N E R   A V E R S E
    T S H I R T   Y E S M E N
```

CROSSWORD 119

```
C L A P   G A B E   P A R
E E R O   E A G A N   O W E N
Y E G G   S T E R S   L A N E
    O N T H E •   S K I E R
E S P   E E E   E L A T E D
S H A T T E R S   G O •
S A L E S   I M A G E   M T S
A D E N   O N E R S   B O O P
Y E S   E G G A R   P O T T O
  • E R   R E S E N T E D
P E S T L E   S P S   O D E
A R C H Y   • A T I O N
R A R E   S H E E N   E T T A
A T O I   H A R R Y   X R A Y
O D S   E N O S   T A R N
```

CROSSWORD 120

```
J A Z Z   A R F S   M U M S
E P E E   R O O T   P I N O T
D E T E R M I N E   I N U S E
    S A S E   Z A Y A K
    B I G   L I N E T O
L O Y A L L Y   P O W E L L
S A D O   L E O S   S H A L E
T R E K   S A Y N O   A S I A
A G N E S   M O O D   L E E K
D E S O T O   S O I L E R S
  R E F I R E   T E A
    O L D I E   O N C E
A N A X E   E X C U S A B L E
R O S E S   I G O T   T E A M
C H A N   O I S E   O R N O
```

DIAGRAMLESS 1

DIAGRAMLESS 2

DIAGRAMLESS 3

DIAGRAMLESS 4

DIAGRAMLESS 5

DIAGRAMLESS 6

DIAGRAMLESS 7

DIAGRAMLESS 8

DIAGRAMLESS 9

DIAGRAMLESS 10

DIAGRAMLESS 11

DIAGRAMLESS 12

DIAGRAMLESS 13

DIAGRAMLESS 14

DIAGRAMLESS 15

DIAGRAMLESS 16

CRYPTIC CROSSWORD 1

ACROSS

1. STOCKING (anag.)
5. CHASTE (hom.)
10. AGAINST (anag.)
11. SEMIPRO (anag.)
12. HO(LLYWO)OD (*lowly* anag.)
13. US + ER + S
14. NE(S)TER + S (*enter* anag.)
16. SAGG + ED (*gags* anag.)
18. P(RATE)D
21. TUR + NIPS (*rut* rev.)
24. CO + CO + A
25. NAR + RO + WISH (*or + ran* rev.)
27. ROT(A) + TOR
28. AC + AD + IAN
29. D(EL)UDE
30. TORTILLA (anag.)

DOWN

1. ST(ASH)ING
2. ORACLES (anag.)
3. K + IN + KY
4. NO + TI + ON + S
5. H(AM + BURG)ER (*grub + ma* rev.)
6. H(AM + BURG)ER (*grub + ma* rev.)
7. SU(PREM)E (*perm* anag.)
8. EGOIST (anag.)
9. A + SIDES
15. EXTRA + aCTED
17. ASTHENIA (hid.)
19. RE(C + I)TAL (rev.)
20. DENIRO (anag.)
21. TORNADO (anag.)
22. I + NIT(I)AL (rev.)
23. S(CARE)D
26. O + PART (rev.)

CRYPTIC CROSSWORD 2

ACROSS
1. BATTER + IN + GRAM
8. RETRAC + T (*Carter* rev.)
9. CLAVIER (*Percival* anag. minus *P*)
11. FLOWS (hom.)
12. AM + BU(LATE)D
13. DISH + ONES + T
15. sTERNS
16. DEFOE (anag.)
18. CARP + ENTER
20. EPISCOPAL (anag.)
23. C + LIMB
24. SWAR(ME)D
25. WHATNOT (anag.)
26. DEMON + ST + RATED

DOWN
1. BUT + TONS
2. TRANSPOSE (anag.)
3. EXTRA (hid.)
4. IN + CUBA + TOR (*rot* rev.)
5. G + RAIL
6. A + V(I)AT + OR
7. DRAFT + DODGERS
10. RED + IS + TRIBUTE
14. ESCAPADES (anag.)
15. TRENCH + ANT
17. F(RIG)ATE
19. TH(INN)E + D
21. CAME + O
22. LOWER (2 defs.)

CRYPTIC CROSSWORD 3

ACROSS
1. TOLL (2 defs.)
3. CREDITABLE (anag.)
9. I + M(BIB)ED
11. R(AU + C)OUS (*sour* anag.)
12. MAN + NA (*an* rev.)
13. IN(VO)KED
15. HA(NG + DO)G
16. ST + RANGE
18. NUMERAL (anag.)
21. T + RIPPED
23. JU + KEg + BOX
25. STEER (2 defs.)
27. CURRENT (hom.)
28. CHERISH (hid.)
29. T(RAN + SC)RIBE
30. SWAP (rev.)

DOWN
1. TRIUMPHANT (anag.)
2. LE + BAN + ON
4. RID(D)ING
5. D(E)RIVES
6. T(R)UCK
7. B(ROAD)EN
8. EASY (first letters)
10. BOARDER (hom.)
14. LEAD + ERSHIP (*perish* anag.)
17. REIS + SUE (*rise* anag.)
19. MAJ + ORC + A (*jam* rev.)
20. LOB + STERn
21. TAX + ICAB (*a Bic* anag.)
22. PREVIEW (anag.)
24. KEELS (rev.)
26. SCAT (2 defs.)

CRYPTIC CROSSWORD 4

ACROSS
1. GO DOWN IN HISTORY (pun)
9. OUT OF COMMISSION (pun)
10. SARDINE (anag.)
11. ED + IF + ICE
12. RESIGN (anag.)
14. GENERAl
17. UPROOT (anag.)
19. TO(LED)O
23. RAREBIT (anag.)
24. AGELESS (anag.)
26. GETS THE BRUSH-OFF (pun)
27. CHEWS THE SCENERY (pun)

DOWN
1. G(LOSS)ARY
2. D(ET)ER
3. W(AFT)ING
4. IRONED (anag.)
5. H(AMPERE)D
6. SIST(IN)Er
7. OR + I + GINATE (*eating* anag.)
8. YONDER (hid. rev.)
13. SO(UBRE)TTE (*rube* anag. + *set-to* anag.)
15. FOR(TIE)TH
16. HORSEFLY (anag.)
18. RE(BAT)ES (rev.)
20. O(VERSE)E
21. TRA(GI)C (*cart* rev.)
22. MA + DR + AS
25. ELOPE (*people* anag. minus *p*)

CRYPTIC CROSSWORD 5

ACROSS
1. BIDDABLE (anag.)
5. SPECKS (hom.)
9. TRA + VERSE (*art* rev.)
10. F(L)ARES
11. E(X)ORCISM (*score I'm* anag.)
12. GREASE (hom.)
14. RENDE(Z)VOUS (*Don's revue* anag.)
18. H(Y)PODERMIC (*chimp rode* anag.)
22. P(LAY)AT
23. PIN(NACL)E
24. ANEMIC (anag.)
25. S + TRIDENT
26. NO + TATE
27. F(RESHM)AN (*Sherm* anag.)

DOWN
1. BUTTER (2 defs.)
2. DRAG + ON
3. AGENCY (hid.)
4. LOSES HEART (anag.)
6. P(O + L + A)RIZE
7. CARD + A + MOM
8. S(US + P)ENSE
13. ADMINSTER (anag.)
15. CHAP + LAIN
16. A + P + PARENT
17. I + DEAL + IST (*it's* anag.)
19. ANTI + ClasS
20. SCR(E)AM
21. NEWT + ON

CRYPTIC CROSSWORD 6

ACROSS
1. FILETS (anag.)
4. F(ARMY)AR + D
9. REVERE (2 defs.)
10. SCAL(D)ING
12. A + S(TROD)OME
13. DUC(A)T
14. M(ART + IN + BALSA) + M
18. STEN + OG + RAP + HER (*Go Nets* rev.)
21. ABLER (*Albert* anag. - *t*)
22. TASK FORCE (hid.)
24. BACH +ELOR (*role* rev.)
25. KIMONO (hid.)
26. GRE + A + TEST
27. B + LASTS

DOWN
1. FIR(EAR)MS
2. LAVA + TORY
3. TORSO (anag.)
5. ARCHEOLOGIST (anag.)
6. M(EL + O + DR)AMA
7. A(PIE)CE
8. DIG + ITS
11. COMB + I(NATION)S
15. IN + TERSE + CT
16. CHA(RIO)TS
17. TR(EET)OPS (rev.)
19. GA + SBAG (*gabs* rev.)
20. CLICHE (anag.)
23. FR + ILL

CRYPTIC CROSSWORD 7

ACROSS
1. CRIB + BED
5. LIB(ERA)L (*bill* anag.)
9. BAT + H + E
10. MA(TRIM + O)N + Y
11. NAM + E (rev.)
12. IN(J)URE
16. END + OWING
17. G(R)AVEL
19. sEXTANT
20. PALOM(I)NO (*polo man* anag.)
22. LUMBER (2 defs.)
23. RAC + Y (rev.)
27. SCREWBALL (anag.)
28. MEC(C)A (*came* anag.)
29. DEMERIT (anag.)
30. AMNESTY (anag.)

DOWN
1. CAB + IN + F + EVER
2. INTIM(ID)ATE
3. BRED (hom.)
4. DOMINANT (hid.)
5. LITMUS (*must lie* anag. - *e*)
6. B(RID)EG + ROOM
7. ROOD (rev.)
8. LAYS (hom.)
13. TWIN(FLOW)ER (*winter* anag.)
14. A + VOI(DAN)CES
15. BLOODY MARY (anag.)
18. CAME + LLI + A (*A + ill* rev.)
21. IM + PACT
24. USED (hid.)
25. D(R)UM (*mud* rev.)
26. OMEN (rev.)

CRYPTIC CROSSWORD 8

ACROSS
1. PREDICTIVENESS (anag.)
8. A(MEN)D
9. I + SLANDER
10. LEG(IT + IM) ATE
11. ABE + T
14. G + LEAMING (*gem in LA* anag.)
15. VORTEX (anag.)
17. TA(PIN)G
19. DI(SABLE)D
22. STAB (hid.)
23. COATIMUNDI (anag.)
25. LANCELOT (anag.)
26. DRAKE (2 defs.)
27. EXT(EMPO)RANEOUS (*poem* anag.)

DOWN
1. PEARLY GATES (anag.)
2. EP + ERGNE (*green* anag.)
3. INDITEMENT (hom.)
4. THIAMINE (hid.)
5. VA + LETS
6. NINE (hid.)
7. S(HERB)ET
12. T + AX + ID + RIVERS
13. M(O + HAMMED)AN
16. DICTATOR (anag.)
18. PHALA + N + X (*Alpha* anag.)
20. LONG AGO (*Goolagong* anag. - *Go*)
21. DOL + LOP
24. ACME (anag.)

DIAGRAMLESS STARTING BOXES

Diagramless 1: box 3
Diagramless 2: box 13
Diagramless 3: box 8
Diagramless 4: box 5
Diagramless 5: box 9
Diagramless 6: box 3
Diagramless 7: box 1
Diagramless 8: box 9
Diagramless 9: box 7
Diagramless 10: box 3
Diagramless 11: box 4
Diagramless 12: box 1
Diagramless 13: box 3
Diagramless 14: box 6
Diagramless 15: box 2
Diagramless 16: box 12

WEBSTER'S
Best of
Crossword
Challenge
PART 2

Solutions appear after
Puzzle 144 at the end of Part 2.

YULE BE SORRY!

ACROSS

1. Stew in one's own juice?
7. Carol start
11. ___ Nidre
14. Clod
15. Yemeni port
16. Before, once
17. Start of a comment by Robert Orben
20. Put the check in the mail
21. Form of comm.
22. Asian mountains
25. Hecuba's hubby
28. The Mertzes' income
29. Throb
31. Nirvana alternative
33. Xenophobe, for one
34. Like rider print
35. Middle of comment
41. Amiss
42. N.Y. city
44. Milord's molasses
48. "It ain't over 'til the ___ sings"
50. Depended (upon)
51. Alpine air
53. Fencing tool
54. Witch's whereabouts
56. Concentrate
58. End of comment
64. Wish undone
65. DEA agent
66. More trim
67. Logan abbr.
68. Acceptable
69. Peter Wimsey's creator

DOWN

1. Marian's deg.?
2. Sulcus
3. Young classicist's verb
4. Put away
5. ___ it! (amen)
6. Excuse
7. Aristide's home
8. Summer refresher
9. Act racy?
10. Wrinkle
11. Alley cat?
12. Set straight
13. Segment
18. Bellini's bread?
19. Oratorians' founder
22. Abbr. for Friday
23. Buñuel of film
24. Pond growth
26. Tuscan tune
27. Dish list
30. Lofty abode
32. Stupefy
34. Hackney carriage
36. Confederate
37. Egyptian tomato?
38. Passage
39. Low tide
40. Florida county
43. The Science Guy
44. Contraction
45. Expire
46. Provided
47. Breathless
48. Ward (off)
49. Roswell landers
52. Compatriot of 14-Across
55. Discerp
57. Norse goddess
59. The way, to some
60. Samovar
61. Nice season
62. Chalice veil
63. Monopoly quartet: abbr.

ACROSS

1. Victor
6. Leave out
10. Peevish person
14. The —— (Dutch city)
15. Constructed
16. Samson's growth
17. Start of a verse
20. Bridge on the Seine
21. Pub pour
22. Vibrato
23. Metric measurement
24. Calm
26. More of the verse
31. Fail to pay (taxes)
32. Destines
37. Cares for
38. 12/24 or 12/31
39. Something worthless
41. Put back
43. Bright star in Orion
44. More of the verse
47. Conditional release
51. Soup vegetable
52. Fleeting passion
53. Paris negative
54. Dormitory furniture
58. End of the verse
62. Bakery purchase
63. Roman historian
64. Buddy
65. Coastal eagles
66. Closemouthed person
67. French landscape painter

DOWN

1. Bloke
2. Religious ring
3. Opposed to, in Dogpatch
4. Mongrel
5. 4-Down, e.g.
6. Egg dish
7. Lion's pride
8. Court vow
9. Comaneci's perfection
10. Balzac's love
11. Arrested
12. Plane passage
13. Belgian balladeer
18. Beef fat
19. Orch. section
23. Single tree house
24. Withered
25. Intention
26. Gross less expenses
27. More than
28. Diminish
29. Appends
30. Be uncertain
33. Courtyards
34. Bearded bloom
35. Approach
36. German admiral
38. Scottish Gaelic
40. Days of yore
42. Texas strike
45. Namesake
46. Spring season
47. *Silver Streak* star
48. Marketing pro
49. House tops
50. Alternatives
52. Fit
53. Russian river
54. Audition tape
55. Eastern prince
56. Type of lily
57. Bow or bowline
59. RN's specialty
60. Actor Bellows
61. Bug resin

ACROSS

1. Ohio city
5. Until, in Uruguay
10. Fall guy
13. Skip
14. Famed violinist
15. Castor's mother
16. Civil War locale
18. Severn feeder
19. Cooks clams
20. Book of nobles
22. Water cooler
23. Planets
24. Iowa religious community
27. Interdict
28. Admit
31. Freeway cloggers
32. Teutonic tongue: abbr.
33. Topper type
34. Sleeve
35. Theme of this puzzle
37. Nonsense
38. Rigg and Ross
40. Singer Janis
41. Pigeon penthouse
42. Wise ones
43. Volume booster
44. Van Gogh home
45. Asylum seeker
47. Two–kind connector
48. ___ out (endures)
50. Does turkey work
54. Burstyn's '78 leading man
55. Revolutionary War locale

58. Holy image
59. Lake Indians
60. Actress Falco
61. Anchor Rather
62. English poet
63. Tournament favorite

DOWN

1. Ship records
2. "___ a man with seven…"
3. Tiny amount
4. Reaches
5. Author Hermann
6. Church togs
7. Dallas inst.
8. Caribbean fish

9. Spleen
10. Crimean War locale
11. *My Life as* ___
12. Stamp sheet
15. Added something extra
17. Village People hit
21. *Les femmes*
23. Period of hostilities
24. Schs.
25. Anita's friend
26. Revelations site
27. Lay odds
29. Wrathful
30. Scruffs
32. Argon, e.g.

33. Marsh
35. Underlying state
36. Pool distance
39. Like Hercules' lion
41. Goes uninvited
43. *Signor* Toscanini
44. At a distance
46. Taunted
47. Plump, plus
48. Refrigerator attack
49. Actress Chase
51. Sea surge
52. Author Wiesel
53. Winter getabout
56. Diarist Anaïs
57. Sight; view

ACROSS

1. Urge on
5. Lady of the house
10. Your *padre*'s *hermanos*
14. PC pop-up
15. George Hamilton's ex
16. Language of Pakistan
17. Host in Valhalla
18. ___ *Bulba*
19. Cascade down
20. Pays dearly
23. Heavy metal combo?
24. Taxing gp.
25. Maimonides was this
29. Wide collars
33. Remnants of Romes
34. 100%
36. Glowed
37. Stout kin
38. Personal pronoun
39. Eye layer
40. *Olympia* painter
42. Musical ability
43. Olfactory hint
44. Orisons
46. Trinkets
48. Before, to Byron
49. ___ Plaines, IL
50. Be firm
59. Croat or Serb
60. Battery type
61. Butter sub
62. Dried up
63. Cheer up
64. Slight strand
65. Powerful one
66. Clockmaker Thomas and namesakes
67. Staff mark

DOWN

1. EPA concern
2. Leggy suffix?
3. Battalion
4. Glances at
5. Photo finishes
6. Kyrgyzstan range
7. Reweave
8. Med. school study
9. 5 iron
10. Rejects
11. Fury, to Ovid
12. Of lyric poetry
13. Down in the depths
21. Rainbow deity
22. Flubs
25. Rascal
26. Like Peary's explorations
27. Sports venue
28. Tenor Roland
29. Jacket praise
30. Hut
31. Anoint, old style
32. Circus barkers
35. Mauna chaser
41. Sea swallow
43. Tallow source
45. Della and Pee Wee
47. Goes gaga for
50. Start of a whispered chat
51. Endings for "glob" and "caps"
52. Fictional plantation
53. Fish served almondine
54. Lacking air
55. Courtroom promise
56. Mishmash
57. Novelist Nathanael
58. Casual negative

ACROSS

1. Triple-A service
4. John, Paul, and John Paul
9. Hollywood Blvd. embedment
13. Noted times
15. Dental work
16. Kvetchy plaint
17. Marathon segment
18. Hester's daughter
19. Stagecoach line
20. Hard drink
22. Fell behind
24. Close out
25. Diarist Frank
26. Genesis figure
27. Hipster's "Got it!"
29. Siphon piece
31. Make a choice
34. A Ford
36. Lagniappe
37. Limo accessory
38. Herbert sci-fi classic
39. Ohio political dynasty
40. Wherever you are
41. Born
42. Ovid's Muse
43. Sucker
44. One of Rita's exes
45. *The Whales of August* star
46. This and that
47. WWII mil. female
49. Abba of Israel
51. Exam trademark

54. God of music
56. First dictionary illustration, often
58. Poet Sandburg
59. Fall from grace
61. Suit to ___
62. Actor O'Shea
63. *Golden Boy* playwright
64. Shot up
65. Air swirl
66. Kegler's request
67. Tight turn

DOWN

1. Arizona city
2. Stellar hunter
3. Orlando stop
4. Uniform trim
5. Runner at first, e.g.
6. Pierre Boulle fantasy
7. Cochlea site
8. Course outline
9. Bilko, to buddies
10. Shakespeare premiere site
11. Gallic girlfriend
12. Split apart
14. Where the buoys are
21. Comet feature
23. Fortas, et al.
28. Welsh river
30. Biblical preposition
32. Links scores
33. Low card
34. Author Ferber
35. Formal fight
36. Ram's remarks
39. French flag, e.g.
40. Lid
42. Even, to Etienne
43. Frog refuge
46. Most Spartan
48. Metal combo
50. Stitch loosely
52. Corners
53. Distorts
54. High point
55. Invoice stamp
57. Hobo, for short
60. July quaff

ACROSS

1. Marsh or Murray of silents
4. Picket-line crosser
8. Knickknack fragment
12. Kringle colleague
13. Brownish purple hue
14. Stinging rebuke
15. Politico Landon
16. Modern Mesopotamia
17. Sooner
18. Start of a frugal maxim
21. Pitch location
23. Actor Carmichael
24. Chub or night crawler
25. Transportation agcy.
26. Caesar of early TV
29. More of the maxim
33. Foxy flat?
34. Son of Noah
35. Make an approach
36. Bee secretion
37. Refer (to)
39. End of the maxim
43. Serengeti sound
44. Joe Orton stage hit
45. Far from robust
48. Reynolds or Young
49. Remarkable one
50. Vast expanse
51. Brother of Cain
52. Son of Zeus
53. Put the whammy on

DOWN

1. Latin pronoun
2. Nothing but
3. Escaping fluid
4. Emulated Nathan Hale
5. Family of French scientists
6. No room to swing ___
7. "Step on it!"
8. Out of breath
9. Collect leaves
10. Biggest place on earth
11. *Silkwood* costar
19. Position, to Pliny
20. Speed
21. Footnote abbr.
22. Thurmond or Archibald
25. ___ *a Camera* (Julie Harris film)
26. Thickset
27. "...___ it my way"
28. Sufficiently cooked
30. Spring event
31. Upper jaw
32. Inuit dome home: var.
36. Excellence
37. ___ *in the Head* (Sinatra flick)
38. Egyptian floral motif
39. Spherical objects
40. Debauchee
41. Speedy projectile
42. Concert bookings
46. Protecting shelter
47. Having a loose texture

ACROSS

1. Huge party
5. Chug chaser
9. Name
13. Greek epic poem
15. Beach bag
16. Winglike structures
17. Mass meeting
18. Mortgage, for example
19. Sister ship of note
20. Hagar creator Browne
21. Marine
24. Rings out
26. Garland costar, often
27. Agitates
29. Give rise to
31. Ambience
32. Vague period of time
34. Bro, e.g.
37. Hearth goddess
39. Fortune
40. Athenian lawgiver
42. Spud bud
43. Acted lovesick
46. Noun-forming suffix
47. Scott of "Mr. Lucky"
48. Itinerant
50. Very touched
53. Marseilles morning
54. American viper
57. Morse "E"
60. Rime
61. Organs with drums
62. Deteriorate
64. Ibsen's town
65. Raisa's denial
66. Moon valley
67. Walleye winch
68. Monastic titles
69. Hidden valley

DOWN

1. Feeder visitor
2. Jai ___
3. Sow's ear antithesis
4. *2001* computer
5. It covers the world
6. Booty
7. Home to the Jazz
8. Nonspecific
9. Heavy gun
10. Earth visitor
11. Surgical tool
12. Like an old tub
14. Poet Thomas
22. Adamson's joy
23. Drove a dinghy
25. Part of "QED"
27. Bear lair
28. Long fellow?
29. Author Alexander
30. Sherlock's prop
33. Give a shellacking to
34. Ellington classic
35. Saint's image
36. Netman Bjorn
38. Acid variety
41. Sitarist Shankar
44. Allowing for contingencies
45. "Phooey!"
47. Routine recon
49. Different
50. Olympian blood
51. Snare loop
52. Like yesterday's bread
53. Necessities
55. BLT topper
56. City in 7-Down
58. At loose ends
59. Driver's-ed enrollee
63. Getup

ACROSS

1. Haruspex, for example
5. Another man's poison?
9. Research room
12. *Cette femme*
13. Basil-based sauce
14. Parting gesture
15. SLEEPER
18. Map close-ups
19. Ages to remember
20. Picnic crasher
21. Unspoken
24. BONNET
30. On ___ (doing well)
31. Chest muscles
32. Arafat's org.
33. Paris pronoun
34. Misminted coins
35. "Take ___ from me"
36. French connections?
37. Rough about header
38. Gothic arch
39. CRIB SHEET
43. Tomlin and Pons
44. Complement
45. Sole possessor
47. *Without ___* (1983 movie)
50. BUNTING
55. Met solo
56. Bedouins
57. Formerly
58. Printers' measures
59. Dole (out)
60. Rod attachment

DOWN

1. Darn it
2. Morlock captives
3. Carolina college
4. "___ in the Sunset"
5. Gibson and Brooks
6. Subj. for immigrants
7. Put away
8. Long measure
9. Popocatépetl product
10. Roman flier
11. Exemplar of busyness
13. Rocker Smith
14. Value
16. Barbra's role in '83
17. Former Israeli P.M.
21. Symbol of ruin
22. Union
23. Mama of rock
24. Bouillon
25. Shake up
26. Small English wood
27. Sight-linked
28. Greek staple
29. Reliable info
30. Watteau's "with"
34. Fencing implement
35. Rabble-rouser
38. Public
40. Hilo hi
41. Late Belgrade strongman
42. These, in Madrid
45. Frond plant
46. He gave us a lift
47. Curé's title
48. Film
49. Noun ending
50. Ms. Busch of silents
51. Paddock mom
52. 49er's find
53. Dietary need
54. Toothpaste type

ACROSS

1. Copier
4. Oorial
7. Gridlock
10. Close acquaintance
11. Sir McKellen
12. Is animate
16. Hidebound one
17. Neil Simon play
19. Corrida accolades
20. Boy in a Menotti opera
21. Free (of)
22. Victoria's consort
25. Be human
26. U2, for one
27. Bossy remark
28. Sargasso swimmer
30. Marmalade ingredient
32. The ___ Living Dangerously
35. Bygone
36. Lacking fortitude
39. Sudden flood
42. Astrologer's concern
44. Inn
46. Four-in-hand, e.g.
47. Pick
50. Second caliph of Islam
51. Campy exclamation
54. Odd bits of info
56. Electrical unit
57. "Had we but ___ enough, and time..."
59. Painter Guido
60. Enigma
63. Spoken
64. Humperdinck hero
65. Nabokov novel
66. Aficionado
67. Supplement (with "out")
68. Dog size
69. Bath, e.g.

DOWN

1. Artemis's twin
2. '40s hairstyle
3. "Family Ties" mom
4. Canine command
5. "Very funny!"
6. "What's in ___?"
7. Moses' father-in-law
8. Skating jump
9. Czarist commune
13. Maroon
14. Pang
15. Wet through
16. Froth
18. Face value
23. Scythe wielder
24. Actress Garr
26. Buoyant wood
29. Famed Chaney
31. More upbeat
33. Organic compound
34. Turkish topper
37. Block division
38. Expurgate
39. Actor Larry
40. Richardson heroine
41. Arthurian isle
43. Masking device
45. Noggin
48. Fiesta crasher?
49. Shadow
52. Royal prop
53. Parade sight
55. Flat tools
57. Calendar row
58. See 16-Across
61. Pilot's hdg.
62. Round Table braggart

ACROSS

1. Rear up
5. Seafood selection
10. "Shoot!"
14. Hautboy
15. Demi or Dudley
16. Concept
17. Start of saying
20. Craving
21. Bush's alma mater
22. Alabama town
23. Slips up
24. Take over
26. Show again
29. Influence
30. Composer Khachaturian
31. First-aid kit item
32. Middling grade
35. Part 2 of saying
39. Indian weight
40. Exacting
41. PC operator
42. Tot's transport
43. By the skin of one's teeth
45. Full of foam
48. Take it easy
49. Leading
50. "Indeed!"
51. ___ choy (Chinese cabbage)
54. End of saying
58. Nagy of Hungary
59. Upper crust
60. Writer Wiesel
61. Promontory
62. Greasy spoon
63. Jutland native

DOWN

1. Like mozzarella
2. Busy as ___
3. Natural satellite
4. Get-up-and-go
5. Stained
6. Monks' togs
7. Architect Mies van der ___
8. Gold, in Granada
9. Singer Shannon
10. Strip (of)
11. Fred's sister
12. Town near the Argonne
13. Grandmas
18. Vega's constellation
19. Publishes
23. Deciduous shade trees
24. Luxurious
25. Primordial goop
26. Scott Joplin tunes
27. Perry's creator
28. Carson's predecessor
29. Motive
31. Russian author Maxim
32. Docket item
33. Daredevil Knievel
34. Spooky
36. Cuts up
37. Locks
38. Pitch
42. Highland lords
43. Inconvenience
44. Burn balm
45. Classics course
46. "___ where the buffalo…"
47. Sprees
48. Actress Lenya
50. Smug look
51. Composer Bartók
52. Lena of film
53. Swiss artist
55. United
56. Samuel's teacher
57. Oyster plot

ACROSS

1. Algol or Altair
5. Post
9. Quito quaff
13. "Rule, Britannia" composer
14. Italian river
15. Conical-cap wearer
17. Be careful
20. European capital
21. High schooler
22. In the open
23. Contrived
25. Bobble the ball
27. Ms. Stevens
29. Wee nip
31. Advantage
34. At the age of: Lat.
35. Gulf emirate
37. Evened a slope
39. Act mannerly
43. Pressure
44. Is a nosey parker
46. Nice season
48. Norman town: abbr.
49. Emulate Ella
50. Red Bordeaux
52. Suede feature
55. Hockey great
56. Leg. eagle
57. Kill, in a way
60. Approach
62. Act appropriately
67. Assagai, e.g.
68. Vanish
69. Aerial hotshots
70. Track figures
71. Wetlands
72. Phi–Kappa link

DOWN

1. Actor Jaffe
2. Numerical prefix
3. Write in the margin
4. Beatty film
5. Lordly home
6. Land unit
7. Split sec.
8. Easy gait
9. Hersey's town
10. Colt creation
11. Ruined
12. Exculpate
16. Ferrara noble name
18. Pamplona cheer
19. Leave the country?
23. At once
24. Graceful equine
26. Interim ruler
28. Consumerist Ralph and family
30. Composer Gustav
32. Salivate
33. "Medical Center" surgeon
36. Norma ——
38. Brain power?
40. More expansive
41. Candy flavor
42. Dread
45. Poem stanza: abbr.
46. 1971 cult film from Mexico
47. Made lace
50. Bounders
51. He threw to Chance
53. Feeds the kitty
54. Favorite
58. Spat
59. Eye lewdly
61. *Pequod* captain
63. Bilked
64. Lady lobster
65. Seine, e.g.
66. D.C. agcy.

ACROSS

1. Songwriters' org.
6. Mao follower
9. Sharif of films
13. Gape
14. Expressive air
15. Refrain syllables
16. Seer's deck
17. Author Waugh
18. Mideastern republic
19. Start of some advice
22. Strawberry's ilk: abbr.
23. Put a match to
24. Rangerlike?
25. Margaret Atwood, for one
27. Bookie's thou
30. Thai, e.g.
33. Env. filler
34. Confederate
35. Part 2 of advice
39. Algerian seaport
40. Greek letters
41. Pillow filler
42. Desire
43. Sterile
46. Jeff's pal
47. Service call
48. Jackson 5 hit
51. End of advice
56. Sale warning
57. Not a dup.
58. Lasso
59. Leftover bit
60. Untouchable one
61. Rye fungus
62. Vicinity
63. Koch and Begley
64. Last name in tractors

DOWN

1. Up and about
2. Supply with workers
3. Grant namesakes
4. Buck chaser
5. Sulking
6. Mah-jongg piece
7. Plantlet
8. Trespass (on)
9. Antipasto item
10. *Femme*'s mate
11. Arthur's middle name
12. Phoned from Piccadilly
14. Toren of films
20. Own, to Burns
21. Hostelry
25. Normandy town
26. 18th-century religious movement
27. Delighted
28. Actress Sommer
29. Girl watcher
30. Nautical yoo-hoo
31. Tender
32. Mrs. David Bowie
34. Friendly Parisienne
36. 12:59
37. Brought up
38. Used the seesaw
43. Fellow
44. Wild irises
45. Gun the motor
46. Perle of D.C.
48. "...iron bars ___"
49. Ulan ___, Mongolia
50. Jalopy
51. Actress Mia
52. Exploitative one
53. Shine's companion
54. Sibilant sound
55. Yorkshire flower

HOT STUFF

ACROSS

1. About
5. Nocturnal fliers
9. Urban problem
13. Undiluted
14. Fond farewell
15. Sunken fence
16. Billie Holiday staples
18. Jot
19. Anybody
20. De Valera's country
21. Cupid's steady
23. Walks softly
24. Rover's restraint
25. Look up to
28. Count (on)
29. They loop the Loop
32. Howled
33. Sicker
34. Wedding gift
35. Hebrew prophet
36. Jessica of *King Kong*
37. Atlas's mom
38. Scale tone
39. Flat of one's own
40. Back of the barque
41. Quit
42. List linkers
43. Caught, in a way
44. Dracula's canines
46. Titled woman
47. Spiff up
49. Adjutant
50. Tee's leader
53. The tentmaker
54. Enthusiastic
57. "Lean ___"
58. "No way!"
59. Cruel monster
60. Hightailed it
61. Costly
62. Penurious state

DOWN

1. Division word
2. Marquee gas
3. Pink inside
4. List ender: abbr.
5. Pervasive qualities
6. Dinner quaff
7. Part of a relay
8. Hitchcock forte
9. Light carriages
10. Luggage group
11. "Oops!"
12. Ready to play
14. Notwithstanding
17. Got wind (of)
22. Kyoto brew
23. Patisserie picks
24. Florida key
25. Humble
26. Pal of Pythias
27. Platters golden oldie
28. Holds together
30. French river
31. Taxi stop
33. Staffs of power
36. Cursive script
37. LLD holder
39. Sacks
40. Spring feast
43. Rock bottom
45. Broadcast
46. Long-term con
47. Eeyore's chum
48. Old Atlanta arena
49. Menlo Park name
50. Brink
51. Confident
52. Stepped on it
55. Shelter
56. A veritable eternity

ACROSS

1. Anna of *The Rose Tattoo*
8. Fatimids, e.g.: var.
15. Flight formation
16. Crested parrot
17. Start of an aphorism
19. Towel word
20. By hook or by crook
21. Clinton, once: abbr.
22. Mindy's honeymoon site
23. Cons do it
24. Greek musical term
25. Tipples
29. Celtic deity
30. Showing more
31. Roget specialty
33. Civil War general
35. Biblical graffiti word
36. Ashtabula's lake
37. Kept tabs on
39. Contains
43. Railroad switch
44. Hostel territory?
46. Have high hopes
47. Butte's cousin
48. Masterstroke
50. VI
51. Supporter's suffix
52. Tries to snatch
55. Riga native
56. End of aphorism
59. Livestock pest
60. Sea trips
61. Lethal Todd
62. Uncomfortable spot

DOWN

1. Means
2. "I gave my love ——..."
3. Minipickle
4. Bird bills
5. Ring legend
6. Year-end quaffs
7. Gold mold
8. Overfussy parent
9. *Dieciseis ÷ dos*
10. Slant
11. Old ballad
12. Whatnot
13. More sullen
14. Of any kind
16. Thick liqueur
18. Post of propriety
24. Concoct
26. Roman family monikers
27. Prepared to propose
28. Ago, to Burns
30. Woe to Job
32. Healthwise
34. Boat in *Jaws*
37. It must go on
38. Morally strict
39. Occupied
40. Doctor's dilemma
41. African land
42. *Cosmo* quiz, perhaps
43. Forgers
45. With grandeur
49. Desiccate
52. Feds
53. Fiddler Stefanini
54. Hardly the expert
55. San —— Obispo
57. U-turn from NNW
58. Extinguished

ACROSS

1. Perth pal
5. Beginning of fall?
9. A virtue, according to Paul
14. Ugandan autocrat
15. Town on the Truckee
16. Egress
17. Patsy
18. Toward the dawn
19. Right-angled pipe fitting
20. Extortionist's practice?
23. Biblical landfall
24. Pisa pronoun
25. Olden times
28. Day in court?
32. Geometry solutions
36. Silkworm of puzzledom
38. Eden's earldom
39. Curio shops?
42. On the summit
43. Aussie fool
44. New York city
45. Excise
47. "Get lost!"
49. *Mahogany* star
51. Bagels' cousins
56. Sneaker salesman's saw?
61. FDR's chat medium
62. Carry on
63. Simple; elemental
64. Enthusiasm
65. Blueprint extras
66. Sporting blade
67. Intended
68. Rotations' durations
69. Cockney cads?

DOWN

1. A Gabor
2. French affair
3. Topper for John Paul
4. Stage direction
5. Magical call
6. Back
7. Handle, to Henri
8. "Take It ___ Limit"
9. ___ fiddle
10. Hero up high
11. "...the enemy and he ___" ("Pogo")
12. Low note producer
13. Cobbler's replacement
21. Assurance
22. Trial, in Tours
26. Out-and-out
27. Sea raptors
29. CLXIX trebled
30. Campus khaki wearers: abbr.
31. Author Seton
32. Hebrew month
33. Neural net
34. Seth's boy
35. Slur
37. Skin problem
40. DeLuise film of 1980
41. Tossed ring
46. Colleague
48. Haunt
50. Basted
52. Concur
53. Lapidary's glass
54. Alpine music
55. Old daggers
56. Mine wagon
57. Fabled loser
58. Icelandic epic
59. Roman evil
60. Hideous

ACROSS

1. Belfry hanger
4. Writer Ferber
8. Rum-soaked dessert
12. Sighting subject
13. Item for fencers
14. City in *Italia*
16. Mahayana sect
17. Ethel Merman role
19. Henry Fonda role
21. Caustic solution
22. Neither pairing
23. Stool pigeon
26. Basalt source
29. Lettery arch
31. Polloi header
32. Numerical prefix
33. "NYPD Blue" extras?
34. Ghana's capital
37. Sportscaster's concern
39. Comparable to a jaybird
41. Extreme
42. Chimney shaft
43. Littlest bill
44. Auction signal
45. Would-be adult
46. Graven image
47. They often get a word in
50. Dowry
52. Samovar
53. Jon Hall role
57. Fess Parker role
60. Reaction of wonder
62. —— march on
63. Toothed whale
64. *Tiergarten*
65. Ms. Bombeck
66. Crave
67. Heel

DOWN

1. Sawyer of the comics
2. Two or three
3. Stage statue
4. Spirit of poetry
5. John Russell's "The Lawman" role
6. Muse count
7. Faux handles
8. Fluffy scarf
9. Genesis craft
10. Guy Madison role
11. Part of a Biblical retribution
14. Pith helmet
15. Terminer's mate
18. Atlantic bird
20. Anecdotage
24. Clan chief
25. Peruvian shrub
26. Standout
27. Indigo dye
28. John Payne TV role
30. Station wares
33. Pairs
35. Splitsville?
36. Yemen town
38. Land of Yeats
39. Pale brew
40. Butch's pal
42. Hang garlands
45. Chicago daily, for short
46. Possessive pronoun
47. Lather
48. Chatter
49. Tex. neighbor
51. Mountain nymph
54. Pith
55. Seepage
56. High time
58. "—— Woman"
59. Guido's note
61. Scuttle

ACROSS

1. Kithara front?
6. Bub
9. D.C. channel
14. Perfect report card
15. Butt end?
16. Iowa commune
17. Factory
18. RR stop
19. Summit action
20. "Mille Bornes" playing units
23. ___-jongg
24. High priest
25. Decree
27. Ms. Stewart
30. City on the Vistula
34. Distinct breaks, in mus.
37. Southern address: abbr.
39. Wild Indian buffalo
40. Plant pouch
41. Relating to seamen: abbr.
42. Runnymede document
46. Small pony: abbr.
47. Colored patch
48. Hair wash, briefly
50. Wimbledon gp.
51. "Battlestar Galactica" villain
55. Kite's org.
58. "Presto!"
62. Poe preceder
64. Southern constellation
65. Part of a proverbial cost
66. New ___, N.Y.
67. Siege weapon
68. Sandal piece
69. "Battlestar Galactica" hero
70. High peak
71. Orgs.

DOWN

1. Hebrew letters
2. God of Islam
3. Urban square
4. Subject of a 1978 treaty
5. Exalted
6. A gender: abbr.
7. Film pooch
8. Scorch
9. Diagnostic tool
10. Wee, in Ayr
11. Chiromancer's reading
12. Singer Paul
13. Nonsense poet
21. Double helix constructions
22. First light
26. Relocates
28. *Discovery*'s sponsor
29. Central Asian people
31. Persian king
32. Fever
33. Unit of power
34. Houston and Neill
35. Light cart
36. Church of Eng.
38. Pituitary hormone
43. One strophe
44. Red-bellied woodpecker
45. Rhyme scheme
49. ___ hatter
52. Aspen lifts
53. Firth of Clyde island
54. Freeway outs
55. Family member
56. Overjoyed
57. Breve header
59. Unusual: Latin
60. Kazakhstan sea
61. Bivouac
63. PIN device

ACROSS

1. Sheik's mount
5. Conk out temporarily
10. Location
14. Soused cake
15. Whatnot item
16. Leander's love
17. Egyptian deity
18. Hokkaido port
19. Aplenty, to bards
20. TV addicts
23. Annapolis letters
24. Above, to Key
25. Preserved (flowers)
28. Pesach feast
30. Yearn (for)
33. *A Chorus Line* number
34. Smiley's creator
37. Opie's pop
38. Post-WWII kids
40. Soothing application
42. Notwithstanding
43. Arm of the UN
44. Ferrara surname
45. Must
49. Go off
51. Greek letter
53. Large cask
54. Some work-force women
59. "___ a man with..."
61. Plus
62. Hamburg's river
63. Yuri's love
64. *Hard Cash* author
65. Scenario
66. Leader lead-in
67. Screwup
68. Makes doilies

DOWN

1. Calculator's forerunner
2. Branched
3. Teem
4. Shoal, to Simone
5. Range
6. Help with homework
7. Smell ___ (be suspicious)
8. Trevi toss?
9. Oaf
10. Diaphanous
11. Retirement cushions
12. Pizarro's desire
13. AAA job
21. Sinai's alias
22. Pindaric poem
26. Football position
27. Ottoman ruler
29. Actor Jack
30. Obeyed the alarm
31. Horsewhip
32. Fractional prefix
35. Charisse, et al.
36. Lend an illicit hand
37. Vicinity
38. Grandma's gym pants
39. Moral precept
40. Encore's kin
41. Mountaineer's challenge
44. Street shader
46. Midler movie
47. Large flatfish
48. Beginnings
50. Tiny amounts
51. Expression of belief
52. He's not loath to loathe
55. Former filly
56. French flower
57. Autocrat
58. Held on to
59. Poorly
60. Oft-quoted one

SUMMER DAZE

ACROSS

1. Springs for drinks?
5. Set ___ (try to catch)
10. Soprano Gluck
14. Diamond cover
15. Span, in Spain
16. Was sorry
17. Simple plantlike organism
18. Still in bed
19. Reuner
20. Like the Fourth
22. Floors it
24. Muscle woe
25. Claim on property
26. Singer Jennings
29. August exodus
33. Weaver chiller
34. Sullies
35. PC chip
36. Deck of seats
37. Grass blade
38. Horseradish additive
39. Blow up, in photog.
40. Norse bard
41. Coastal avians
42. ___ and blue (timely color scheme)
44. Obstreperous
45. Give an edge to
46. Tony
47. Poltroon
50. Summer strand
54. PhD qualifier
55. Sardonic humor
57. Lout
58. Nothing more than

59. Prosodist's study
60. ___ about (circa)
61. Ages and ages
62. Dueling pieces
63. Shaggy bovines

DOWN

1. Doe's dear
2. Chalice cover
3. Colchis-bound ship
4. Light stick for the Fourth
5. *Darkness* ___ (Koestler opus)
6. Dolly Varden, e.g.
7. Mild oath
8. ___ Darya (Asian river)
9. Hot-weather cooler
10. Silvery
11. Angler's bait
12. Honey liquor
13. Puts together
21. Told about
23. Pod group
25. Ayr aristocrat
26. Tear up
27. Skirt style
28. Relent
29. Hot-weather fabric
30. Bakery pros
31. Spreads out
32. Cuckoo

34. Outburst
37. Flip over and take the plunge?
38. Mike Love, e.g.
40. Tatar tribe
41. Speaker in the Hall of Fame
43. Pod group
44. Rutherford ___ (19th Pres.)
46. Use a thurible
47. Appear
48. Creme snack
49. Caution
50. Seeing red
51. Lady Chaplin
52. Fleece
53. Strays
56. Ribbed fabric

ACROSS

1. Secretary, e.g.
5. Dress down
10. Duel prelude
14. Keynes sci.
15. Put one atop the other
16. Bight of Benin state
17. Host of "Jeopardy!"
20. New York neighbor
21. Cropped up
22. Maude player
23. English, e.g.
25. In smithereens
29. Dilute
30. Health hangout
33. Additional
34. Future diamond
35. Lola's portrayer
36. Former host of "Jeopardy!"
39. Off-key
40. Pith
41. Uhlan's weapon
42. Italian direction
43. Baker's shovel
44. Potential harm
45. Bonnie and Clyde's target
46. Clique
47. Toned down
50. Depones
54. "Jeopardy!" response, given correctly
58. Informal negative
59. Begins to drill
60. Austen opus
61. Style
62. Raise glasses
63. Look both ways?

DOWN

1. Blade drops
2. Sound return
3. Before long
4. Mend (bones)
5. Was merciful
6. Eyelashes
7. Bun topper
8. Latin rule
9. *Silent Spring* toxin
10. Unrelenting
11. Gray wolf
12. Shakespearean septet
13. Pig's place?
18. Fencing steels
19. Reason for a tarp
23. Treat badly
24. Medicine ball?
25. Use a divining rod
26. Porthos' pal
27. Carrying call
28. Will notable
29. Bottom line
30. Jazzy '30s sound
31. Cheshire change
32. A deadly sin
34. Narrow inlet
35. Fed
37. Ave ending
38. Puffs up with pride
43. Brest bet
44. Abominate
45. The Divine Miss M
46. Frame uprights
47. Didn't sink
48. Mississippi feeder
49. Plain ring
50. Light blue
51. Footfall
52. Watch info
53. A little
55. Jet-set jet
56. GIs' address
57. Dagwood's delight

ACROSS

1. At ease
5. Predilection
9. Keloid
13. Without ___ (broke)
14. Marsh plant
15. Contain
16. Lyric's opening
19. Alopecia mask
20. Skater Stojko
21. Tablet verb
23. Velvety
24. Middle of lyric
28. Upcoming Olympic site
29. Copyright infringement
30. Brotherly bloke
33. Springiness
34. Nervous trait
35. Item in Dracula's closet
36. Parachutist's domain
37. Woodcutter's daughter
40. Saône town
41. Singers of the lyric
43. Emulate Como
45. Mr. Ertegun (Atlantic Records founder)
46. Time and ___
47. British boatman
50. End of lyric
55. Rainbow
56. Jumblies' boat
57. Cut short
58. Sweep's makeup?
59. A little
60. Arizona city

DOWN

1. Cornfield call
2. Pelée particle
3. Old card game
4. Walrus feature
5. Horn note
6. Loiter
7. Novelist/critic James
8. Poseidon's element
9. Bounty from 8-Down
10. Make a bust
11. Shun
12. Zebras in a field?
14. "Stifle yourself!"
17. Tintinnabulate
18. Divine nature
21. Comedic gimmick
22. Profound
23. High moccasin
24. Fleet at dockside
25. Takes the bait
26. Overused
27. Diacritical mark
30. Check recipient
31. Leftward, boatwise
32. Optical item
35. Mild weather
37. Explode
38. Seek office
39. Three-mile measure
41. Persecute
42. Tea genus
43. Entertainer from Murcia
44. Ham's medium
46. Author Kingsley
47. Verve
48. Morning time: slang
49. Peregrinate
51. CIA forerunner
52. Actress Joanne
53. May honoree
54. Smog foe: abbr.

ACROSS

1. Airport aid
6. Set the pace
9. Fail to stimulate
12. Hopping mad
13. Man of Madrid
15. Can
16. Molly's hubby
18. Computer-programming lingo
19. Joy Adamson's cub
20. See 27-Across
21. Off
23. Veracity
27. With 20-Across, Sri Lankan park
30. Old English letter
31. West Point sch.
32. Single advance
34. Dance concert
38. Cancel
39. Bow or Barton
40. Poker-faced
43. Chanticleer
45. Moolah
46. Rita's royal mate
47. Morose
48. "…a single tear has ___ fame" (Byron)
53. Panting
54. Berman of sports
55. Mystery mutt
59. Gossip Smith
60. Polygraph
64. Hail
65. Roofer's hangovers?
66. Emulate Witt
67. Blushing
68. About half of us
69. Sen. Kefauver

DOWN

1. Prevalent
2. Seed coating
3. Small amounts
4. Up, in Shea
5. Befuddled: Scot.
6. Grandson of Judah
7. European land: abbr.
8. Woodland female
9. Dracula's heartache?
10. Staff members
11. Nibbles
13. "Andy Capp" cartoonist
14. Not substitutes
17. Bad losses
22. Edible gastropods
24. Video-vérité show of the '80s
25. Parka trim
26. Exploitation
27. Egg on
28. Stuart queen
29. Russian river
33. Moves a little
35. Does a lace job
36. District
37. Fat
41. Landon from Kansas
42. Of an unknown ordinal
43. Hindu royals
44. Fragrant
48. Of the cheek
49. Diagonal archway
50. Torn down
51. Of antiquity
52. Adds (on) a rider
56. ASAP, in the OR
57. Lug
58. Hawkish god
61. "___ the Walrus"
62. Second person
63. Native: suffix

ACROSS

1. With 63-Across, theme of this puzzle
5. "ICURYY4ME," e.g.
10. Duel memento
14. Brainstorm
15. ___ *Romance*
16. Draw nigh
17. Adverb-based pun
19. Bedouin
20. Theater sign
21. Ninny
22. Winged
23. Chihuahua cheer
24. Re a line wherein each word has one syllable more than the last
27. Piqued
30. Soft
31. Lowly brass
32. Easy gait
33. ___ *Sanctorum*
37. Cryptic clue
39. "Waltz, nymph, for quick jigs vex Bud," e.g.
41. Ms. Lamarr
42. English river
44. Emulate Demosthenes
45. Holy book
46. Lear heir
47. "Violence—nice love," e.g.
51. Summer quaff
52. Minstrels
53. Yalie
54. Φ
57. Writer Wiesel
58. "Senseless-nesses," e.g.
62. Hubbubs

63. See 1-Across
64. Dry: prefix
65. Fine spray
66. Fiery stones
67. First place

DOWN

1. Intelligence
2. Kitchen aura
3. San ___, Italy
4. German article
5. Poker ploy
6. Bad marks
7. Took the lure
8. Corn header
9. "Get it?"
10. Roman steps
11. Reef stuff
12. Cremona craftsman
13. Early string instrument
18. 1983 Nobelist
22. Mil. address
23. Eared seal
24. Cruise port
25. Chance (upon)
26. Highly rated
27. Septennial occurrence?
28. Rest, in Rheydt
29. "And not ___ little dancer"
30. Lung lining
33. Go along
34. Precipice
35. "So long"
36. Churchly sitcom
38. Way out

40. Skiing style
43. Tec Spade
45. Metric units: abbr.
47. Perpendicular to the keel
48. Nita of film
49. Small bands
50. That is: Lat.
51. At ___ (confused)
53. Daredevil name
54. Argued a case
55. Take on
56. Sacred image
58. Actor Tognazzi
59. Siesta
60. Ms. Hogg
61. Opposite of 55-Down

ACROSS

1. Frogman
6. Roughly
10. Whodunit sine qua non
14. Poets' inspiration
15. Crackers
16. Right-hand man
17. PDT and PST?
20. Chemical suffix
21. Wringer's descendant
22. Also-ran Perot
23. *Gypsy* star
24. Sandwich cookie
26. Verdi opus
29. Carnival of mirrors?
34. Demonstrate
36. Concert halls
37. La lead-in
38. Generous elf
39. Hwys.
40. Grasp mentally
42. Singleton
43. Entreaty
45. Purplish red hue
46. The French Open?
49. Outfits
50. Elevs.
51. Bellicose deity
53. Greek consonant
56. ___ rye
58. "Star Wars" letters
61. Guard in Florida?
64. Make better
65. Test variety
66. *M.* Zola
67. Park path
68. Till bills
69. Deserved

DOWN

1. Salami shop
2. Player's club?
3. Rose holder
4. Attic letter
5. Concerto movement
6. New York Indian
7. Govern
8. Olympic taboo
9. WWII spy group: abbr.
10. "A ___ star-cross'd lovers"
11. Wheels of fortune
12. Paeans
13. Hardy lass
18. Orchard
19. ___ *Laughed* (Hepburn film)
23. Would like
25. Map line: abbr.
26. Fabulist of note
27. Ex-Trump
28. Hash house
30. ___ home (out)
31. Game company
32. Like seconds: abbr.
33. Carries on
35. Rotating shaft
39. Coast
41. Gable trademark
44. K–O link
45. Timekeeper's prefix
47. Pierce
48. Caravan lopers
52. Insert
53. Chancellor Helmut
54. Zone
55. Blueprint
57. Simile phrase
58. Pet
59. Take out
60. ___ *Three Lives*
62. Pixel
63. "___ Yankee Doodle Dandy"

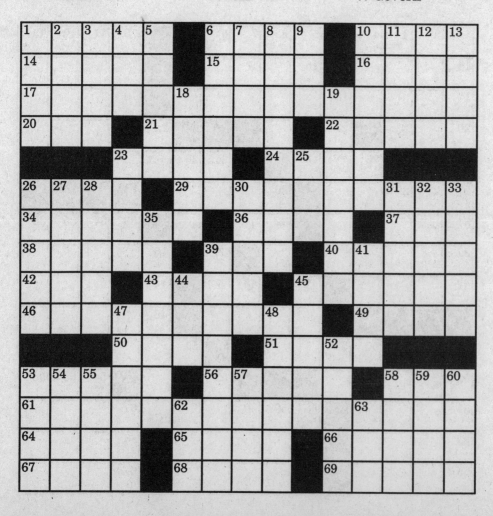

ACROSS

1. "The jig ___!"
5. Subway feature of yore
10. Rewards for Fido
14. Stratagem
15. Choreographer Tharp
16. Smell up the place
17. "I cannot tell ___"
18. Butcher-shop buy
19. "Dies ___"
20. String groups
22. 1040 topic
24. Chan affirmative
25. Aged dirk
26. Saws
29. Bhutto's land
33. Irish export
34. Use the grill
35. Poetic pugilist
36. Maiden
37. Aileen or Aidan
38. Interrogate
39. Dijon donkey
40. Leader
41. School fool
42. 880, in a sense
44. Hang around
45. Camera innovator
46. Steer (a ship)
47. Progenitor
50. Shrill pipes
54. Soap additive
55. Baranova of the WNBA
57. PBS science show
58. Round: abbr.
59. Doctrine
60. VIP in stuntdom
61. Mitty player
62. Intuit
63. Posted

DOWN

1. OPEC member
2. George Takei role
3. America's PR organization
4. Noble groups
5. Ulcer irritant
6. "One down, ___ go"
7. Scandinavian rugs
8. Capp and Capone
9. Broadway star Mandy
10. Inflation indicators
11. Of jets
12. Nets or Knicks
13. Snow runner
21. Subsequently
23. Vocal Diamond
25. Rhone feeder
26. Koran Creator
27. Artemis's counterpart
28. Photographer Adams
29. Peacock's sin?
30. Jeer
31. Teddy R.'s first wife
32. Trial lawyer Louis
34. Physique
37. Classical combos
38. Di-keto derivatives
40. FBI agent
41. Thus: Fr.
43. Rip off
44. Spot
46. Flicks
47. Prepare to move
48. Inter chaser
49. Actor Calhoun
50. Madonna's ex
51. Zip
52. Baker's need
53. Seasoned tar
56. Sheltered side

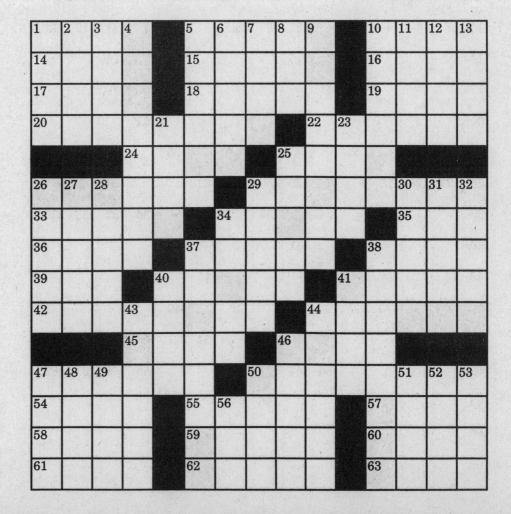

ACROSS

1. Ricochet
6. Shatt al Arab port
11. Mideast lang.
14. Basque province
15. Fab follower
16. Be, for two
17. Turgenev text, in Tours?
19. Dander
20. Bouquet-laden
21. "That's the ___ my worries"
23. Algerian city
25. With a cold shoulder
26. Desiccated
30. Act the dilettante
33. Gibson film
35. South of Spain?
36. Cartoonist Thomas
40. Soviet Fabraycation?
43. Pelion's partner
44. Ivy Bulldog
45. King of pop music
46. Closer to Kareem
49. Galley goofs
50. On foot: Fr.
53. Hindu queen
55. Musician's moment of glory
58. Tertiary epoch
63. Pac. counterpart
64. Soviet cultural export?
66. Michigan region
67. Roast figure
68. Russian lake
69. Rocker Brian
70. Lennon and Penn
71. Ate

DOWN

1. Toy-gun ammo
2. A Baldwin
3. Thin, as air
4. Drying chamber
5. Archaic pachyderm
6. Kid's protest
7. TV alien
8. Turf
9. Hold sway
10. Lambaste
11. Hispaniola, in part
12. Big name in swashbuckling
13. Quite muscular
18. Poetic contraction
22. Stage hangings
24. Less nice
26. Bond movie
27. Beams
28. Halogen endings
29. Executors' concerns
31. Patty's home?
32. Bric-a-___
34. Marrow: prefix
37. On
38. Town on the Vire: abbr.
39. Golf gizmos
41. Annex
42. "...a ___ shopkeepers" (Adam Smith)
47. Sun-dried bricks
48. Seti's father
50. Demean
51. Climber's aid
52. Northern hemisphere?
54. Medical research org.
56. Heavy fabric
57. Killer whale
59. Motion picture
60. Scratched (out)
61. "Forget it!"
62. Author Hunter
65. Desire

COME TO YOUR SENSES

ACROSS

1. Gender: abbr.
5. WWII menace
10. Go up, up and away
14. Countertenor
15. Oslo folks
16. Doozy
17. Gets suspicious
19. Ester endings
20. Not as punctual
21. Go along with
23. Rousing success
25. Southpaw
26. Like some modern music
29. Firstborn
32. Crater issuance
33. Puppeteer Bil
34. It's now the CIA
37. Rung
38. Mild expletives
39. Hip dance
40. Atop, to Keats
41. Fragrant seed
42. A Nobel Prize category: abbr.
43. Layers
45. Struck hard
47. Wildly funny one
49. Canine cries
51. London landmark
53. 2-edged steels
57. *Dos* cubed
58. Tacky
61. Executive power
62. Certain seeds, old style
63. Nairn negatives
64. Once, once
65. Overfills
66. Form of *être*

DOWN

1. Sheet support
2. Diva Gluck
3. Follower of young and old
4. Indian summer's end
5. Open, in a way
6. Guys in sties
7. Bruin star
8. Botanist Gray
9. French bean?
10. Hits the rough
11. Incommunicado
12. State of readiness
13. In need of practice
18. Flat bean
22. Huskies' haul
24. Inadmissible testimony
26. As well
27. British gallery
28. Omissions
30. Weapon for Walton
31. RNs' associates
33. Chum, e.g.
35. Wild plum
36. Dune material
38. Genetic letters
39. Revolutionary mercenaries
41. Siena skill
44. See 26-Down
45. 53-Across, for example
46. Date: abbr.
47. Higher in rank
48. Chef's gadget
50. Get the lead out
52. Tangs
54. Bible twin
55. Famous US hwy.
56. Court mtg.
59. Sch. union
60. *Fledermaus*

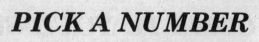
ACROSS

1. Roman deeds
5. Prepared the way (to)
10. Qualified
13. Finance for a fee
14. Minneapolis suburb
15. Barrett of Tinsel Town
16. Equal split
18. Hence, to Hadrian
19. Skilled performer
20. Electra's brother
22. Ms. Arthur
23. Carry out orders
24. Military barracks
28. Balkan land
31. Currier's mate
32. Practice
34. High-pitched sound
35. Waterway: abbr.
36. Wee colonizer
37. A Bobbsey Twin
38. Like Yale, now
40. Werner from Vienna
42. Cantinflas title role
43. Elevate, in a way
45. Lab vessels
47. Walked heavily
48. Old French coin
49. Nowadays
52. Transport for Dorothy
56. Medical amount
57. Perfect test mark
59. Arabian VIP
60. Sultry singer
61. Eye slyly
62. Regal title
63. Trimmed
64. Roulette bet

DOWN

1. Code-communication letter
2. Coconut fiber
3. He beat Bryan
4. Resort on the Riviera
5. ___ right (indiscriminately)
6. TV's McClurg
7. Unlike: abbr.
8. Poetic preposition
9. Overhead cost
10. Gold-rush participant
11. *Picnic* author
12. New Mexico art center
15. Perch again
17. North Sea feeder
21. Abate
24. *Odyssey* enchantress
25. Flier from Orly
26. Trombone count in *The Music Man*
27. Obliterate
28. Hitching post
29. Not suitable
30. Meg Tilly role
33. Squid squirt
39. Gable window
40. Dusky color
41. Echo
42. Hit repeatedly
44. Rebuff loudly
46. Rent
49. Hebrew month
50. Alaska cape
51. Oklahoma town
52. Friendly word
53. Jason's craft
54. Hero counter
55. Baltic feeder
58. Work unit

ACROSS

1. Arts branch
6. Poultry pen
10. Inspiration for this puzzle
14. Moses' brother
15. Wax enthusiastic
16. Golfer's choice
17. Canine lover's lament?
20. Ollie's pal
21. Part of us
22. Banished ones
23. Some feds
25. Clairvoyant's words
26. Confuses
29. Short-order order
30. Sea extract
34. Halloween transport?
35. Song of joy
37. Caviar source
38. Canine king?
41. Charged atom
42. *On the Beach* author
43. Speech affectations
44. Ms. Lanchester
46. Somewhat: suffix
47. Bluto's foe
48. Quaver, e.g.
50. Strikes out
51. Irish dialect
54. Cut off
55. Luke Skywalker's mentor
59. Colorful canine?
62. Declare
63. Grant Wood's birthplace
64. Tea treat
65. Lacrosse teams
66. Whirlpool
67. Leading

DOWN

1. Speaker's spot
2. Finn's floater
3. Met highlight
4. Theme from *Picnic*
5. Shaker mystic Lee
6. A shoulder to ___
7. Kailua's isle
8. Eggs
9. Idol's perch
10. Makes shipshape
11. Spoken
12. Muscle strength
13. Wad bulkers
18. Leached materials
19. Chop down
24. Business notes
25. ___-France
26. Activist Hoffman
27. Go gaga (over)
28. Treeless uplands
29. *Giles Goat-Boy* author
31. Originate
32. A bit bonkers
33. Uptight
35. Take ten
36. Stocking material
39. Very formal
40. Mouth the lyrics
45. Goads to fury
47. Family figure
49. ___ *Town*
50. Sudden raid
51. Base kid?
52. Wander
53. Hot chamber
54. Licentious
56. Bassoon's kin
57. Lisbon lady
58. Full of wonder
60. Mason's need
61. O.T. prophet

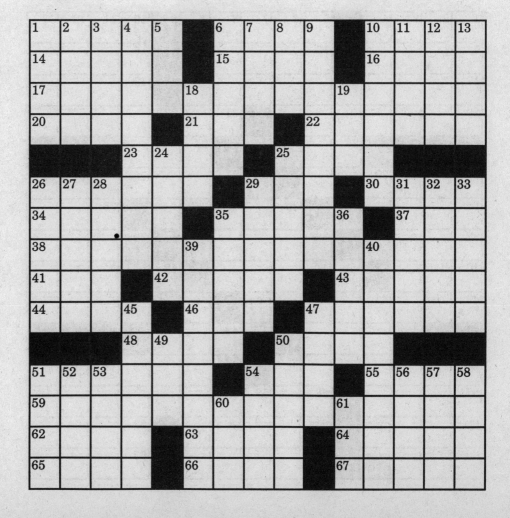

ACROSS

1. Particle descriptor
5. Wood shaper
10. Fraud
14. Composer Khachaturian
15. Diarist Nin
16. Designer Schiaparelli
17. Find the road to riches
19. Witty Jack of TV
20. Use shears
21. Old photo
23. Egyptian seaport
25. Gore, e.g.
26. Lodestone
30. Rubber bands
34. Pile up
35. Impinges (on)
36. Malabar Coast state
37. Secular
38. Sutherland title role
39. Auto mishap
40. Soft, white metal
41. American painting family
42. Like a chimney sweep
43. Certain California urbanite
45. Leatherworker
46. Gully washer
47. Place for polish
49. Children
52. *Vertigo* star
57. Julia of film fame
58. Bulldozer, e.g.
60. Writer Sarah ___ Jewett
61. Cussed
62. Open weave
63. DOJ agents
64. Hairnet
65. Ginger's partner

DOWN

1. Scornful cries
2. Actor Bogosian
3. Hulot portrayer Jacques
4. Rock boosters
5. Arrangement
6. *My Dinner With* ___
7. Asian people
8. Trumpeter Al
9. Summer asleep
10. Musical group
11. Skeet target
12. Hurry-up letters
13. Broody one?
18. Pack animals
22. Caledonian Canal link
24. Pike of peak fame
26. Sicily neighbor
27. Suddenly
28. Make progress
29. CIA overseer
31. Guitar kin
32. Tale, in Tours
33. Faun
35. Writer Sillitoe
38. Acuity
39. Put on
41. Bend at a barre
42. Hawthorne's hometown
44. Aerie makers
45. Gave a tenth
48. Jetson's pet
49. Campus figure
50. Tenuous
51. React to a bore
53. Philanderer
54. Declare
55. Actor Auberjonois
56. Stomped
59. Joey's parent

ACROSS

1. Pirate shouts
6. "Oh, woe!"
10. Rhyme scheme
14. West Pointer
15. Extraordinary
16. Wahines' gifts
17. Start of an alleged Chinese proverb
18. Provoke
19. Inauguration ritual
20. Sparoid fish
21. Part 2 of the proverb
24. Prom attenders
25. Scarf down
26. Wear down
29. Drop the ball
30. Courtroom railing
33. Bulb bloom
34. Chemists' corners
37. Site
39. Dispatched
40. Part 3 of the proverb
42. Two-dimensional mark
43. Trout abodes
45. Perky Meg
46. Dramatist Bagnold
47. Mag. VIPs
48. Hullabaloo
50. Visions
52. Title for Kay
53. Gown fabric
55. Part 4 of the proverb
59. Used to be
62. Nasty
63. Soft fruit
64. End of the proverb
66. Pressing need
67. Sommer of cinema
68. Hopping mad
69. Monopoly card
70. Raced
71. Rhino relative

DOWN

1. Play parts
2. Buried fence
3. Polecat's defense
4. Toady's reply
5. Simmered
6. Hot felony
7. Wood strips
8. Domingo ditty
9. Tray or cart
10. In the air
11. Salmon stalker
12. Snack
13. 1975 Wimbledon winner
22. Rye ends
23. Face flankers
24. Savor
26. Wedding walk
27. Moola
28. Skaters' havens
29. This, in Toledo
30. ___ and Nothingness (Sartre work)
31. Movie Hall of fame?
32. River grass
35. Space header
36. Horse hue
38. Spotless
41. Fits of fury
44. Go windsurfing
49. Prepares a pattern
51. Oddball
52. Exhuast
53. Burger accompanier
54. Broadcast
55. Enthusiastic
56. See 52-Down
57. Burn soother
58. Dog distress sound
59. Don a sari
60. Piedmont town
61. Drag closer
65. Author Levin

ACROSS

1. Essential meaning
5. Formal statements
10. Peruse
14. Iroquoian folk
15. Matriculate
16. Crossword bird
17. Tenure
18. Tiny alga
20. Show vanity
22. Assuaged
23. Prepare pages for binding
25. *Willard* extra
26. Chicken cut
27. Jumps ship
31. Force to flee
32. Entree embellishment
34. Métier for Miró
35. Spots for snoops
37. Boundary
38. Algerian currency
40. Paddle wheeler: abbr.
41. Delight
43. Vincent Lopez theme
44. African pests
46. Improve the lawn
48. Joplin forte
49. Opening movement
51. "Abou Ben ___"
54. Milk train, e.g.
55. Furnish with battlements
58. Asian sea
62. Grazing group
63. Consumed
64. Hold the watch
65. Woolly wives
66. SALT subject
67. Cut the rushes

DOWN

1. Understand
2. Fury
3. Title of respect
4. Stencil; overlay
5. Waterloo
6. Cove
7. Whooping wader
8. Dress (up)
9. Pub pint
10. Give an account of
11. Notable periods
12. Feed the kitty
13. Legal paper
19. Turned the pages
21. *Kidnapped* monogram
23. Zagreb residents
24. Body of work
25. Audit slip: abbr.
26. Bug River port
27. Dress up
28. Went by birchbark
29. Irish town
30. Fine fiddle, for short
32. Earthly septet
33. Farm animal
36. Tahini base
39. Prepare for winter
42. Trip segment
45. Inclinations
46. Modern
47. Old high note
49. Armor sheet
50. Surf sounds
51. Hurt all over
52. Extracted
53. Roll-call reply
56. Forager's field
57. Ancient lang.
59. Make free (of)
60. Pierre's pal
61. Tennis call

HOUSEHOLD WORDS

ACROSS

1. A ton
5. Set of principles
10. Bonnet contents, for some
14. Object of devotion
15. Not o'er
16. Pen name of 43-Across
17. Aerated quaff
18. Hot dip
19. Red-waxed delectable
20. Churchillian partition
23. Conceptual artist of note
24. Indiana town
25. Take in (a sail)
27. Run a blood test again
30. Made kabobs
34. Bard of boxing
35. Redacted
37. "Ixnay!"
38. Wild cats
40. Postman's Creed word
41. Cicely of film
42. April 13, e.g.
43. Charlotte, Emily or Anne
45. SC summer setting
46. Spelled out
48. Wipes clean
50. Lick ___ promise
51. Steak order
52. Oleo container
54. Getting censured
60. First name in mysteries
62. Part of "RKO"

63. ___ Camera
64. On in years
65. Bert's pal
66. Biting
67. Post meal
68. Surges
69. Rents

DOWN

1. Virna of *Queen Margot*
2. Nose offender
3. Fuss
4. Highly colloquial
5. Nailed down
6. Moist-eyed
7. Sentry order
8. "___ Grand Night…"
9. Presided over
10. Burrows of Broadway
11. Cushy situation
12. Panache
13. Salt's saint
21. Headlands
22. On the cutting edge
26. Start of an "it" decider
27. Fleet
28. Get away from
29. Schedules
30. Tolerated
31. Composer Jerome
32. Horatian lyric
33. Dimples

36. As to
39. Simile link
41. Caesar's land
43. Covering
44. Trains
47. Altar assent
49. Reception aid
51. Fix one's cravat
52. Yoked pair
53. Strong itch
55. Ms. Hatcher
56. Hart's mate
57. Walk the waiting room
58. Give off
59. Little bits
61. Masthead VIPs

ACROSS

1. Monte Carlo game
5. Surveyed on the sly
10. Divine apostle
14. Links club
15. French steel
16. Part of the eye
17. As the gobs go
19. Bacterium
20. Fleecers of myth?
21. Be one
22. 24-Across director
23. Wall growth
24. ___ *Gotta Have It*
25. Specs support
26. Second Stuart king
29. Barrett and Jaffe
32. Wraparound reptile
33. Trim line?
34. Start of some book titles
38. Georgette's glove
39. Tabloid
40. Street fillers
41. Ancient Syrian capital
43. "So ___!"
45. Arm bone
46. Head handles?
47. School group: abbr.
50. Not digested
52. *Apollo* rider
54. Rhee's GIs
55. *Mir* manners
56. Merriment
57. *Paper Moon* moppet
58. Blackthorn fruit
59. Diner sign
60. Sean and William
61. Seat of Irish kings

DOWN

1. Ultimate
2. "What ___ mood I'm in…"
3. Blusher
4. Aware of
5. Chocolate sources
6. *Rebel Without* ___
7. Sands' smaller kin
8. Slippery ones
9. Towel off
10. Powerful force
11. Ignored alarms
12. *Ici*
13. Headliner
18. Closest to the heart
21. "Eureka!"
24. Thick pile
25. Chambered mollusks
26. Cote cry
27. Feedback
28. "The ___ the limit!"
29. Sitar piece
30. Son of Judah
31. Island off Cape Cod
32. Vast
35. Piebald whale
36. Ebenezer's utterance
37. ___ d'être
42. Part of Can.
43. Cowled hero
44. Flynn, et al.
46. Krupp's city
47. Prentiss of pictures
48. Teach, in a way
49. Lost
50. Exhort
51. Lopez theme
52. Tops
53. Political cartoonist
55. Beat rover

ACROSS

1. Scouting outing
5. Precipice
10. Give to get
14. Alcohol burner
15. Wrangler derby
16. Pisa dough
17. Links star
19. Automotive pioneer
20. Chair a meeting
21. Pantry musts
23. Financial setback
25. Trawler trailer
26. Steel ropes
30. Dangerous fly
33. Spiced stew
34. Silly one
35. His book was red
38. Hoop star
42. Actor Mineo
43. Barnstormers' moves
44. Jane of fiction
45. Play a flute
47. Puzzling problem
49. Agitates
51. Daily fare
53. Most sacrosanct
56. Airbrush, perhaps
61. Man Friday
62. Ring star
64. Valley
65. Threefold
66. Toe the line
67. Mailed
68. More lucid
69. Major ending

DOWN

1. Beatles flick
2. Pliny's path
3. Patella's place
4. Wolfs
5. Sets of principles
6. Significant others
7. Strongman Amin
8. Damp spots
9. Short distance
10. Inclines
11. Diamond star
12. Shakespearean forest
13. Out-of-date
18. Heat up
22. Daisylike flower
24. Danced at the Savoy
26. Intimidates Elsie?
27. Others, to Otho
28. Court star
29. Realtor's parcel
31. Tears up
32. Compass point
34. Wilde's prison
36. French flower
37. Unique person
39. Cathedral precinct
40. Sweltering
41. Ewe's yard
46. Point toward the east
47. Move unsteadily
48. Famous last words
49. Chases fly balls
50. Simple linen weave
52. Goddess of peace
54. Some NCOs
55. Japanese monastery
57. Free, in a way
58. Single thing
59. Small coin
60. London park
63. Anaïs of note

ACROSS

1. On cloud nine
5. Activists
10. Old Possum's monogram
13. Nautical preceder
14. Start
15. Elegant wingding
16. Dowser
18. Numbered work
19. Charismatic quality
20. A fictional Queen
22. Society-page word
23. Made tracks
24. Become enraged
28. Human volition
32. Hawkeye's craft
33. A marked man
34. Minor continent?
35. Wields
36. Trunks of trees
37. Palaver
38. British pool
39. Banner maker of note
40. "___ Street Blues"
41. Dawdler
43. Posh dry-goods merchant
44. Brazilian macaws
45. *East of Eden* lad
46. Held out
49. High octane stuff
54. Spindle
55. River rapids
57. Bergman's last role
58. Sick one
59. Isinglass
60. Lunch order
61. Sidereal times
62. Invites

DOWN

1. Rubberneck
2. Albany's father-in-law
3. Jester Johnson
4. Warren matrons
5. Drank hastily
6. In safekeeping
7. Italian town
8. Make a video: abbr.
9. Mt. ___, Washington
10. 8-Down essential
11. Sling mud
12. No problem
15. 1964 also-ran
17. Richards of tennis
21. Wind-free site
23. 60-Across accompaniment
24. Pond films
25. Prop for Wyeth
26. Cool time in Castile
27. Delicate perfume
28. More than misleading
29. Jacob's pa
30. French city
31. California cager
33. Simmers
36. NYC rialto
40. Under
42. Face starter
43. High-tech tools
45. Work weddings
46. Cosset
47. Rink jump
48. Fine aperture
49. Arizona river
50. Tibetan monk
51. "How sweet ___!"
52. Isthmus
53. Times in mind
56. Hightail it

ACROSS

1. Bond fee
5. Rascal
10. Tar
13. City in Uttar Pradesh
14. Some roses' is red
15. Inkling
16. Hapless hummer?
18. Filter fallout
19. Vote on the Hill
20. Change of a fin
21. Put an end to
23. Skidded
24. Vicar's assistant
25. Astrologer's belt
28. Second film version
29. Merits
30. PC data converter
31. See 34-Across
34. With 31-Across, plush floor covering
35. Manhandled
36. Iberian river
37. Ship's tower
38. Some Olympic honors
39. Cheek-y stuff
40. In excess
42. Sacred Indian flower
43. Knuckles and elbows
44. Moor sights
45. Summer cooler
46. Senator's sidekick
47. Scribe's need
50. Code letter
51. Play-off pest?
54. In the pink
55. "...emblem of the ___ love"
56. Tatter's all
57. Sly operative
58. German steel center
59. Worn jeans spot

DOWN

1. Endearing term
2. Big chill
3. "My Friend ___" ('50s sitcom)
4. Room for experimentation
5. Picturesque
6. Hollowed out (apples)
7. Clothing for the masses?
8. Skier Tommy
9. Implied
10. Fluttering flasher?
11. Pint part
12. Golfer Daniel
15. Dagger partner
17. Falana, et al.
22. Overstuff
23. Tell all
24. Gives ground
25. Verve
26. Pearl Harbor isle
27. Coercive critter?
28. Rough
30. Retail havens
32. Egg on
33. Splits
35. Like a tent
36. Ages
38. DNA sequence
39. Street show
41. Essential
42. Novelist Gail
43. Minty cooler
44. Mark of Señor Zorro?
45. Adages
46. Barley beards
47. Terrible Tsar
48. Pleasant
49. Artist Paul
52. Western org.
53. Large cervine

ACROSS

1. Cheerer's chants
5. Kuwaiti cash
10. Advantage
14. Succulent plant
15. *Waterworld* girl
16. Hibernia
17. Unrefined airtight excuse?
20. Surcoats
21. Small band
22. Night spot
23. Tony-winner Daly
24. Urgent plea
26. Spoil
28. Footwear for the furtive
32. Jason was one
37. Dividing word
38. Pure antiwerewolf ammo?
42. Punt park
43. Pin path
44. Calms
48. Bronze coin
49. Most unconvincing
51. Shoat supper
55. Welcome site
58. Son of Jacob
59. Winyah Bay feeder
61. Elemental bird dogs?
64. Stage presence
65. Like Gatsby?
66. Preppie collar
67. Small shark
68. Curvy characters
69. Solitary

DOWN

1. Heyerdahl transport
2. Alaskan native
3. Callused
4. Old World finch
5. Century divs.
6. Bus. abbr.
7. 1982 Murphy costar
8. Warnings
9. Circle part
10. Sniggler's catch
11. Smidgen
12. Scoff
13. Playwright Bagnold
18. He who cometh
19. Tops
24. German number
25. Regular paper
27. School subject
29. Got the gist of
30. Sundance's sweetie
31. All ablush
32. Blackjacks
33. Buffalo canal
34. Matured
35. Wild
36. Sarnoff's corp.
39. Sheepish statement
40. Brazil rubber tree
41. Renter
45. Soft stone
46. Become manifest
47. Cuts off
50. Internet addresses
52. Carpenter's tool
53. "__ Billy Joe"
54. South American leader
55. Spinnaker spar
56. Prefix with pilot
57. Hazard for Tiger
59. Fruit detritus
60. Unappreciated laborer of old
62. Choler
63. *Norma* __

ACROSS

1. Conceal (a card)
5. Bewitching spot?
10. Docks
14. Ben Adhem of verse
15. Barcelona beach
16. Scatter?
17. First person
18. Eye cosmetic
19. Celebrity
20. Urban chaos
23. Shipping route
24. Bother
25. Least ornamented
28. Indy entries
33. On the qui vive
34. Big name in Baroque
35. Animated
36. Sheepish complaints
37. Indian territory
38. Hilltop
39. Qty.
40. Angers
41. Seditious one
42. Reckless drivers
45. Leatherneck
46. Pooh creator's monogram
47. Atlantic City game
48. One cause of 20-Across
56. Opinion
57. Was bold enough
58. Little one
59. Italian commune
60. Weather over time
61. Part of "QED"
62. Diving bird
63. Passenger motorboat
64. Bean curd source

DOWN

1. History
2. Bonn conjunction
3. *Damn Yankees* girl
4. Neck wraps
5. Break brace
6. Role for Mia
7. *M* director
8. Watcher
9. Latin street band
10. *Cautionary Tales* author
11. Mixture
12. Power coalition
13. Submerged
21. Shun food
22. D.C. monogram
25. Fictional pachyderm
26. Cottonwood
27. *Giant* setting
28. Chest sounds
29. German exclamations
30. Excuse
31. Aloft
32. Memorial stone
34. Arctic float
37. Hero at Troy
38. Detours
41. Avis header
43. *Beagle* sailor
44. Skeptic's cry
45. Tick off
47. "___ cold..."
48. Track shape
49. Don Corleone
50. Architect Saarinen
51. Swiss river
52. Walked
53. Newcomer
54. Give a nod to
55. Plant bristle

ACROSS

1. Intimates
5. Succotash bits
10. Lake catch
14. Sharpen one's clause
15. Uniquely
16. Baby brook
17. Oz traveler
18. Towhead
19. *Lakmé* lilt
20. Start of Richard Nixon's request to 42-Across
23. Paul's *Exodus* costar
26. Oldster, to Otto
27. Wears down
28. Enrobe
30. U.S. youth org.
31. More of the request
34. Talent
38. They make it all matter
39. Son of Apollo
40. Dumbfound
41. Pigskin play
42. Onetime King of the Cowboys
44. Biddy
46. Cooks fat-free
47. Pod's cousin
51. Food for hackers
53. Fast flier
54. End of the request
57. Actress Downey
58. Duffer's strike
59. Hand (out)
63. Gas or water co.
64. Run off with the honey
65. Life instinct
66. Soil aggregates
67. Impressions
68. Swampland resident

DOWN

1. Fish, to some
2. Excitement
3. Set ablaze
4. Put a cork in
5. Identified, in a way
6. ___ ease (nervous)
7. Northern deer
8. Last Stuart
9. Marsh plants
10. Salute for Sills
11. Shook out (the sheets)
12. Viscous mud
13. Annihilates
21. Bert and his biographer
22. Tax-deferred CD
23. Remnant
24. Valiant's lady
25. The Word
29. Brae berets
30. Rhine port
32. Ink
33. Nail askew
34. Sticky stuff
35. Jots
36. Eton grades
37. Rendezvous
40. Baneful
43. High-priced spreads?
44. Cub's query
45. Struck out
47. Corn product
48. Robert of "The Rogues"
49. Weather word
50. Some exams
51. Exeter's shire
52. Take as one's own
55. Store in order
56. Utopian spot
60. Danish coin
61. Ignoble
62. Guess: abbr.

NATIVES

41

ACROSS

1. Limo alternatives
5. Island in the Aegean
10. SoHo space
14. Potpourri
15. Walking trip
16. Woody's kid
17. Bearing
18. Gretzky, once
19. Diamond nine, e.g.
20. Some feminists
21. Helen Reddy and Rod Taylor
23. Moderately, musically
25. Travels
26. Western Amerind
27. Seasoned sailors
29. Arlene Francis and Madeline Kahn
33. Apply lightly
36. Wedding
37. Christina's dad
38. New York city
40. A Ritter
41. Benny Hill and Paul McCartney
43. Exam answer
45. Born
46. First name in nursing
48. Moves swiftly
52. Lorenzo and Cosimo de' Medici
55. Small seed
56. Leeway
57. Been in a mess?
58. PC fodder
59. Church area
60. Kilmer classic
61. Torte trimmer
62. Belgian river
63. Moselle feeder
64. Work station

DOWN

1. Pause mark
2. Roswell lander
3. Coffee choice
4. Bushmen
5. Add girth to
6. Come up
7. Brewer's need
8. Hebrew measure
9. Hogs the bed
10. South Americans, e.g.
11. Mountain nymph
12. Cádiz custards
13. Alley prowlers
21. Playwright Chekhov
22. Obstruction
24. Jam participant
27. Drill pro
28. Blue dye
29. On the other hand
30. Roll of a die
31. Another roll of a die
32. Fleming and Holm
33. Unclear
34. Cockpit expert
35. Malediction; curse
38. Computer owners
39. Friendly pronoun
41. Hawklike birds
42. Deeply felt
43. Field worker
44. Land unit
46. Pony sounds
47. Free
48. Villainous visage
49. Rapidly
50. Kin to 41-Down
51. Young fop
52. Wear into rags
53. O'Hara's home
54. Journey for Juvenal
58. Took care of

ACROSS

1. Penetrating taste
5. Deli purchase
11. Neighbor of Ga.
14. Father, in Medina
15. *The ___ Winter*
16. Tutelary god of Rome
17. Big-mouthed banger
19. Doctrine
20. Had a feeling
21. Retards, in a way
23. Biblical verb
25. Start of a Fats Waller title
26. Toxic gas
29. Question starter
32. Spring bloom
35. Foster a felon
36. Morning fare
38. Done, to Donne
39. Hindu weights
40. Took on
41. 4,840 square yards
42. Organ with a drum
43. Laugh at
44. Leap with joy
45. Amused expression
47. Compass point
48. Resource
49. Almost there
51. Latest thing
53. Tiered temple
55. Teach, for one
59. Sparklers
60. Wild West weapons
64. Gawain's title
65. Privileged groups
66. Part of "QED"
67. Soap breaks
68. Take on
69. Inside info

DOWN

1. Chits
2. Seaman's rating
3. Proper word
4. Theme words' thunder
5. Pung and luge
6. Tune
7. Tennis stroke
8. Babylonian god
9. Beethoven's ___ *solemnis*
10. Impart
11. Old muskets
12. Persevere
13. Shootin' irons, e.g.
18. BMOC
22. Lead-in for corn
24. Not ours or yours
26. Levels, to Brits
27. Crossing the keel
28. Pocket pistols
30. Perfume root
31. Hoe wielder
33. Condor condo
34. Crawled
36. Guevara of note
37. Tart drink
41. Stated
43. Salty expanse
46. Papal name
48. Exchange fee
50. Tracks
52. Strike ___ (model)
53. Galileo's home
54. Etcher's bath
56. Of flight
57. Golf hazard
58. Noble Italian
61. Nu followers
62. Actor Erwin
63. Skirt fold

QUIP AHOY!

ACROSS

1. March movement
5. Walk down the aisle
9. Santa's eschewal
14. Natural fertilizer
15. Lhasa chaser
16. Inlay hardwood
17. Pac-10 member
18. Shroud
19. Lewis and Clark carrier
20. Start of a Leacock quote
23. "How ___ love thee?"
24. Shannon of pop
25. Part 2 of the quote
34. No matter which
35. Where whales wallow
36. More cunning
37. Asther of old movies
39. Thug
42. Safe from storms
43. ___ It (Skelton farce)
45. Straight
47. KO hook?
48. Part 3 of the quote
52. ___ generis (unique)
53. Latin port
54. Part 4 of the quote
61. Image transfer
63. Noted shrew
64. End of the quote
65. Flying
66. Arc goddess?
67. A Saarinen
68. Catchers' catchers
69. Chow
70. Dust for a downpour

DOWN

1. Blue lingo
2. Rpm meter
3. Dashiell's colleague
4. Glengarry garb
5. Most shrewd
6. Blunt sword
7. ___ were (so to speak)
8. Erie port
9. Motown lemons
10. Blind as ___
11. Designated area
12. Lennon's love
13. Bread for a Reuben
21. Milan "mark"
22. Electric unit
25. Paralyzing fear
26. Joined, in Juárez
27. Stocking stuff
28. Classic car
29. Animals
30. Wave: Sp.
31. Author Cather
32. Appears
33. Game site
38. Gorby's people: abbr.
40. Figure out
41. Glabrous
44. Processes sea water
46. Hard labor
49. Čapek opus
50. Indian state
51. Cow catchers
54. Northern Celt
55. Tool handle
56. Standard diet
57. Lift chap
58. Joyful shout
59. King's address
60. Snake, for example
61. Aswan sight
62. Bush was one

ACROSS

1. *Miss Lonelyhearts* author
5. Gardner and namesakes
9. Bonny beanies
13. External: prefix
14. Bohemian dance tune
16. Actor Jannings
17. Beginning of an epigram
19. Allison of jazz
20. Geological times
21. Plies the pitch
22. French cleric
23. Vigilant
24. More of the epigram
26. 1985 Cy Young winner
28. Esprit de corps
29. Type widths
30. Lenient
34. Founded
35. More of epigram
38. Kayak's cousin
41. Toddler
42. "Gag me with a spoon!"
45. Shuns
47. *La Nausée* author
50. End of the epigram
54. Bucolic
55. Wait
56. Stand rampant
57. One-eyed god
58. Got down
59. Author of the epigram
62. Swell
63. Rock's frequent costar
64. Rosebud, e.g.
65. Margin
66. Assail vigorously
67. Out, in Orléans

DOWN

1. Smearable
2. Troop arrangement
3. Music boxes
4. Approaching
5. Tax mo.
6. African waterway
7. Actor Robert and son
8. Bypass closely
9. Poster paints
10. Primordial organisms
11. Govern poorly
12. Showered down slush
15. Indian state
18. Bone: prefix
23. Lifetime
25. Asian desert
27. Wedding-announcement word
31. Fitting
32. Like a fox
33. Chatter
35. Fashionable attire
36. Lamarr of *Ecstasy*
37. Endorsement
38. Greenbacks
39. Resulted in
40. Drifting off
42. Montmartre painter
43. More stately
44. Underworld goddess
46. Young haddock
48. Lined up
49. Almost uncivil
51. Famed fabulist
52. Holy: Fr.
53. Follow
60. Q–U connection
61. Rag VIPs

ACROSS

1. Biggest part of the fish?
5. Health no-nos, for short
9. Tennessee Williams heroine
13. Painter Nolde
14. Sharp ridge
16. Moon landing, for mankind
17. Early Buñuel collaborator
18. Aired again
19. Not fooled by
20. Vacation problem?
23. Vain
24. Tavern tipple
25. Congressman Sanders
28. Best of the movies
30. Darwinian's kin
33. WWII craft
34. Horatian in style
35. Power network
36. At present
39. Beat a retreat
40. Ryun's run
41. Growing out
42. Scrooge of 1951
43. Vintage, in Vienna
44. Certain rockets
45. Dear follower
46. Weight allowance
47. Repeatedly
53. Split city
54. Greystoke swinger
55. Soap shape
57. Invest in
58. Pal of Pythias
59. Final word
60. Roman fury
61. Acidulous
62. Dip liquid

DOWN

1. Ruth's Denishawn partner
2. Warm word from Caesar
3. Caron flick
4. Strike out
5. Lombard lady
6. Byzantine empress
7. Microorganism
8. Legal postponement
9. Solo
10. Impart for a while
11. Catchers for Korbut
12. GI mail drop
15. Heighten
21. Head of wardrobe
22. Earlobe, e.g.
25. Aficionados
26. Campania town
27. Composer Ned
28. Old Roman official
29. Thin coin
30. Early heretic
31. Historic ship
32. Borders
34. Porter's Miss
35. Pertaining to heredity
37. Lapidary cut
38. Sire
43. Links position
44. Notorious
45. Hot issue?
46. General drift
47. Lacerate
48. Manco Capac, for one
49. Dictate
50. Author Janowitz
51. Doll cry
52. Stretched
53. Shea stat
56. Compass point

ACROSS

1. Outer space
5. Marinated meat
10. Irving character
14. Simplicity itself
15. *Veni*
16. Plains native
17. Prone to bellow
19. Daze
20. Master's requirement
21. *Follow* ___ (1936 musical)
23. Black
25. Shunned restaurants
26. What 1-Across is, mostly
29. Gore and Green
31. "...___ merry"
34. Actor Calhoun
35. Calendar abbr.
36. It fell at Ragnarok
37. Made of: suffix
38. Happy
40. Xanthippe
41. Like some songs
43. Hellenic vowel
44. Behold, to Brutus
45. Fred's sister
46. Curved course
47. Charger
48. Grammy gp.
50. Sound
52. Had the answer
55. Pursue provender
59. Nichols' hero
60. "I could have been ___!"
62. Aperture
63. Fun city, to farmers
64. Roadster
65. Roosters, in a way
66. Add data
67. Gamboling sites

DOWN

1. Suit extra
2. Court ritual
3. "Eureka!"
4. Mass–volume ratio
5. Summerhouse
6. Puzzle abbr.
7. Switch's mate
8. Some Amerinds
9. Poet William Rose
10. Baby honker
11. Teachers' take?
12. Rake
13. Confined
18. Tim's epithet
22. Regale
24. Spun strands
26. Author Jong
27. Single unit
28. Claim to honor
30. Metric unit
32. Hound twosome
33. Sidled
35. Vaudevillian Eddie
36. Maximal collection?
38. Colette novel
39. Impress artistically
42. Red wines
44. How hope springs
46. American art school
47. Wild drupe
49. One kind of love
51. Following
52. Laundry
53. Fit
54. Legal wrong
56. Together, to Toscanini
57. Wooden shoe
58. Another kind of love
61. Born

ACROSS

1. Respighi's *Fontane di* ___
5. Old herbal remedy
10. Filing aids
14. Joss or tiki
15. Land nymph
16. Noted US highway
17. Softer
19. Hence, to Domitian
20. Foot part
21. Elegant equine
23. Flying high
26. Musical symbol
27. *Il Trovatore* highlight
31. Favor follower
32. Manila termite
33. Instrument in La Scala's pit
35. Line, as a ship
39. Wagnerian band?
40. Violinist Mischa
41. Serve the soup
42. Capitol Reef's state
43. Tempo
44. Behan's birthplace
45. However, briefly
47. Rare fungi
50. London district
52. *Common Sense* man
53. Lease
55. Tempest site, at times
60. Cod's kin
61. Very soft
64. Showy bloom
65. Actor Davis
66. Role for Liz
67. Wee barracuda
68. Clan groups
69. Yarn quantity

DOWN

1. "___, Pagliaccio" (Leoncavallo aria)
2. Rune deity
3. Family members
4. Landed
5. Join together
6. Actress Mary
7. Asian coin
8. 1978 Nobelist
9. News for a nose
10. Musical symbol
11. Courtyards
12. Fathered
13. Swiss commune
18. Approach
22. Astern
24. Papal scarf
25. Musical pause
27. Japanese ship
28. Pt. of a monogram
29. Mideast capital
30. Musical symbol
31. A Fleming
34. Parental prefix
36. Nottingham noble
37. *Each Dawn* ___
38. Camera part
40. Tropical tree
46. Tap word
48. Slips knots
49. Service charges
50. Musical symbol
51. Jack of old flicks
52. Use leverage, in London
53. Phi followers
54. Bunch of poems
56. Author Sholem
57. Ballgame, to Ovid
58. Sign
59. Captured
62. Nile ophidian
63. Wee bug

ACROSS

1. One of 40-Across
5. Troublemakers
9. Gatsby epithet
14. Inner: prefix
15. Work hard
16. Sugar servings
17. Arabian gulf
18. Kelly creation
19. Do a coup
20. Cajun country (with "The")
23. Black snake
24. Rousing success
25. Took to the fore
28. Sans escort
31. Team spirit
33. In the sack
37. Buffalo's lake
39. "___ is an Island"
40. This puzzle's theme
43. Glutinous goo
44. Ms. Pavlova
45. Sultry Nigerian singer
46. Wholehearted
48. New Zealand evergreen
50. "Why not!"
51. Squabble
53. Sweetheart
57. One of 40-Across
61. Rand's shrugger
64. Talking toy
65. Cat, in Cádiz
66. One of 40-Across
67. Target
68. Biblical kingdom
69. Fit times
70. One of 40-Across
71. Corded fabric

DOWN

1. Bound
2. Subservient position
3. Inscribed marker
4. Stimulant
5. Disclosed (knowledge)
6. Lapse into idle reveries
7. Symbols of 9-Down
8. One of 40-Across
9. One of 40-Across
10. Trick
11. Aussie nonflier
12. Mo. of reckoning
13. Dose amt.
21. French pronoun
22. Oakley's forte
25. She-demon
26. Large antelope
27. Thickheaded
29. Zone
30. Dean's final film
32. Southern sea
33. Analyze
34. Ball girl
35. Dark forces
36. Audio tryout
38. Ms. Ferber
41. Disorders, of a sort
42. By the book
47. "Mazel ___!"
49. Ritz and Unser
52. Cram
54. One of 40-Across
55. Union leader
56. Bar at the bar
57. Hand-reared
58. Animated one
59. Norse ruler
60. Coarse hominy
61. Inclined
62. Numeric prefix
63. Covering

ACROSS

1. Swindle
5. Poet's product
10. As far as
14. Joint swelling
15. Marry in haste
16. Finish third
17. Put on the rocks
18. Fiery fragment
19. Burn balm
20. Poisonous cottonwood?
23. Long in the tooth
24. Trencherman
25. Fax precursor
27. The fungus that made Milwaukee famous
31. Do another draft
34. Steely Dan album
37. Beer topping
39. Dickens of a Dodger manager
40. Heavy northern weed?
44. *The Story of —— H.*
45. Tub idleness
46. Off the market: abbr.
47. Hesitates
49. Select group
52. Cornhusker city
54. Gather
58. Interdict
60. Metallic southern plant?
64. Pros
66. Hooded killer
67. Carreras carol
68. Verbal stopper
69. Mass units
70. Calm a baby
71. Bobcat
72. Was somnolent
73. Angled support

DOWN

1. Marsh bird
2. Winter warmer
3. Proficient
4. Musical mix
5. Change direction
6. Shade givers
7. Flowing garment
8. Used up
9. More uncanny
10. Dos Passos opus
11. Breathtaking garden beauty?
12. Plane or level
13. Was indebted to
21. Is for two
22. Chin feature
26. Etc.'s kin
28. "Just as I suspected!"
29. Match parts
30. Western lake
32. Legendary chanteuse
33. Wraps up
34. Inst. of learning
35. Green stone
36. Very bright showy flower?
38. Clock face
41. Double salt
42. Directive to the Pied Piper
43. Hit the slopes
48. Corn piles
50. Lao-tze's path
51. Board the *QE2*
53. Stirred up
55. A Burr
56. Golf goof
57. Vampire bane
58. Wail
59. Sore
61. Skilled
62. Duster's target
63. Autograph collector?
65. Lester Young's instrument

ACROSS

1. Painful rebuff
5. Physicist Niels
9. Short-needled evergreen
14. Last wife of Henry VIII
15. Author Wiesel
16. He who whets
17. 1961 Brando oater
19. One from the heart?
20. Enmity
21. Violent uproar
23. Organic compound
24. Fills with fear
26. Corrupt
28. Wild canine
31. Casino coup
34. Transmitted
35. U.S. Grant opponent
37. Extract by boiling
39. Actor Ed and kin
40. Houston pro...
41. ...and his pursuit
44. Conceits
45. Court
46. Pressure unit
49. Mulberry family member
50. White Sea bay
54. Wordy
57. Cause
58. "...the opening of ___" (Dickinson)
59. Halloween decor
62. Fool
63. Garden spot
64. Gaelic
65. Shoe shapes
66. Assay
67. Looks, both ways

DOWN

1. Fungi seed
2. Cantrell and Turner
3. Ain't right
4. Mr. Chips, for one
5. Suds
6. Medieval
7. Steal by force
8. Go back to "go"
9. Paving tools
10. ___ out (becomes exhausted)
11. Concerning
12. Tidy profits
13. "QED" word
18. Long ago, long ago
22. Sounds of hesitation
24. Hail
25. Actor Cariou
27. Alphabet trio
28. Lacking skill
29. Dynamic leader
30. Of lower rank
31. Crow relative
32. Cuban coin
33. Number prefix
36. Devitalizes
38. Soothes
39. Priest's vestment
41. Swabbie
42. First caliph
43. Ignited
47. 1040 agcy.
48. Yemen port
49. Military footwear
51. Rhone feeder
52. Scandinavian
53. Henry's second and fourth
54. Lower respectfully
55. Icelandic opus
56. French kings
57. Rave's partner
60. Lyric verse
61. Arles article

WRETCHED EXCESS

ACROSS

1. Perch, e.g.
5. Grade of meat
10. Crystal gazer
14. Little bit
15. Put a new label on
16. Whirlpool
17. Automobile collector's excessive dream
20. Muppet eagle
21. Astride
22. Froth from the surf
23. Custard dessert
24. Throat-clearing sound
25. Pious office
28. Cans abruptly
29. Peppery
32. Stowe lass
33. Like some tales
34. Michelle's rink foe
35. Hearty diner's excessive dreams
38. Walked
39. Tram fillers
40. Brown ermine
41. Giant Mel
42. Sacked out
43. Name on a news story
44. Cause to skid
45. Track trial
46. Musical groups
48. A March girl
49. Switch setting
52. Baseball fan's excessive dream
55. Indo-Aryan language
56. Shake awake
57. Be uxorious
58. Washington bills
59. Fencing tools
60. Bland expletive

DOWN

1. Makes room for
2. Amana locale
3. Stanch
4. Princely nickname
5. Go unbilled
6. Casing, of a sort
7. Call __ evening (leave)
8. Blemish
9. Chick protector
10. Blood fluid
11. Dutch treat
12. Margin
13. Bakery choice
18. God of fire
19. Greystoke's adopters
23. Disconcerted
24. Auto shafts
25. Basil sauce
26. Watchful
27. Central point
28. Sighed deeply
29. Asian capital
30. Body part
31. Sample
33. Chucked
34. Library catalog entry
36. "Certainly!"
37. Cupid's love
42. Tons
43. Takes a tub
44. Nasal cavity
45. Diamond's Pee Wee
46. Go sour
47. Midway draw
48. In the dumps
49. Redolence
50. Greek cheese
51. Worry
52. Status chaser
53. Balloon-bursting sound
54. Append

ACROSS

1. *Secrets & ___* (Mike Leigh film)
5. Dietary need
10. That guy's
13. Tell prop
15. Fred's partner
16. Tamandua's treat
17. Stevies, he and she
19. Drain cleaner
20. On tiptoe
21. Meaningless
23. Unfriendly
24. Vane direction
25. Waylay
29. Edge
32. Theirs is a colorful job
33. ___ *Mrs. North*
34. Recent addition?
35. Israeli port
36. Highland hotshot
37. Erode, in a way
38. The word?
39. Black humors
40. Desert
41. Keyboard feature
43. Suffused
44. More appealing
45. Little, in Lyons
46. Guppy troop?
48. Ramose
53. Isabella's half sister
54. Glenns, he and she
56. List shortener: abbr.
57. Lamb product
58. Fashionable
59. "A mouse!"
60. Blunt pencils
61. Pre-Christmas purchase

DOWN

1. Some have riders
2. Pressing need
3. Coastal raptor
4. Bar mixer
5. Role for Barbra
6. "___ Rock and Roll Music"
7. *Alouette*'s bill
8. Norwegian barker
9. Echo
10. Daryls, he and she
11. Death Valley county
12. Simmer
14. "___ in a Shadow"
18. Sumptuous
22. Inc.'s kin
24. Emulates 3-Down
25. *1776* role
26. "___ runneth over"
27. Shelleys, he and she
28. Actress Mary
29. Heath bush
30. Rob, old style
31. Cried in pain
33. Cheeky
36. Defamer
37. Understand
39. Turns into
40. *Gemini* start
42. AFL mate
43. Withstand
45. Ravens (upon)
46. German admiral
47. Quote
48. Leak
49. Raptor's rake
50. Time unit
51. This, in Toledo
52. Like a basso profundo
55. Shreveport sch.

ACROSS

1. *Sans'* opposite
5. Sitcom nurse, offscreen
9. Small haddock
14. Broad bean
15. Subcontinent language
16. ___ *Day's Night*
17. Garfield's chum
18. Novgorod negative
19. They dream of knighthood
20. Theme song of Egypt, once?
23. Not quite shut
24. Bray opener
25. Corday's victim
27. Liberal policy
32. Barbados export
33. Puzzled comment from Jane Addams?
35. Touched down
37. Actor Charleson
38. Stands on the grass?
39. Russophobe's ultimatum?
44. Cry of approval
45. Reveal
46. Men who would be queen?
48. Keystone character
49. Gripping tool
50. Emerge, à la meat inspectors?
57. Twister shout?
58. Penurious
59. Animated Betty
60. Blender button
61. Actress Raines
62. Spindle
63. Even ___ (number choices)
64. Jack of oaters
65. Bread and booze

DOWN

1. Diamond family
2. Blue of ball
3. Fatimid royal
4. Suetonius subject
5. Tanning process
6. More ironic
7. Mind spark
8. Fonteyn's flounce
9. Wise
10. Fretted over
11. Brand of sauce
12. Russian town
13. Tooth-tender's deg.
21. Town by Oxnard
22. Not now
25. Purpose prefix
26. Faulty
27. Elliptical
28. Phnom follower
29. Large amount
30. Tub spreads
31. Dried bread
32. Incursion
34. Broadcasts
36. Wore (out)
40. Assigned positions
41. Last year's frosh
42. Satirical statement
43. Hen fodder
47. Mixologist's post
49. Pansy hybrid
50. Aspersion
51. Architect Saarinen
52. Duelist's tool
53. Laze around
54. Clever
55. Clinton foe
56. Copies
57. GI address

ACROSS

1. Holy Land line
5. Immense rent
10. Soviet news agency
14. Bossy declaration from Nero
15. Little Iodine creator
16. Plains native
17. Pat and Vanna's boss
18. "...my only study, ___" (Borrow)
19. Raucous yawp
20. Overview of *The Tempest?*
23. Low, in Lyon
24. Celtic Bob's family
25. Jazzman in *Hamlet?*
31. Converse
32. Tectonic unit
33. Contribute
36. Like ___ deserting...
37. Isn't fair?
38. Thompson Twins, e.g.
39. Hardin and Cobb
40. Synthetic fiber
41. Leading
42. Nautical command in *Othello?*
44. Flight portions
47. Like Cl ions
48. Unplanned *Julius Caesar?*
55. Make ___ with (delight)
56. Crane domain
57. Whine
58. Rich strike
59. Uneven
60. Son of Oileus
61. Squint
62. Shepherd order
63. Good advice, often

DOWN

1. "Cope Book" aunt
2. Letch look
3. Cultural topper
4. Stubing's command
5. Phi–omega link
6. Bungle
7. Sphere opener
8. Blind, in part
9. Grass class
10. Libyan city
11. A Titan
12. Unrinsed
13. Namesakes of Adam's youngest
21. Lean
22. Auction word
25. HS exam
26. Grand Ole site
27. Eclogue sites
28. Once–time bridge
29. Swung around
30. Loose and crumbly, as earth
33. L x W
34. Bias: abbr.
35. Late bird
37. Has the nerve
38. Femur cushion
40. Adriatic town
41. "Just ___" ("Hold it")
42. Devon nurse
43. Paean
44. Hair holder
45. Nevada lake
46. Digression
49. Delhi wrap
50. Key denizen
51. African fox
52. King slobberer
53. Actor Mowbray
54. DMV call

ACROSS

1. Skin virus
5. Oriental beverages
9. Bloke
13. Latin love
14. ___ Rookh (Thomas Moore poem)
16. Hounds' prey
17. Asian range
18. Prussian lancer
19. White-tailed sea bird
20. Drake, for example
23. Century divs.
24. Avec, in Aachen
25. French bay
28. Wraparound reptiles
30. Arab robe
33. "Be there ___ ..." (Crabbe)
34. Windows to the sea
36. Heavy reading
37. Kind, to Henri
38. Salt Lake area
39. Intersections
41. Trite
42. Coop rooster
43. Sweeten the pot
44. Fern reproducers
45. Germanic god
46. Rude fellow
47. Destiny's spinners
56. Gain by working
57. Bede's creator
58. Above
59. Has a misery
60. Psalm ending
61. Don
62. Swiss artist
63. Dotted with stars, in heraldry
64. Brief downtimes

DOWN

1. WWII distaff gp.
2. Indian tree
3. Laugh loudly
4. Tykes' wheels
5. All thumbs
6. Nobelist Otto
7. Nazimova of silents
8. Croat, e.g.
9. Defraud
10. Hind's mate
11. Tuscany river
12. British aristocrat
15. Enliven
21. Russian river
22. Dorothy or Lillian
25. Bread from one baking
26. "...a tulip, and ___ a big red rose"
27. A disciple
28. Dane Victor
29. Lunch scraps
30. Ritual table
31. "___ Street Blues" (Handy)
32. Cigar cinders
34. Seine crosser
35. Away from home
37. Skull cavities
40. Yacht
41. Trade jabs
44. Placate
45. On edge
47. Frail
48. Crop damager
49. Contemporary of Agatha
50. Spanish cheers
51. Rasp
52. Sea spray
53. Eye part
54. Certain tide
55. Does the human thing

ACROSS

1. Move on all fours
6. Footnote abbr.
10. Bonkers
14. Horse opera
15. Zola novel
16. About
17. Carol, Carole, Carroll
20. Botanist Gray
21. Thinks
22. Jones of *A Night at the Opera*
23. Fuse together
24. Streams
25. Spinning
28. Lincoln feature
30. Market mammal
31. Comic opening
32. *Alice* star
35. Diane, Dyan, Dianne
39. African desert
40. Leaves out
41. Spread served in bars
42. Impish ones
43. In partnership
45. Mount
48. Tra trailer
49. Beach area
50. Divvy up
52. Terse affirmative
55. Madeline, Madlyn, Madeleine
58. Famous palindrome part
59. Zoning unit
60. Trunk
61. Visit a bistro
62. In brogues
63. Dessert

DOWN

1. Pop selection
2. Sol lines
3. Sicily's smoker
4. Sushi choice
5. Like better
6. Put one's John Hancock on
7. Temporary release
8. Hostelries
9. Trygve's successor
10. Used a rotary phone
11. Place for a spat
12. Devotee
13. Small shorebirds
18. Cry out
19. Grave mound
23. Finish line
24. First felon
25. Fit
26. Become frayed
27. Exhibit, at the Prado
28. Inclinations
29. Aphrodite's son
31. Foul mood
32. Lay your cards on the table
33. "Aha!"
34. Powerful particle
36. Tree
37. *Diary of ___ Housewife*
38. Scottish isle
42. Actor Kopell
43. Boru's seat
44. Warnings
45. Queried
46. A Lewis
47. Songwriter Leonard
48. Threaded
50. Of a kind
51. Long lunch?
52. The dim past
53. Ultimatum word
54. Novel necessity
56. Isn't out of
57. Brawl

ACROSS

1. Served to a tee
5. Scandinavian herders
10. Prepare to tour
14. Hors d'oeuvre spread
15. Stop, in Sèvres
16. History variety
17. Feel sore
18. *Mona Lisa* feature
19. Bulrush
20. Look for the woman: Fr.
23. Auction ender
24. Archaic advice
25. Coal quantity
26. Leftist
27. Sweet age
31. Someone else's office
34. Yard components
36. Land unit
37. Too much of a good thing: Fr.
41. East, e.g.: abbr.
42. Egg holder
43. Speck in the sea
44. Metallic taw
47. Beaver building
48. Gun the motor
49. *Café* enricher
51. RR stop
54. Without rhyme or reason: Fr.
59. She fell for Aeneas
60. Actor Navarro
61. Shia republic
62. Humdinger
63. Vendor's site
64. Goya's *Maja*, for one
65. Needlefish
66. Canvas holder
67. Hebrew measure

DOWN

1. Swiftly
2. Secret supply
3. Outer space
4. Forest denizen
5. Attacked verbally
6. Ready to fight
7. Purse
8. ___-mell
9. Soapstone
10. Powerful
11. Hooded plant
12. Storm preceder
13. Swiss painter
21. Mass statement
22. Brush wagger
26. British rule, in India
27. Family branch
28. London peer
29. Canal, city or lake
30. Barber's cry
31. Morals: abbr.
32. Roof, in Rouen
33. Seine feeder
34. Untrammeled
35. Road curve
38. Cosmic expanse
39. Lariat
40. Mil. decoration
45. Typos, for example
46. Tennis call
47. Alpine skirt style
49. Mongol monks
50. Expiate
51. Antitoxin
52. Occupation
53. Lou Grant portrayer
54. Sick as ___
55. Ike's ex
56. Silesian stream
57. British ciao
58. *In* ___ *veritas*

ACROSS

1. *Andrea Doria* call
4. Numerical norms: abbr.
8. Schnoz
12. RN dispensation
13. "___ Quarter to Nine" (Jolson hit)
15. First name in architecture
16. Rita's prince
17. Cudgels, down under
19. Rachel Carson book
21. Headpiece for gridders
22. Dallas sch.
23. Welsh river
26. Chump
27. Nightmare street
30. Share the load
32. John Knowles book
35. Tours river
38. Past *due*
39. Bridal path
40. Arthur Miller play
43. "...seven churches which are ___" (Revelation)
44. Newt
45. Anvil site
48. Econ. index
49. Refrain starter
51. Jeered
54. Hepburn movie (with *The*)
57. Guidance related
60. Conditional words
61. Collar style
62. Farm machines
63. Agent, briefly
64. Ms. McEntire
65. Tweed 'toonist
66. Afore

DOWN

1. Be squirrelly
2. North and Hardy
3. Six-headed monster
4. Touched (upon)
5. Ency. units
6. Swallow hard
7. Celebrities
8. Euro. kingdom
9. Grown elver
10. Pavo neighbor
11. Stats for Holyfield
13. Queen from Cleves
14. True selves
18. Seldom seen
20. Vast dominions
23. Adjusts, as headlights
24. Düsseldorf donkey
25. French I verb
28. Mono attachment
29. Tide, in Toulouse
31. Beam continuously at
33. In the surf
34. Hildegarde of films
35. Secular
36. ___ importance
37. Type abbr.
41. Seer decks
42. Crosswise
46. Garb
47. Peacoat
50. Negatively charged atom
52. Some paintings
53. Hang fabric
54. Siberian river
55. Ames' state
56. Compass points
57. German article
58. Native: suffix
59. Rip off

ACROSS

1. Michelle Phillips, once
5. Personal pension letters
8. Anna Leonowens' bailiwick
12. Mangle's relative
13. Kelpie kin
14. O'Neill offspring
15. Toxic paint ingredient
16. Greenhorn
18. "Dust in the Wind" band
20. Make amends (for)
21. Eugene's state
24. Give a rendition of
27. Lacking smoothness
32. Got down
33. Make a bow
34. Double negative?
35. Snobbish
37. Unaffected song
38. Darcy's creator
40. Laughable Viking
44. Lacking in pomp
48. All-powerful
51. Luau land
52. General Bradley
53. Electrical measurement
54. Buds on spuds
55. Kitties
56. Tucked into
57. Foolish individual

DOWN

1. Extract, as venom
2. Geometric measurement
3. Haunted house sound
4. Et cetera
5. Marked by great zeal
6. Disencumber
7. Cord splitter
8. Delicate in texture
9. Grand total?
10. After a little while
11. Capture the king
17. Phoned from Penzance
19. Hand holder?
22. Displays canine carriage
23. Numerical opener
24. "Nonsense!"
25. Whitney of gin fame
26. Fit out or outfit
28. In the dark
29. Survivor of Sodom's fall
30. Formicary resident
31. Singer Orbison
33. Sigma–upsilon connector
36. Celtic instrument
37. Cozy retreat
39. Epithet
40. Target for Magic
41. Magazine contents
42. Midge
43. Affectations
45. BLT topper
46. *The Clan of the Cave Bear* author
47. Heel over
49. ___ *pro nobis*
50. Principle

ACROSS

1. Indian chief
5. Bass boosters
9. Bright star
13. Distressing factor
14. Be furtive
15. Back awhile
16. Data-storage device
17. Aerobics gear, often
19. Start of a Mickey Rivers quote
21. "___ Right" (Impressions tune)
22. Hostile force
25. Town-meeting votes
27. Pindaric tribute
28. Sound of surprise
30. Straighten
33. Quote, Part 2
36. A vague quantity
37. Woodworking insert
38. Transport for Peary
39. Quote, Part 3
41. Manner
42. Typesetter's spaces
43. Bobby of hockey
44. Boom or gaff
46. Cooper's piece
48. Telemark toasts
52. End of the quote
56. Show piece
59. "Dancing Queen" quartet
60. Green carpet
61. TV justice squad
62. Cheers potable
63. Wheel rod
64. Robin's roost
65. Perry's maker

DOWN

1. Pie cuts
2. "...word better than ___" (Bible)
3. Quips
4. Michael, e.g.
5. All over again
6. Large prefix
7. Hock
8. ___ thin ice
9. ___ plume
10. Singleton
11. TV adjunct
12. Ancient bronze coin
14. Like a fox
18. Extend an option
20. Panache
23. *Ulysses* character
24. Rustic
26. Vilify
27. Nebraska Indians
29. Conceal
30. "___ forgive those..."
31. Diving birds
32. "...___ to the greenwood go"
34. Letter carrier: abbr.
35. Sextant ancestor
37. ___ band (small combo)
40. Channel town
41. Rice brew
45. David's song
47. Have ___ to pick
49. Caution color
50. Sticker
51. Bag
53. Staff mark
54. Citrus sips
55. Protein source
56. EPCOT state
57. Remiss
58. Pussycat's partner

ACROSS

1. Bohr's concern
5. Ribbon holder
10. Temple bell
14. Leghorn lucre
15. Singer Cole
16. Celeb
17. Bereft of brightness, in *As You Like It*
19. Menlo Park handle
20. Raspy
21. Joffrey, e.g.
23. Luau treat
25. Harsh
27. Poker challenge
28. Remove clothes, in *The Taming of the Shrew*
30. Like fine pasta
32. Winning margin
33. Nichols' hero
34. A Chaplin
35. Sordid aspect, to Emilia in *Othello*
40. Mouths: Latin
43. In a bit
44. Cover with leaf
48. Inge classic
50. Bluster, to Puck in *A Midsummer Night's Dream*
53. Marsh bird
54. Advantage
56. Veto vote
57. Dingo's family
59. Recorded, in a way
61. Give off
62. Showing restraint, to Prospero in *The Tempest*

66. Church hour
67. Happen again
68. Lunar horn
69. Stretches
70. Bounds
71. On the Black

DOWN

1. Totality
2. Juan's aunt
3. Hothouse blooms
4. Game shark
5. Sudden jets
6. Bowl plays
7. Objective
8. *Corrida* yell
9. Dress with fat
10. Brief look
11. Lube tools
12. Quaint gizmo
13. Twisted or knotty, in *Measure for Measure*
18. Beam out
22. Lent a hand
23. Groan inspirer
24. Lennon's love
26. Collars
29. Legal matter
31. XIII x IV
33. Author Rand
36. Devoured
37. Toledo time
38. Does the deck
39. Quiche protein
40. Offensive to decency, in *Love's Labour's Lost*
41. Go nuts
42. Simple
45. Rock class
46. Poet's field
47. Anhydrous
49. Offends
50. Made fun of
51. Hoses down
52. He raised Cain
55. Puccini opus
58. London peer
60. Type size
63. Skep dweller
64. Exploit
65. Belgian town

ACROSS

1. Inflexible shoe
6. Grow pink
11. City in India
12. Spotted with mud
13. D.C. middle name, 1869–77
14. D.C. middle name, 1909–13
15. Detonators
16. Prepare a torte
17. Tax-deferred fund
19. OPQ follower
20. Herodias' daughter
23. First Ruler of all Russia
24. Sweet word, in *Roma*
25. Author Zola
26. Canea's island
27. D.C. middle name, 1921–23
29. D.C. middle name, 1963–69
30. Court dividers
31. Hothouse items
32. D.C. middle name, 1825–29
35. D.C. middle name, 1877–81
39. Apple-cart mishap
40. Hebrew prophet
41. Ms. Arthur
42. Rowers
43. Heavenly grouping
44. Vessel: abbr.
45. Genetic material
46. Word on a wall (Daniel, 5:25)
47. Bark, e.g.
48. D.C. middle name, 1933–45
50. D.C. middle name, 1974–77
53. Belted coat
54. Smitten
55. Zasu of film
56. Watered fabric

DOWN

1. Doctor's clue
2. Nile vipers
3. Derek and Diddley
4. Cortes' quest
5. Metric multiple
6. Soho guy
7. "West Wing" star
8. All fifty: abbr.
9. Pardoned
10. Mix with water
11. Bad influence
12. Mortification
13. Stunted tree
16. Cotton pod
18. Pierre's farm animals
20. Choice
21. Peace
22. Epitaph word
23. From Cork
26. Appealing, as music
28. Meara and others
29. Cleaning agent
31. Type size
32. The slammer, to Brits
33. On the ―― (honest)
34. Haifa native
35. Choler
36. Acquit
37. Use a VCR again
38. Villain Vader
40. Landed estate
43. Chromosome carriers
46. A Dillon
47. Rude rube
49. Mil. vehicle
50. Lip
51. Toledo *numero*
52. 551, to Ovid

ACROSS

1. Run out of steam
5. Summer ermine
10. Medieval Venetian leader
14. *Othello* black hat
15. Bridge strand
16. Town on the Oka
17. Stupefy
18. Edible bulb
19. Laptev Sea feeder
20. Musical land
23. Publicizes
24. Worn smooth
25. Onassis' diva friend
28. Act the ecdysiast
30. Bread spread
31. Put on ice
32. Got into a mess?
35. Musical sky
39. Tip
40. Door section
41. Noble element
42. All in
43. Others, to Otho
45. Moving en masse
48. Biblical gift bearers
49. Musical sea
55. Shadow, in a way
56. Sham blow
57. Bat beginner
58. Out of action
59. Broad satire
60. Eye drop
61. Manx or Breton
62. Guide
63. Novelist Ferber

DOWN

1. Tyson's toppler
2. Plaster foundation
3. Malarial fever
4. Dangling banner
5. Cleans and brightens
6. Ancient Egyptian city
7. Write of passage?
8. Medicinal plant
9. With kid gloves
10. Small amount
11. Mountain nymph
12. Wish giver
13. Large oxlike antelope
21. Inlet
22. Small pellet
25. Set of signals
26. Greenspan of finance
27. Licentious
28. Fragment
29. Cultivate
31. Work with wicker
32. Critic/novelist James
33. Thunderous god
34. Lab burner
36. Richard's veep
37. Winter wear
38. Close
42. Dosage form
43. Easy gait
44. Coop crop
45. Storage space
46. Tint
47. Brecht's musical collaborator
48. Hash
50. Undiluted
51. Warning of disaster
52. Served a winner
53. Moslem nation
54. Screenwriter Ephron

ACROSS

1. Earned an A
5. Overrun
10. Economist Smith
14. Porter of notes
15. 58-Across, for instance
16. Beak, in Barcelona
17. Forestall
19. Ratio words
20. Splitting asunder
21. Luxury purchase
22. Sancta
23. Evil leaders?
25. *Tennessee: Cry of the Heart* writer Dotson
28. Creep (along)
29. Kiev's land: abbr.
32. "I've half —— to…"
33. Predominant quality
34. Large knife
35. Flustered
38. At a previous time
39. Millennia
40. Make corrections
41. Recent
42. Dined again, to Mammy Yokum
43. Mist
44. Power units
46. Beach architect's tool
48. Actress Sharon
50. Utters again
54. —— avis
55. Unplug
57. Cassini of fashion
58. Asian mountain chain
59. Hindu holy book, for short
60. Play in the surf
61. Pitcher's site
62. Toil

DOWN

1. Elec. options
2. Helix
3. Otherwise
4. Period of decline
5. Fabulous bear
6. Deserves
7. Riverboat hazard
8. Nog need
9. Golf gizmo
10. Bee linked
11. He can get it for you wholesale
12. Pituitary prod.
13. Academic
18. Go to extremes
21. Slangy assent
23. Highbrows
24. Pale brown
25. Toxic gas
26. Ammonia derivative
27. Found out
28. Personal denial
30. Footballer Turner
31. She is woman
33. Double reeds
34. Tastes
36. Comply with
37. Injury
42. Literary monogram
45. Siouan tribe
46. Pie nut
47. Eschew
48. Enlarge
49. Scatter's syllables
50. Queue after Q
51. Endome
52. Plasm prefix
53. Dateless
55. Paddock mom
56. Workers' gp.

ACROSS

1. Impetuous
5. David's weapon
10. Corrida acclaim
14. Taft turf
15. Of timbre
16. High-protein bean
17. Actress Pitts
18. Greet the day
19. Like Yale today
20. Something sure
23. *Looking for Mr. Goodbar* star
24. Train unit
25. Rock chips
28. With competence
30. "Caught you!"
33. Islam's God
34. Rights org.
35. Amorphous mass
36. Nutty notions
39. Change for a five
40. Freshly
41. Monsoon-season forecasts
42. Numerical prefix
43. Big leaguers
44. Means of remuneration
45. Favoring
46. Canadian prov.
47. Stinging rebuke
53. Grain storage
54. Footpath
55. Horseman's gait
57. Bulb lighter?
58. Boxer Griffith
59. Role for Gwyneth, 1996

60. Sugar source
61. Less risky
62. Applied henna to

DOWN

1. Cartoonist Chast
2. *Pequod* skipper
3. "Yes, indeed, Pedro!"
4. Simple timepiece
5. Flight
6. "Bonanza" Ben
7. Acronym part: abbr.
8. English satirist Thomas
9. Singing group
10. Pianist Levant
11. Lake diver
12. Snuck a peek
13. A bit blue
21. Sultanate sacked by Tamerlane
22. Foal food
25. Wooden shoe
26. Smoothing tool
27. Redo
28. Exercise aftermath
29. Puffed
30. Michael Caine role, 1966
31. Keratotic
32. Chasm

34. —— time (never)
35. Covered completely
37. Does voice-overs
38. Jagged
43. "Lenore" penner
44. Austrian composer
45. Pool accessory
46. Wall crossover
47. Staffer
48. Hightail it
49. La Douce
50. Guileless lad
51. Military host
52. Trevi's locale
53. Sis, e.g.
56. Small fry

ACROSS

1. Takes curtain calls
5. Teutonic deity
9. Faves
13. Landed
14. Muhammad's creator
15. Highlight of 24-Down
16. "Why did you fire your masseur?"
19. Dark sauce source
20. Rakes over the coals
21. Antiquity of yore
22. Tadpole haven
23. "What do firemen do?"
28. Continental coin
32. Express a view
33. Sugar suffix
34. Energy booster
35. Sci-fi skipper
36. Genres
38. Major end
39. Palindromic word
40. Bobby of rink fame
41. Saucer crewman
42. Board file
44. "What's up?"
47. Alpine wild goat
49. Collar
50. Surgical blade
53. Baby braves
58. "Does jogging tire you?"
60. Author Ludwig
61. Free-for-all
62. Cat scratcher
63. Relief of a sort
64. German river
65. Mendicant's mite

DOWN

1. Scroogian retorts
2. Melt for muffins
3. Lean and fit
4. Ticket scrap
5. Actress Jackson
6. Auto pioneer
7. Brae beret
8. Wars of —— (1455–85)
9. Easter activity
10. Mythic heart specialist
11. Light dye
12. Loses tone
14. Have —— (enjoy oneself)
17. American naturalist
18. Got the prize
22. Nudnick
23. Hopeless case
24. Classical musical
25. Multiplication word
26. Lennon's love
27. Hopkins role, 1999
29. *Wait —— Dark*
30. African badger
31. Has a premiere
36. Now and then
37. Eland's kin
38. Yalie
41. Top monk
43. Predicament
45. More fatuous
46. Moral slip
48. Wax worker
50. Spun yarns
51. Sphere starter
52. File target
53. Rug nap
54. Toothed whale
55. Window part
56. Mild cheese
57. Works seams
59. Spread hay

ACROSS

1. Tire out
5. Photo finish
8. "When My Baby Smiles ——"
12. Ingrid's last role
13. Give up
14. Bullets
15. Detail of 10-Down
16. French shade tree
17. Cruise film
18. G. B. Shaw quote, Part 1
21. Charles, to Philip
22. Finish paying for
23. Quote, Part 2
24. Filly fodder
27. Plod through puddles
29. Ankle bones
31. Quote, Part 3
35. Three-part cookie
36. Bubble, in Bologna
37. Bedazzled
38. Quote, Part 4
41. Fact-finding facilitator
42. Shankar's strings
43. Peepers, on Jura
44. Quote, Part 5
47. Tuneful Tormé
48. Cry out loud
51. End of the quote
55. Romanov ruler
57. Night light
58. Make merry
59. Damage
60. Baseball's Speaker

61. African river
62. Copies
63. Bird's instrument
64. Assay

DOWN

1. Waikiki warbler
2. *Hellzapoppin* comedian
3. Brainstorm
4. King of crooners
5. Mogul Griffin
6. 'Fess up
7. Places for braces
8. Choir voice
9. Doris Day film
10. Glove-compartment item

11. Ames and Asner
12. London fools
13. Turnstile adjunct
19. Sugar-box wt.
20. Himalayan mystery figure
25. Deadly pale
26. Knotted
27. British weight
28. Lightens the load
30. Light comparison
31. Pax's counterpart
32. Requires tending
33. Right demanders

34. Court sipper
35. Tom Joad, e.g.
39. Former Nebraska senator
40. Conspicuous
45. Branch offices?
46. Newsy's shout
48. Hose woes
49. Combo of size
50. Stein serving
52. Weaponry
53. Rue de la ——
54. Author Wiesel
55. Asian brew
56. Hit with a ray gun

ACROSS

1. Shows one's age?
5. Pipsqueak
10. Viands
14. Trendy ta-ta
15. Van Gogh haunt
16. Hook plus hackle
17. Lack confidence in the woodsman?
20. Auth.'s originals
21. Author Shere's kin
22. Primes the pot
23. Frat sticker
24. Go to bat for
25. Succeeding at woodsmanship?
33. World-class
34. Painter Guido
35. Baron appendage
37. Lacking
38. Lazy lady?
39. Hack's collection
40. High-priced oil?
41. What the skeptic smells
42. Torso tube
43. "Good luck, woodsman!"?
47. College players assn.
48. NJ's ocean
49. Malled it up
52. Solarium succulents
55. Proverb
58. Woodsman's threat?
61. Hel's father
62. Hamstrung
63. Actor Dullea
64. Paper section
65. Yankee land?
66. Dexterous

DOWN

1. Racket
2. Haughtiness
3. Chews the fat
4. Michigan region
5. Act of domestication
6. Court order
7. If not
8. OSHA concerns
9. Greek letter
10. Billie Burke role
11. Least of the litter
12. Psych up
13. Harry's lady
18. It's held by Swiss banks
19. Rocky resort
23. Plant seeds
24. Not fer
25. Tableland
26. Eye opener?
27. Relatives of
28. Cornish town
29. *As—— It* (Roosevelt)
30. Maternally linked
31. Nin's notes
32. Keep an —— the ground
36. Dilute *le vin* with this
38. Indian actor
39. Fake out
42. Room for old Greeks?
44. Offensive
45. "I could —— horse!"
46. Not for kids
49. Corn coffer
50. Sit heavily
51. Ms. Sommer
52. Benny's instr.
53. Vapor: prefix
54. Joan of "Twin Peaks"
55. German *Graf*
56. Like
57. Archaic verb
59. Law deg.
60. Authorized

BELOW THE BELT

ACROSS

1. From —— riches
7. Whither the wagon trains
11. Filial relative
14. Conductor's word
15. Sore
16. Hail, to Hadrian
17. Casbah entertainer
19. Sheriff's concern
20. Futons, for some
21. Win all the events
22. Pool-table surface
23. Give —— whirl
24. Takes off
25. Out, in Arles
27. 007
28. Within reason
31. Blot
34. Late morning
35. Cabin warmer
38. Toward the head
39. Woods walks
40. Unsteady
41. Voting group
43. Court plea, for short
44. Tallow source
45. Not the sire
48. Large wine cask
50. Ananias and Munchausen
52. Try one's wings
53. Silk spinner
54. Adam's lack?
56. Bother
57. Give the heave-ho
58. Pearl's luster
59. Convent dweller
60. Yuletide, to some
61. Light carriage

DOWN

1. Temple leader
2. Red as ——
3. Meir from Kiev
4. Mineo and Bando
5. Sample
6. Pretty sure
7. Ebbs
8. Behold, to Brutus
9. Young David, for one
10. Son of Odin
11. Record for Willy Loman
12. Track-shaped
13. Salamander
18. Bowled over
22. Distraught
24. Regan's sib
26. Single performance
27. Curio
28. Pedal part
29. Zero, to Becker
30. Chemical endings
31. Train with Tunney
32. Color value
33. Corporal's order
34. An evergreen
36. Floor covering
37. Hearth burner
41. Cover up
42. Home to Sappho
44. Seasons
45. Excessively fond one
46. Unescorted
47. *The Full* ——
48. Conk
49. Pakistani language
51. *Casablanca* role
52. Rouse
54. Kite style
55. Braz. neighbor

ACROSS

1. Little swigs
5. Galley worker
10. English spa
14. Grimm guy
15. Waters of song
16. Lost; bewildered
17. Cut of meat
18. Liquid removers
19. Yard, e.g.
20. Pitcher's pride
21. Tombstone notables
22. Unadorned
23. Depletes
25. Junk space?
26. Cow curb
28. "Zounds!"
30. Michaels and Hirt
33. Fatimids with power
34. Become a buff
35. Indian state
36. CSA men
37. Capacious
38. Mixed-up canine
39. Switch positions
40. Joined a file
41. Well-spiced
42. Bar beginner
43. Sweet wine
44. Morals arbiter
45. Rural tract
47. In dreamland
49. With high purpose
51. One of the Allens
52. Milan direction
55. Sheltered
56. Malay canoes
57. Play tricks
58. Titled one
59. Fish sauces
60. Spoken
61. Mushy
62. Vexatious
63. Ferrara family

DOWN

1. Lopez theme
2. Borodin prince
3. What's for dinner?
4. Kyoto cash
5. Meal
6. Hokkaido city
7. What's for dinner?
8. Smorgasbord dish
9. Literary monogram
10. Moisten the meat
11. What's for dinner?
12. Binge
13. "Pay attention!"
21. Greek vowels
22. Faction
24. Catchy tunes
25. Begin making 7-Down
26. "*Vive ——!*"
27. Ritual responses
29. 49er's find
31. Bingo kin
32. Faun
34. Roman Eros
37. Fermi's concern
38. Horsehair
40. Nimble
41. Prom goer
44. High-toned
46. On one's toes
48. Hut
49. Downy surfaces
50. Dinner spread
51. Gardner of whodunits
53. Tiff
54. Prefix for type
56. Baby's dinner
57. Average guy

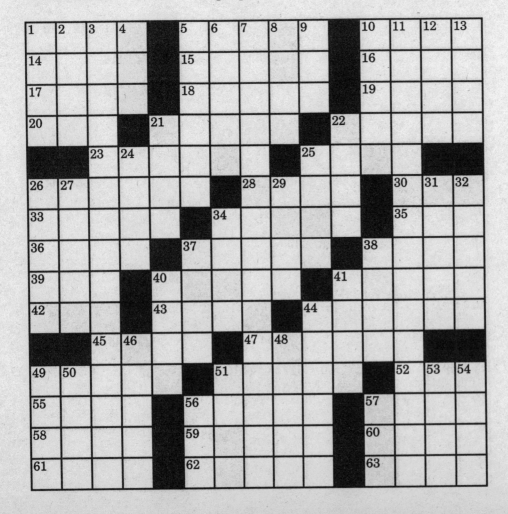

BARROOM FLAW

ACROSS

1. Bohemian Manhattan district
5. Melodic
11. Cowboy Tom
14. Jacket style
15. Pain-sensitive cell
16. One of the Khans
17. Bar order from the Ritz Brothers
19. "Frasier" role
20. Morelia matron
21. Corrosion
23. Bartender's reply to 17-Across, Part 1
29. Puffs
33. Drink with sukiyaki
34. Big story
35. Dolt
36. "This is only ——"
38. Siege breaker
39. Playwright Imamu Amiri, once
40. Bartender's reply, Part 2
41. Make happy
43. Spanish article
44. Orléans office worker
46. Poet Alfred
47. HRE ruler
49. Biblical duke
50. Holy Grail trail, e.g.
51. Bartender's reply, Part 3
54. Type of type: abbr.
55. Electron tubes
60. Insert more

62. End of the bartender's reply
66. Take to court
67. Garage style
68. *The King* ——
69. That girl
70. Titans, before
71. In case

DOWN

1. Sound stages
2. Will-——-wisp
3. Antler
4. "——'Clock Jump" (Basie theme)
5. Down Under soldier
6. Old auto
7. Element suffix
8. Sphere
9. Evening entertainments
10. Follow
11. *Jumbo* star
12. UN agency
13. Alphabet trio
18. Disputatious
22. Beatified ones: abbr.
24. Clear ——
25. Sans artifice
26. Not detailed
27. Playing marbles
28. Most mild
29. Weeping tree?
30. Agee novel opener
31. EMT
32. Overly

37. It equals 200 bob
42. Mr. Brock
45. Wahine of song
48. Giant Mel
52. Cowboy's cheer
53. Fragrances
56. Verbose exam
57. Sup
58. Swan songs
59. Revue segment
60. Former ember
61. Expected
63. Speedometer reading: abbr.
64. Archaic "forever"
65. Paver's patch

ACROSS

1. Steamer's stem
5. Sings à la Ella
10. Screwy
14. Facility
15. *Romola* author
16. African lily
17. Is under the weather
18. Autumn drink
19. Spaulding portrayer
20. With 49-Across, is meticulous
23. Vault site
24. Leakey's milieu
25. Sit in on
28. Steinbeck story
33. Generous barroom buy
34. Opportunity
35. "How —— love thee?…"
36. "Behave!"
40. Mentor to Samuel
41. Tinters' tubs
42. Ebb
43. Acoustical measures
46. Film festival site
47. Stoat's coat
48. Kismet
49. See 20-Across
55. Wrinkle remover
56. Writer Jong
57. Eurasian river
59. Feathery herb
60. Illuminated
61. Custody
62. Comply with
63. Pad paper?
64. Fictional alter ego

DOWN

1. Shooter ammo
2. Sortie
3. Akerskirke fortress site
4. City in Wisconsin
5. Place place
6. Slammer
7. Deputy
8. Nails obliquely
9. Giant-steppers
10. Civil-suit assessment
11. Zen author Watts
12. Motown mogul
13. John Ritter's dad
21. Broadway barker
22. Enjoy a soda
25. Like some criminals
26. Linen fabric
27. Military jacket
28. Wrongful acts, in law
29. Brewery needs
30. Append
31. Lawn-game variation
32. Heels over
34. Twofold
37. Make excessive claims about
38. Lined stone
39. Paragon
44. Exasperated cry
45. Jitney, e.g.
46. Cocktail accompaniment
48. Adjust a lens
49. Slatted bed
50. Actor's quest
51. Dunkirk's lake
52. Indra's wife
53. Salver
54. Reddish chalcedony
55. Last single phrase?
58. CSA hero

ACROSS

1. Seed capsule
5. Mouth, in Madrid
9. De Brunhoff's pachyderm
14. Bhutan location
15. Comedienne Martha
16. Manila hemp
17. Sheaths
19. Streamlet
20. Singer Janis
21. Covers confectionery
22. Card game for two
23. Was sullen
25. Noted Transylvanian, for short
26. Jarreau and Jolson
27. Fitting
31. On the double
34. Reneged
35. Bench, in Bordeaux
36. Garden root-munchers
37. First-class
38. At odds
40. Eastern bishops
41. In a uniform way
42. Make a gaffe
43. African flower
44. Prepared croquettes
48. Upbraid
51. Normandy town
52. Nigerian native
53. Aviator Balbo
54. Heroes of Judea
56. Rhino's relative
57. Polar prefix
58. Brute
59. Kett and James
60. Howls
61. Fly larvae

DOWN

1. Laptop lingo
2. Actor Homolka
3. Climbing plant
4. Hunting dog
5. Soho suspenders
6. Drove a dinghy
7. Charisse namesakes
8. Brutus' bronze
9. Bearing berries
10. Charming word?
11. Victor over Carnera
12. Vinegar: prefix
13. Garden tool
18. Douay book
22. Leif's father, et al.
24. Roman revel
25. Roman military commanders
27. Overseasoned
28. Simpleton
29. Moon deity
30. They start in *juin*
31. Blood-typing systems
32. Catch one's breath
33. Prepay the pot
34. Attic council
36. Sheer material
39. Prose polishers
40. Sports venue
42. Puts up
44. Hillbilly's chaw
45. Painter Rivera
46. Critic Roger
47. Doc's portions
48. Champ
49. Paris record
50. Deep in study
51. Face, to Fernando
54. Fairy queen
55. Bing's bro

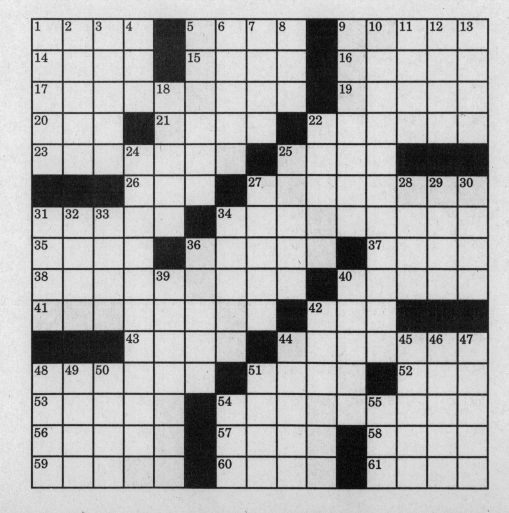

ACROSS

1. Gender abbr.
4. Racked one
8. Indian potentate
13. N China river
15. Negri of the silents
16. Massey of *Rosalie*
17. Dramatic conflict
18. —— even keel
19. Tossed
20. Montemezzi's *The Love of* ——
23. Salt container
24. Suppress
25. End of Lent
28. Son of, in Mecca
29. New Hampshire city
31. Miraculous food
34. Split into lots
38. Shawm's kin
39. Today it's Tokyo
40. Heinous
41. Hell
44. Garden creeper
45. Make —— over (lionize)
46. Race in neutral
47. Man at the bar
50. Drill command
54. *Exodus* hero
55. Thomson's —— *In Three Acts*
59. Caught 40 winks
62. Dinah's mom
63. Categorical inexactitudes
64. Dark corundum
65. *Der* —— (Adenauer epithet)
66. Hook's sidekick
67. Home for some
68. Turn
69. Marine flier

DOWN

1. Opera decor
2. Prime-time time
3. New Zealand native
4. Recited
5. Ms. Morrison
6. Novelist Paton
7. Crew
8. Moroccan mountain range
9. Wholly
10. Camelot combat
11. Year, to Yves
12. Mother of Ishmael
14. Aria for Cio-cio-san
21. Exile isle
22. Germ
26. Blackbird
27. Strauss' "Dance of the ——"
29. Praise
30. Inky, in poems
31. Char's gear
32. Writer Burrows
33. Correlative
34. *Dos* x *tres*
35. Majoli of tennis
36. 502, to Nero
37. Old cloth measure
42. Bowstring hemp
43. Home territory
44. Plant bristle
46. Bacon unit
47. Stevedore, e.g.
48. Bouquet
49. Shrivel up
51. Lively: French
52. Take the helm
53. Ruhr town
56. Norwegian king
57. Ubangi tributary
58. Assess
60. Work unit
61. Recolor

NUMBERS GAME

ACROSS

1. Plot measure
5. Explore thoroughly
10. Allergy symptom
14. Tribal division
15. Carpenter's tool
16. *The —— Fingers of Dr. T*
17. Shakedown cruise
18. Goes public
19. Spring fling
20. A fifth
22. Logic
23. Shake up
24. Tout, hopefully
26. Field of greens
29. Tangy coolers
31. Take back
35. *Hamlet* setting
37. Lack of vitality
38. One of the saxes
39. Rick's ivory tickler
41. Personal denial
42. Cookery item
45. Mum
48. "Bewitched" character
49. Skinny strip
50. Nonsense
51. Punjabi princess
53. Hera's son
55. Cast out
58. Controlling interest
63. Fyn islander
64. Love, to Luigi
65. Toast topper
66. Bard's flower
67. Admit
68. Cavort
69. Sail support
70. Small amounts
71. Rumor catchers

DOWN

1. Part of *Camelot*
2. Marc's love
3. Irritate
4. Stage direction
5. *Sr.* Domingo
6. Party people
7. Part of the range
8. Lahr and Parks
9. High rides
10. Eatery extra
11. In distress
12. Cote calls
13. Runner's goal
21. Rust-colored steed
22. Viewed
25. Gooden stat
26. Takes a hurdle
27. Barbara Bel Geddes role
28. Michaelmas daisy
30. Ticket entitlements
32. Lover
33. Explosive mix
34. Corrupt
36. Agent's chunk
40. *The Rivals* word mangler
43. Med. school course
44. A Bobbsey
46. Lurches
47. Roman way
52. "—— on the dead man's chest"
54. Rifle add-on
55. Dutch export
56. Café coffee
57. Seth's scion
59. Just a jot
60. Actress Raines
61. At hand
62. Fiddles (with)
64. Unser, et al.

ACROSS

1. "If ever —— any good man's feast" (Shakespeare)
6. Leaves dressed?
11. Ragtag bunch
14. Sheer laziness
15. Author Loos
16. Keg quaff
17. Fictional fantasizer
19. Maiden-name preceder
20. Rebellious activity
21. Request
23. Refrain openers
24. Thespis, et al.
25. *Die Hard 2* or *Aliens*
28. Soluble salt
29. Chopin opus
30. Taro, for one
31. Night drop
34. Anger, to Agrippa
35. Axed
36. Vamp of silents
37. Legal thing
38. *Mlles.* of Majorca
39. Urban VIP
40. Sail-deflating rope
42. Florida Park
43. Somme city
44. Bit style
45. Start of two Henry Miller titles
46. Coercive
50. Handgun
51. Swift figure
53. GI rec center
54. Thai or Lao
55. Golfer Pate
56. Some RPI grads
57. Innuendoes
58. Puzzle laborers

DOWN

1. Compass points
2. Wings
3. Apprised
4. Cocky manner
5. "...she gave me of ——, and I did eat."
6. Aegean island
7. Have —— with (enjoy pull)
8. Blazing
9. Set upon
10. Sun
11. Aides, Defoe style
12. Fatty spreads
13. Malt brew
18. Iranian cash
22. —— Nidre (Hebrew prayer)
24. Archaic vestments
25. Lotan's father
26. Raison d'——
27. 1959 Nobel poet and kin
28. Hearing-linked
30. Vespasian's son
32. Slangy suffix
33. Sound the tocsin
35. Charles V's rival
36. Materialists, à la Lewis
38. *Beloved Infidel* author Graham
39. Marxist Herbert
41. Short snort
42. Baby sound
43. Stood
44. Mints
45. Legitimate
46. Soho pad
47. Good, to Henri
48. Wash
49. Compass points
52. Artist Maya

ACROSS

1. Burn the midnight oil
5. *Carmina Burana* composer
9. Thicket
14. Trevino target
15. Soccer great
16. Professes
17. Hersey's romance about Venus?
20. Source of strength
21. Wheelhouse
22. Genetic letters
23. Husky haul
24. —— *ouverts* (with open arms)
26. Pigeon English?
27. Mil. medal
30. Weasel's kin
31. Gray wolf
32. Going price
33. Anouilh's herb cookbook?
36. *Damn Yankees* lady
37. Rime
38. Spry
39. Sugary suffix
40. Lots and lots
41. Corning solution
42. "Alas!"
43. Mag VIPs
44. Pulsating
47. Muddled by mead
52. Steinbeck's *Portnoy* rewrite?
54. Shakespearean Athenian
55. Twenty quires
56. Wall pier
57. Accord
58. Composition
59. Highland hop

DOWN

1. Scorch
2. Sugar Ray's wrap
3. A Baldwin
4. Overwrought production
5. Mozart creations
6. Line watchers
7. Polar bear raft
8. Iron, in Aix
9. Key groups
10. Like Humpty-Dumpty
11. Place for a perch
12. More than a sip
13. Existence, to Antonius
18. Crescent-shaped
19. Flowering
23. Grave
24. Greek peak
25. Actor Peter
26. Torpors
27. Singer Bobby
28. Stone marker
29. Sign over
30. Normandy town: abbr.
31. Sierra tailer
32. Campus figure
34. Certain parallelograms
35. The —— Avon
40. Troublesome
41. Twig brooms
42. Lingo
44. Aleutian isle
45. Dilute
46. Fractional prefix
47. Page
48. One of Rebekah's boys
49. Apt anagram for note
50. Feminine suffix
51. Arabic letter
53. Favoring

ACROSS

1. Pyrenees people
8. Mustard metropolis
13. Child's dish?
14. Novelist de Balzac
15. Recipient of recognition
16. Spanned (over)
17. Dramatist's trick
18. Chief thinker?
20. Large mug
21. Pound and Stone
22. Quick engagement?
25. MO monogram
26. Ranch
28. Flying start?
29. Eyeshade
30. Playtime
32. Preservation place
35. Morrow
36. Replacing (with "of")
37. Shows of emotion?
38. Trumpeter at the bank?
39. "That's What You ——" (Charly McClain)
41. TV network to the north
44. Cobb and Hardin
45. Rented ltr. drop
46. Death defier
48. Swabbie's force
50. "—— woman crazy for me…"
51. Drone domicile
53. People with "I" strain
55. Isaac, almost
56. Setbacks
57. Lensman Adams
58. Growly one

DOWN

1. Major claims?
2. *Anything for —— Life* (Middleton)
3. Renowned restaurateur
4. Royally roomy
5. Pulpy fruit
6. Choice words?
7. Cold sufferer
8. Campus digs
9. Ancient Andean
10. *Reds* role
11. Heavy-metal combo?
12. Writer Buntline
13. Skirmish
14. Lapsed into reverie
19. Southern constellation
23. Bear of the skies
24. Prying
27. Alias
28. Goes into gear
29. Silver streak?
31. Efficiency expert
32. Ring delivery?
33. Airstrip: abbr.
34. Rubber bands
35. Moon drawback
37. Devon fodders
40. Benin king
41. La ——, WI
42. Improving
43. Loutlike
45. Risk
47. *There's —— in My Soup*
49. Great distaste
51. One of Mickey's exes
52. Green sight
54. Eggs

ANYTHING GOES

ACROSS

1. Line o'type?
8. Canada bay
14. Planetarium displays
16. In an unpleasant way
17. Actor Harvey
18. Certain accents
19. Twice —— (semiannually)
20. Poirot's *problème*
22. Wall Street acronym
23. Matt of "Friends"
25. Take-home
26. Comparison vis-à-vis a whistle
28. Antediluvian
30. Hirsute Addams
33. Sack cloth
34. *Sr.'s esposa*
35. Nagy of Hungary
36. Primary colors in photography
39. Danish measure
40. Slack
41. Grow sluggish
42. Part of a word: abbr.
43. Filmmakers' org.
44. Upright exerciser
45. Pryor's "Oz" role
47. —— one's beer (was maudlin)
49. *Star Wars* dancer
50. Pac. counterpart
51. Monograms at Annapolis
54. Tax times

56. "Of course, Alexander the Great ——" (Gogol)
58. Soft fabric
59. Choir piece
60. Make precious
61. Texas topper

DOWN

1. *Nana* novelist
2. Inside picture
3. Remark from the despondent
4. *On the Town* costar
5. *Song of the South* ursine
6. Noted diarist
7. Hajj city resident
8. PC glitch
9. "You're —— Old Flag"
10. Sweetheart
11. Heiden and Borg, e.g.
12. Holm oak
13. Pataki constituency: abbr.
15. A Penn
21. Contempt
24. Jacket flaps
26. Coptic clerics
27. Besmirch
29. Berwick boy
31. Head lock

32. Doctrine
34. Bird's reed
35. Strike while the ——
37. Asian capital
38. June celeb
43. Showy shrub
44. Cadiz columns
46. "Merrily shall ——" (*The Tempest*)
48. Famed droid
49. Shop sign
52. Jackie's ex
53. In due time
54. Hail
55. Orch. section
57. Made a lap

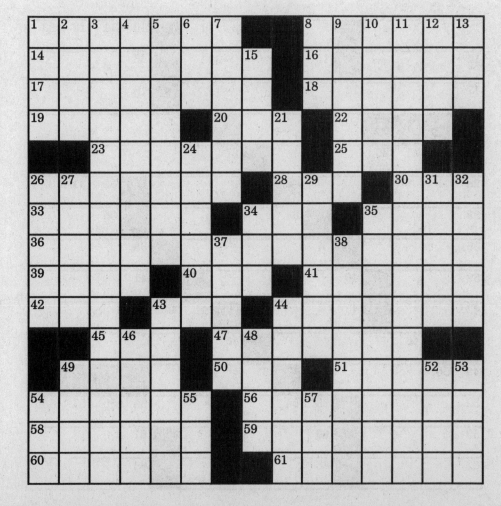

ACROSS

1. TV dare-Devil Roberts
5. Cato, for one
10. "... like —— the sky"
14. Courts, to 5-Across
15. Province in Spain
16. Sting
17. Metric area
19. Aware of
20. Yacht spot
21. Egg holder
23. Unfriendly manner
27. Onward
28. Houndlike
29. Very small sum
30. Decline
33. Netman Lendl
34. Stellar barker
35. Čapek play
36. Theorem creator
37. Crete dialect
38. Some arias
39. Medieval tale
40. Short dresses
41. Large cattail
42. Common abbr.
43. Hash-house sign
44. Old hand
46. Mirror
48. Solemn
49. Panay Island town
51. Make —— with (please)
52. Part of speech
53. "The fault, dear Brutus, is —— ..."
59. Eco's title bloom
60. White poplar
61. Stirs
62. Going around ——
63. Ruled
64. Finn floater

DOWN

1. Out —— (misaligned)
2. Seoul soldier
3. Uris hero
4. P.M. Shastri of India
5. Multibranched
6. Extras
7. Curve catcher
8. Tavern order
9. Soporific
10. Cancel
11. Talented tyro
12. "Tell —— Sweeney!"
13. Broadway gas
18. Reveal
22. Olympic hawk
23. Eave hanger
24. Warning
25. Trapped by difficult problems
26. O'Neill heroine
27. Conclusion
29. Home-run king, 1961
31. Cartridge
32. Prickly
34. Short tale
37. Twill pattern
38. Hart
40. Mill product
44. Fished with a net
45. Josip Broz
47. Gets from the earth
48. Whereas
49. Cross letters
50. Diving bird
51. Solar disk
54. Kyoto cummerbund
55. Onetime Mideast initials
56. Food label abbr.
57. —— David
58. One of the jet set?

ACROSS

1. Barb
4. Beard of grain
10. Puzzler Sisson
14. Mil. mail drop
15. Puzzler Rhoades
16. Cruising
17. Crossword puzzle makers
20. Kin's kin
21. Jacob's bro
22. Warn
23. More cunning
25. Henna user
27. Ubiquitous bean
28. Low note
31. Puzzler Osborn
33. Winning serve
36. Stubborn
39. Zenith
43. Many long puzzle words
46. Puzzler Miller
47. Thwart with a tough clue
48. Malt quaff
49. *M.*'s *femme*
51. "— See Clearly Now"
53. Topper from Ayr
56. Draw with acid
59. Talk-show diva
63. Walking — (joyful)
65. For fear that
68. Puzzler Randolph
69. Ambiguous clues
72. Town in Italy
73. Conditional release
74. Before, before
75. Voice votes
76. At all
77. Gender

DOWN

1. Trunk items
2. Shower time
3. Ailing in the joints
4. Black cuckoo
5. Be itinerant
6. Furies
7. Prized fiddle
8. Shopper's quest
9. Saw collection
10. Crook's bond
11. Puzzlers' word stretchers
12. Nostalgic
13. Sapid
18. Masticate
19. Yuri's love
24. Actress Downey
26. Heathen
29. Start
30. Dart about
32. Golf score
33. S&L convenience
34. Greek letter
35. Comic-strip outcry
37. Uncordial
38. Truck type
40. OSS offshoot
41. Puzzler Rosen
42. Compass point
44. *Nun* lead-in
45. Rend
50. Puzzler Reagle
52. Dijon direction
53. At the present time
54. Make — of (jot down)
55. Puzzler Jacobson
57. Laved
58. Puzzler Hook
60. Saddle pains
61. Rhone feeder
62. English shire
64. Sacred Nile bird
66. Pack
67. Brain tissue
70. Anti-smog gp.
71. French marshal

ACROSS

1. Plotters
7. Bitty beginner
11. Bikini bit
14. Charlotte ——, St. Thomas
15. Drive off
16. Paramedic's purpose
17. Mexican state
18. With 20-, 61-, and 63-Across, how to decipher 39-Across
20. See 18-Across
22. Take apart
23. Pop, in Mecca
24. Rarin' to go
25. Goneril's victim
26. Between *hic* and *hoc*
28. —— *Heard the Mermaids Singing*
30. Battle mark
33. Level
38. NOW issue
39. THE CRYPTOGRAM
43. Hack's ID
44. Where attendance is taken
45. A Cobb
47. Carte leaders
48. Minced oath
52. Idolator
55. Conscription org.
58. Chemical suffix
59. Tempest site
61. See 18-Across
63. See 18-Across
65. Optimistic
66. Torah holder
67. Bovine fly-swatter
68. Add CO_2
69. Scale tones
70. Haywire
71. NYSE worker

DOWN

1. Algiers fort
2. Simple life-form
3. Franc changer
4. Baseball family
5. Turkish coins
6. '60s activist Bobby
7. British exclamation
8. *Der*, *die*, or *das*
9. Close-fitting hat
10. Offspring
11. Ledger pro
12. Take long odds
13. Woodworking tool
19. Chalices
21. Protein diet doctor
25. Say differently
27. Den denizen
29. Speech sound
31. Escort's offer
32. Fink
34. Utmost ordinal
35. Once-familiar road sign
36. "Evil Woman" band, briefly
37. Dad header
39. Angled annex
40. Compete
41. Sprain helpers
42. Kilted uncle
46. Mock
49. Genesis mount
50. With a handle
51. Valentino player (1951)
53. Must, slangily
54. First string
56. Crouch
57. High-grade
59. Sign of sorrow
60. To be, in Aix
61. Shoe cleat
62. Canyon mouth
64. Carioca city

BATTLING THE BOXES

ACROSS

1. Golfer's sine qua non
5. Grid coups, for short
8. Amount (to)
13. Daughter of Eurytus
14. Whence Mork
15. Samuel Finley —— Morse
16. Dangerous tropical fish
18. Full of spirit?
19. Problem with 19-Across and 12-Down
21. Author Anita
22. Start of a Shakespearean title
23. Hurts badly
25. Clampett patriarch
26. Ear core
29. Beaked Muppet
30. Rugged rock
32. Loud outburst
33. Problem with 33-Across and 28-Down
36. Sale caveat
37. Hentoff and Cole
38. Confusion
39. Gumshoe
40. Capitol Hill climber: abbr.
41. Wrapped à la Batman
42. Smooth wood
43. Miffed
44. Problem with 44-Across and 48-, 49- and 50-Down

51. "You'll get ——"
52. One percent of a millennium
53. "Clair ——"
54. Tavern order
55. Ms. Woodhouse
56. Spectated idly
57. Poet Robert
58. Optimistic

DOWN

1. Essence
2. Portnoy's penner
3. Nastase of net fame
4. Fines
5. Some statues
6. Attracts
7. Scottish isle
8. Traitor of 1780
9. Campus bigwigs
10. Cause for chapter 11
11. Mil. flight fleet
12. Wee? *Oui!*
15. Cowboy's affliction
17. Sundial pin
20. Bombay VIPs
23. Huge deer
24. Caper
26. Go no further
27. Obeyed the coxswain
28. Sanctified
29. Winged pest
30. When, in Lima
31. Group of troops: abbr.
32. Frank Oz, e.g.
34. Monotonous
35. Marble home?
40. Silky-smooth
41. Ex-heavyweight fighter Gerry
42. Hedge item
43. Beach find
44. Trendy youth of the 1960s
45. Eye layer
46. Manx, e.g.
47. Wield a snee
48. Emotion for Ovid
49. *6 —— Riv Vu*
50. Recite

ACROSS

1. CA clock zone
4. Thai tower
10. Arizona town
14. Swiss river
15. Become communicative
16. Ex-Czech Lendl
17. 1986 funky film comedy
20. Definite no-no
21. Diarist Anaïs
22. Every last thing
23. Airline's French connection?
24. City on the Rio Grande
27. Baseball stat.
28. Charlotte of TV
29. Top-notch
30. "—— Ron Ron"
32. Season of celebration
35. Lanky
36. With "A," the director's description of 17- and 55-Across
39. Ishmael's boss
40. Wood protectors
41. Show spots
43. Zen, e.g.
44. Three, on some holes
47. Cher, to Chastity
48. Say for sure
51. Dixie gridders, briefly
52. Snacked
53. Chart
54. Job's tormenter
55. 1989 racial-tension satire
60. Pike sight
61. Not tense
62. Pindar work
63. Put aside
64. Cyclist's must
65. Blue

DOWN

1. Flock leader
2. North African expanse
3. High-pitched
4. Walt Kelly creation
5. GI address
6. Obtain
7. Toronto's province: abbr.
8. An Allman
9. Plant pest
10. 1,004, once
11. "Our Miss Brooks" star
12. Windjammer, for example
13. Insect-eating insect
18. Versatile bean
19. "Can read —— ... " (Swift)
24. Ear parts
25. Old-womanish
26. PR statement
29. Diving bird
31. Baba and MacGraw
32. Agree
33. Conger catcher
34. Toss out
36. Dodge showdown
37. Cabbage tree
38. Table scrap
39. Battle fleets
42. Identical
44. Picnic sites
45. Ms. Plummer
46. Roamed freely
49. Isaac's mom
50. Ill will
51. Scrooge's cry
54. Rescind a dele
56. Cub's question
57. Set
58. Ark rider
59. It's on the tip of his Tung

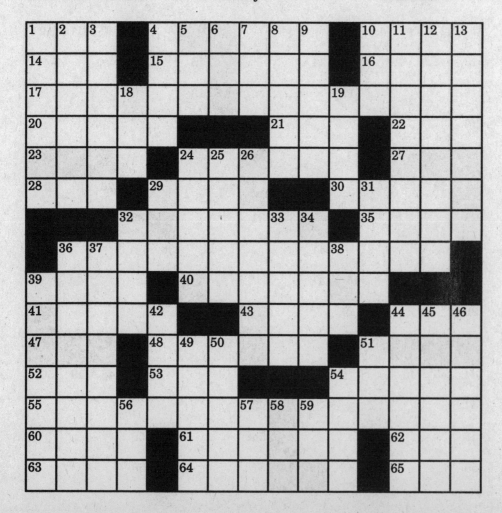

ACROSS

1. Drag along
5. Actress Maria
11. Singer Cooke
14. Night bear
15. His work was done by Friday
16. Kaz Dagi
17. Hillary's attainment
19. Light time
20. Fast-food fare
21. Dies (out)
23. Custom
24. Exigencies
27. Surfing milieu
28. Bacteria
30. Gains a lap
32. Durable cotton
35. Point
37. Changed clothes, in a way
39. Bitter herb
40. Place in four states
45. Novelist Umberto
46. It can hold water
47. Heavyweight?
48. Bawdy
50. Vientiane's land
52. Contract extra
56. A Reagan, for short
58. Vapor
60. Blackbird
61. Mosey with attitude
64. He calls Nome home
66. Fourth caliph
67. Retro garb
70. A Beatty
71. Musical with a Twist
72. Suit to ——
73. River in Wales
74. Melds
75. Glabrous

DOWN

1. Balderdash
2. Stir up
3. Loan shark
4. Chanteuse k.d.
5. Give a start
6. Crunches, of a sort
7. Europe invader
8. Leghorn direction
9. Barnstormer's maneuver
10. Cartoon Pepe
11. Cheeky growth
12. Jewish month
13. Hall-of-Famer Willie
18. Stretchable
22. Spread hay
25. *Encyclopédie* editor
26. Charon's river
29. Loony
31. Religious faction
33. Trim
34. Pivotal
36. Cry weakly
38. Sole cleaner
40. Actress Harris
41. Hot rocks
42. The cons
43. Oodles
44. Verse opener?
49. Key signal from Sparks
51. Ocean floor
53. Sioux member
54. Paint finish
55. Washed out suds
57. Mogul governor
59. Then, in Thiers
61. Beach blanket
62. The way the wind blows
63. Holler
65. Effort
68. Stretch the truth
69. MD's aide

ACROSS

1. Child, e.g.
5. Texas panhandle city
10. Stuffs with packing
14. Tokyo tummy
15. Ludwig and Jannings
16. Medley
17. Like —— out of hell
18. Kegler's button
19. Crucifix
20. Cut-rate stock trader
23. Watt's energy
24. Go gliding
25. Prom attendees
29. Furnace feeder
33. Abstaining from
36. Revel in victory
38. Aware of
39. Cut-rate clothing source
43. Personal: prefix
44. *Murder in the Cathedral* dramatist
45. Existed
46. Legally bars
49. Nobelist Root
51. Zeno's school
53. —— ease (awkward)
57. 1978 cut-rate whodunit? (with *The*)
62. Nasal wind
63. Macho guys
64. Actor Novello
65. Xiaoping
66. Trojan War saga
67. Golda from Kiev
68. Residue bit
69. London lords
70. Actor Garcia

DOWN

1. Everett and Lowe
2. Sister's garb
3. Wipe away
4. Big shot
5. Cuzco's country
6. Grace ender
7. Haze
8. Common people
9. Dome team
10. The Oval Office, for one
11. Soap additive
12. Designing Christian
13. Turf
21. End of a series
22. Trendy tidbit
26. Actor Wallach
27. Fifth canonical hour
28. Plush fur
30. Was cognizant
31. Famed volcano
32. Goes bad
33. Theater award
34. Fleeting fashions
35. Glassmaking material
37. Manx's lack
40. Zero
41. ——-*disant*
42. Moral standard
47. School gp.
48. Role for Meryl
50. Last syllable
52. Writer Rogers St. Johns
54. Make merry
55. Steer clear of
56. Robe material
57. Good buddy, briefly
58. Whet
59. Kuwaiti kingpin
60. Small duck
61. Remnants
62. Unmatched

ACROSS

1. Epsilon follower
5. Ancient Asian kingdom
9. Diplomat's asset
13. Uneven
14. Sphere of conflict
15. Mormon mecca
16. Cyclist's inflater
17. Mel Sharples' establishment
18. Wander
19. With 24-Across, Mandrell hit
22. Born
23. Posts
24. See 19-Across
30. Spring sign
31. "___ Theme" (from *Doctor Zhivago*)
32. UN agency
35. Pinnacle
36. Cucumbers
37. Fruitless
38. Theorem abbr.
39. They have bark but no bite
40. Divide equally
41. Tall order, at the deli
43. Concert hall
45. Author Levin
46. Country-music duo
53. Desk item
54. Maine town
55. Hebrew month
56. Town on the Oka
57. Clear wrap
58. Mayberry boy
59. Walk in water
60. Ailing trees
61. Mute salutes

DOWN

1. Shoots, arcade-style
2. Hebrew month
3. Weighty reading?
4. Book supplement
5. Yeats' homeland
6. Former Chinese VIP
7. Fin parts?
8. Percussion instruments
9. Swollen
10. Bikini, e.g.
11. Prehistoric condos
12. Common article
14. François' farewell
20. Laborer
21. Burns' vetoes
24. Recent US foe
25. Terse refusal
26. Resting
27. Censor's sound effect
28. Carnation site
29. Irregularly notched
32. Use your feet
33. Pollen pantry
34. Unique person
36. Evening bloom
37. Hiatus
39. Accurate
40. Presenter's word
41. Sacred site
42. City in E France
43. John or Maureen
44. Like some stadiums
47. Asian sea
48. Average
49. Genetic abbrs.
50. Short shot
51. Invade
52. Mesabi extractions
53. Base

ACROSS

1. Tent locale
5. Union foe
9. Israeli statesman
14. Jai ——
15. Sit for Seurat
16. Eweish
17. Ineffectual
18. Pot portion
19. Musical lamentation
20. Newspaper special
23. Pismire
24. Full of moisture
25. 551, to Flavius
28. Made a chess move
32. Poet pugilist
35. It's straight from the heart
37. Put on
38. "Step —— !"
39. Newspaper bonus
42. Swagger stick
43. Title role for Bette
44. Sacred song
45. No matter which
46. Bridge tactic
48. Those, in Lyon
49. Shore raptor
50. Wrap up
52. Newspaper staffer
60. Fragrant flower
61. Catalog
62. Exercise suffrage
63. Author Jong
64. Daughter of Laban
65. Not for
66. Perches
67. North Sea feeder
68. Light element

DOWN

1. A little lower?
2. Wings
3. Peggy Wood role
4. Sacred sculpture
5. Dorian city-state
6. Sight cell
7. Movie pooch
8. Keg contents
9. Full follower
10. Toss out
11. Lass
12. "Picnic" penner
13. Formerly named
21. Hawkeye's pal
22. Twit
25. Bangladesh capital
26. Ship-finding system
27. Literary wit
29. Faint
30. Concise
31. Takes on cargo
32. Aussie/Kiwi soldier
33. French city
34. Listings
36. Half a fly
38. Parts of lbs.
40. Squeeze dry
41. Turn over
46. Melee
47. Boil
49. Put into law
51. Salon sitter
52. Bog
53. *Inter* ——
54. Man, for one
55. Yule song
56. Snatch
57. Pitch
58. Palindromic Teuton
59. Bit adjunct
60. French article

ACROSS

1. Vocal range
5. Screen Gunga Din
10. Ganges river landing
14. Puma hideout
15. Some reeds
16. Futhark script
17. Decorators' doings
20. Soda flavoring
21. Underdog's coup
22. Raise, for one
23. Actress Sondergaard
25. Lovers' liaison
29. Sea extract
30. Indicate assent
33. Small bottle
34. Commemorative slab
35. Columbus coll.
36. Football end
40. Slow down, in music: abbr.
41. Old Kingdom of Burgundy
42. Plum variety
43. Oink spot
44. Chicken condo
45. Island of the Colossus
47. Sawyer's pal
48. Drover's command
49. Steeple
52. Zealous one
56. Hidden intentions
60. At no time, poetically
61. Punjab pundit
62. Nothing
63. Gravel mound
64. Blessed table
65. Over again

DOWN

1. Muhammad's son-in-law
2. Rangy
3. Cold War leader
4. Oka port
5. Enlistee
6. More or less
7. Army post
8. Washington agent
9. Language suffix
10. Complain
11. Bear embraces
12. Stuart queen
13. Tryout
18. Physicist Isidor
19. Harem lord
23. Highlanders
24. "... monarch of ___ survey"
25. Declares
26. Mister ___ (handyman)
27. Lard laden
28. Pub order
29. Throat woe
30. Rover
31. Orange variety
32. Gobi sights
34. Greek lawgiver
37. More risqué
38. Press agent?
39. Conceit
45. French painter
46. Summer woe
47. French cleric
48. Galen's initial
49. Torpedoed
50. Entreaty
51. News bit
52. Campus gp.
53. Ike's ex
54. Terrible tsar
55. Give over
57. "There ___ tide ..."
58. Pussycat partner, in a poem
59. Pruner's tool

ACROSS

1. Minn. neighbor
5. Kin of a creek
8. Primitive: prefix
13. Repository
15. Make corrections
16. Concocted deceitfully
17. Josh
18. Place for a retort
19. Ess trailer
20. Fetter
21. Night hunters
23. Achieve desired results
28. Augsburg article
30. Signs at the Palace
31. Sulawesi ox
32. Hub of old Rome
34. 1040 collector
35. Ready to party
36. Rule out
37. Seem likely
40. Page size: abbr.
41. Hoofer Miller
42. Aix ailment
43. Bore's effect
45. Pirate's plunder
47. Inkling
49. Poor mark
50. Destined
53. Veldt fox
56. The broody bunch
57. "Eureka!"
59. Strew hay
60. Eastwood of Carmel
62. Road sign
65. Sub finder
66. Precisely
67. Unmollified
68. Minsk assents
69. Since, in Ayr

DOWN

1. Bedding material
2. Big gamble
3. Elbow support
4. Held on to
5. Cowboy contests
6. Promissory note
7. Roadie's tote
8. Roland of ballet
9. Egyptian sun god
10. Pointed inquiry
11. Printers' measures
12. Paean
13. City on the Vire: abbr.
14. Pipe material
20. Blues singer Smith
22. Elton's title
24. Insincere flirt
25. Haifa dance
26. Raccoon's kin
27. Boxer's coup
29. Main point
32. Pope's cape
33. Apes
36. Indonesian island
38. Art cult
39. Circ.
44. Pedagogues' org.
46. Thumb ball
48. Conforms
51. Headword
52. Pahlavi title
54. Mother wit
55. Sidle
58. Enzyme endings
60. Reb's govt.
61. Actor Chaney
62. Blynken's chum
63. Bet —— sure thing
64. Hull bend

ACROSS

1. Uncouth
5. Jaipur honcho
10. Jockey's accessory
14. Seed covering
15. Go bananas over
16. Sidekick
17. 31401
20. Woodshop tool
21. Dozes (off)
22. Hill denizen
23. Hellenic vowels
26. Spill the beans
28. Fought
31. Map lines
34. Missile trajectory
35. Auriculate
37. Spring bloom
39. 80302
43. Chancellor Bismarck
44. Diamond great
45. Amazon weather outlook
46. Salome's audience
49. Follows advice
51. Speaker's post
53. Line a roof
54. Ruction
57. Pack away
59. Tightfisted one
63. 55806
67. Summer quenchers
68. German port
69. Get game
70. Arizona town
71. Medieval manor officer
72. Cry of distress

DOWN

1. See 20-Across
2. Russian range
3. La Scala performer
4. Bird of the hawk family
5. Operated
6. Nabokov novel
7. "Revelations" revealer
8. Jargon
9. Obedient one
10. Train section
11. Baltic capital
12. Host at Valhalla
13. Fossil fuel
18. Used a seine on
19. Ibsen's city
24. Winglike parts
25. Missionary Junipero
27. Snug abode
28. Soup for sipping
29. Sharp
30. Design transfer
32. Depicted
33. Facets
34. Finnish seaport
36. Architectural style
38. Tosspot
40. Parliament member
41. Finish fourth
42. Punctual
47. Malt kiln
48. Confusion
50. Inventor Otis
52. Amiens river
54. First mate's man?
55. City slicker
56. Cordoba cheers
58. Expansive
60. Spirit
61. Lab burner
62. Hamelin's bane
64. Dos Passos trilogy
65. Elko's st.
66. Compass point

ACROSS

1. Famed chanteuse
5. Trade
9. Learn to fit in
14. Transport for 35-Across
15. Ms. Sarkisian, now
16. Chap
17. Tip, in Toulouse
19. Melancholy
20. W. J. Lederer book
22. Sleeper, at times
23. "—— a little nut tree ..."
24. Ring moves
28. The yoke's on them
29. Burns' ego
32. In conflict
33. Indigo
34. Wrestling style
35. Jason's quest
38. Robe monogram
39. Like —— in the manger
40. Yellow-fever mosquito
41. Exist
42. Granular snow
43. Says yes
44. Priceless
45. Common food additive
46. "Light and beauty on ——" (Masefield)
53. O'Hara brogue
54. Like lampoonery
55. Pulitzer Prize poet of 1929
56. Uniform
57. Titled one
58. Suspicious
59. Puppeteer Tony
60. Galway girl

DOWN

1. Family member
2. Use a mangle
3. *Rio* flower
4. Worth, in Texas
5. Reporter's dreams
6. Snivelling
7. Of flight
8. Opening, in a way
9. Crocheted coverlet
10. Crossed out
11. Lily relative
12. Sound of a flat dive
13. Kilmarnock cap
18. Café
21. Cabinet content
24. Earl Hines' epithet
25. Clear air
26. "If —— a Rich Man"
27. Rosinantes, e.g.
28. Tie —— (binge)
29. Soft leather
30. Host
31. Fertile loam
33. Info on envelopes
34. Prophet
36. Wealthy Scot
37. Slowpoke
42. Flawed
43. Gone fishing?
44. Shell mover
45. Angled joint
46. Canada native
47. Track course
48. Hot rock
49. Final writ
50. —— Bay, Dominican Republic
51. Items for 44-Down
52. Jurists' degs.
53. Dup.

ACROSS

1. Champagne rating
5. Fixes holes
10. Round cheese
14. Newspaper section
15. *The Cocktail Party* playwright
16. Town on the Truckee
17. Start of a punny saying
20. Overhauls
21. Sidesteps
22. Luau strings
23. Jazzman Kenton
24. Menu item
27. On a mission
31. Breathing passages
32. Riding whip
33. Saul's uncle
34. Citrus sips
35. Swears off
36. Capital of 45-Down
37. Asian coin
38. Pumps gas
39. Strings for Orpheus
40. Quartermaster's concern
42. Young Turks
43. Change course
44. Philistine
45. Top-of-the-line
48. Implies
52. End of the saying
54. Jazz jargon
55. Bread bit
56. ——-bitty
57. Roman road
58. Hebrew letters
59. Cajole

DOWN

1. Sibling in Dixie
2. Be footloose
3. Western Amerinds
4. Coerces through pain
5. Extent
6. Botanical balms
7. Spanish streams
8. Gesture of dismissal
9. Church begun under Julius II
10. Wandering
11. Action
12. George I preceder
13. Witticisms
18. Shoulder poles for pails
19. Nautical command
23. Chanel specialties
24. Give guns to
25. Darling of '76 Olympics
26. English river
27. Pen
28. Habituate
29. Absolute denial
30. Kid food
32. Peculiar
35. Least boisterous
36. Not literal
38. Cheeky
39. Nuts
41. More closely matched
42. Tours tales
44. Painter Hieronymus
45. Pacific land
46. *Whose Life —— Anyway?*
47. Part of 9-Down
48. Review: abbr.
49. Slavic leader
50. Madrid pronoun
51. Mythic river
53. Paris holm

ACROSS

1. Weather
5. Development division
9. Velcro alternative
14. Putting-in place
15. Base tot
16. Rider's togs
17. Knowing the scoop about
18. Chum or chub
19. Persian Gulf floater
20. Long time
23. Ante- alternative
24. Diminutive ending
25. Bizarre
26. Outside: abbr.
27. Dehydrate
28. Horse soldiers, for short
31. Cellular item
34. Homecoming attendee
36. Painted metal
37. Long conflict
40. Wright angles?
41. Thous
42. Tin Man player
43. Route
44. Author Rand
45. Because
46. Nile reptile
47. Exploited cruelly
49. TV hosts
52. Long song?
56. Nilotic language
57. Common contraction
58. Aesop animal
59. Gomez Addams portrayer
60. Lateral
61. Nice notion
62. Roman roarer
63. Get an earful
64. Vim

DOWN

1. Small ape
2. Integrity
3. Sans escort
4. Shut (up)
5. Funnyman Bud
6. Artisan's forte
7. Poker maneuver
8. Reproach to Brutus
9. Poorly made
10. Water nymph
11. With competence
12. Sales pitches?
13. Cruise ship: abbr.
21. Witch, at times
22. Shearer on film
26. Some gridders
27. Club fees
28. Monk's hood
29. Wings
30. Truly
31. Sigh of relief
32. Island dance
33. Part of "SRO"
34. Yemeni port
35. Soap ingredient
36. Russian royal
38. Site of Pharos
39. Mary's buddy
44. Take —— to (like)
45. Rot
46. One more time
47. Count of jazz
48. Actress Carter
49. Union general
50. Harvest deity
51. Trapshooting
52. Leisure
53. Ratio words
54. China piece
55. Hissing sound
56. —— de mer (seasickness)

ACROSS

1. *Casa* room
5. Cook a casserole
9. Emmy honoree
14. Hawkeye State town
15. Discharge
16. Lacking in restraint
17. Barrelmaker dined?
19. Bell inserts
20. Campaign
21. Use a bulldozer
22. Reliable
23. Spiritual loner
25. Irritant
26. Dogfight hero
27. Affectation
31. Iridescent gemstones
34. Dressed
35. Pro follower
36. Lady of rank
37. Masticates
38. Trade jabs
39. Hebrew letter: var.
40. Student subsidy
41. Boat berths
42. Beltway bigwigs
44. Hang back
45. Give up
46. Of an eye layer
50. Employs stickum
53. Coiled chokers
54. New Deal abbr.
55. At the apex
56. Jailbird's poetry?
58. Gaze
59. Importune
60. Family member
61. Medieval guild
62. Soup legumes
63. Many planes

DOWN

1. *Le —— du Printemps*
2. Love affair
3. Sierra ——
4. Cleo's undoing
5. Chide
6. Surprise and then some
7. March toy
8. Seine season
9. Not quite
10. "On Sale"?
11. Carryall
12. Sugar suffixes
13. Quiescent state
18. Ambler and Blore
22. Takes careful notice
24. Y chromosomes?
25. Shrimp relative
27. Entreaties
28. Scruff
29. Lawman's emblem
30. Specs supporters
31. Harem rooms
32. Colorless
33. Mass statement
34. Bit of drudgery
37. Dunderheads
41. Analyze critically
43. Home of the brave
44. Bakery items
46. Line dance
47. Result
48. Ain't the way it ought to be
49. Shoe forms
50. Swanky
51. Door column
52. Ollie's mate
53. Cause ennui
56. Trophy of sorts
57. Rule, in India

ACROSS

1. Facedown
6. Turku, once
9. Singe
13. *Bolero* composer
14. Meaning, in Marseille
16. San —— (Ligurian port)
17. Fences, e.g.
18. Alka-Seltzer sound
19. Sutherland solo
20. Debussy's sea
21. Rickenbacker comic strip
24. Period for the books
25. Rake
26. Southern belle?
32. Cold War abbr.
35. Benefit
36. Firm denials
37. Nice *saison*
38. Dispute
41. Cut quickly
43. Hold title to
44. DDE's command
45. Celebrated
46. Youth organization: abbr.
47. "... —— shall come in" (Psalms)
51. Amati adjuster
52. Capri completer
53. Royal matriarch
58. Central
61. Coffee servers
62. Marathon sensation?
63. Speechify
65. "—— Rhythm"
66. Nova, e.g.
67. Spoken for
68. Basilica benches
69. Hindu mantras
70. Man's name

DOWN

1. Hyde Park stroller
2. Playwright David
3. Surmounting
4. Bottom-line word
5. Fashion's Schiaparelli
6. *The —— Papers* (James)
7. Old lady
8. —— about (roughly)
9. Muscle woe
10. Grinder
11. Idi of note
12. Way
15. Incites
22. Corp. honcho
23. 1982 Lemmon film
26. Esau's bro
27. Acknowledges
28. Tropical herb
29. Equipment
30. Make svelte
31. Election night celebrants
32. Tissue partition: prefix
33. Range rover
34. "Delta Dawn" vocalist
39. Brands
40. Cargo count
42. Party organizer?
48. NYC epithet
49. Extras
50. Legal charge
51. Nuisances
53. Gibe
54. Prod
55. Poet's plenty
56. Eight: prefix
57. Surf noise
58. Shark breed
59. Caesar's way
60. Gainsay
64. Drive into

ACROSS

1. Rustic mail abbr.
4. Religious ring
8. Caress clumsily
11. Insect wing
12. Bakery pro
13. Puccini's *patria*
17. With 59-Across, early studio report about 38-Across
20. Work up
21. Opposed to
22. Cry of enthusiasm
23. Occupied
25. Scores, in a way
27. Redgrave and Williams
30. Chickadee treat
31. Cackleberries
32. Seaside scavengers
34. Put off
37. Israeli hill
38. Film legend
40. Tray trifle
41. Looks
43. Take on
44. It's not enough, for Susann
45. Patsies
47. Good sore-throat drink
49. Brief pause
52. Actress Dominique
53. *Je vais*
54. Creator of Portnoy
56. Affliction suffixes
59. See 17-Across

62. Having a handle
63. Bulletin
64. Devilkin
65. "You rang?"
66. Hit the saddle
67. Barracks bed

DOWN

1. Event for Nurmi
2. Fiber source
3. First step for 38-Across?
4. Interruption
5. Gains entry
6. Net call
7. Pied cetacean
8. Some beans
9. View

10. Used to be
14. Perfect adjectives for 38-Across
15. Arrow poison
16. Mellows
18. Stickers?
19. Hoofer Reinking
24. Ground
26. Bee pursuer
27. Ex-GIs
28. *The African Queen* screenwriter
29. Pokey one
33. Fathers
35. End of coal?
36. Ostrich kin

38. Suck in
39. Forwarded packages
42. Tour guide?
44. Rouen rumor
46. Mick and co.
48. Prompt
49. Costa ——
50. Actor Richard
51. And so forth: abbr.
55. He's got the will
57. Salt's saint
58. Clan
60. Sunny time
61. Where a scale rests

ACROSS

1. No longer fizzy
5. Coarse hominy
9. Muscle surprise
14. Not fully marbled?
15. Netman Nastase
16. A Muppet
17. Roman poet
18. Like a roué
20. 1981 media events
22. Utter
23. Game pieces
24. Hoedown instrument
28. One of Smiley's people
29. Apathetic response
31. Hook's aide
33. Slippery customer?
34. Tolkien being
35. Royal duo in 20-Across
40. NRC precursor
41. Egypt, once: abbr.
42. TV prize
43. Sanitary
46. Team honor, for short
47. Star, in Paris
48. —— *Dalmatians*
49. Have a rap session
52. Soap opera duo in 20-Across
56. Campus area
59. Baby's wear
60. Basketmaker's choice
61. Cutlet source
62. Holy image
63. December word
64. Homophone of 57-Down
65. Phoenician port

DOWN

1. Circulates
2. "I —— Parade"
3. Tart
4. One of Liz's hubbies
5. Director Lumet
6. Get into a row?
7. Hit's alternative
8. Mexican moolah
9. Opposite of 43-Across
10. Truth, in Russia
11. *Them!* mutant
12. German pronoun
13. Label abbr.
19. Embrace
21. Thrust forward
25. Reverie
26. Bruce biopic
27. Madrid pronoun
28. Hindu weight
29. "—— not amused"
30. Biddy
31. White-sale item
32. Computer instruction
35. Canary keeper
36. "Aha!"
37. So, to Scots
38. One with soul ownership?...
39. ... and his little brother
44. Less harsh
45. Light snow
46. Runway rovers
48. Mate's kin
49. Sensational
50. Enthusiasm
51. Indiana fort
53. A deadly sin
54. Critic James
55. Miner's entry
56. Iranian city
57. Exploit
58. Football filler

ACROSS

1. Conks
5. Fictional dandy with a trunk
10. Org. for Els
13. Greek dialect
14. Image: prefix
15. Bern's river
16. Those in the know
18. Horror-tale maven
19. Author France
20. Books of prayer
22. Pizarro aide
23. Duty list
24. Everglades denizen
26. Obliterate
29. Tummy muscles
32. Sortie
33. Ruminant, at times
34. Open to debate, or not
36. Bellini opera
38. Nicholas II was the last
39. Groups of eight
41. Wisconsin town
43. Campaign victors
44. French composer
45. Egglike
46. Web linked
48. Thin coating
53. Bill
55. Advanced course
56. Classic car
57. Light and shade, in painting
59. List-ending abbr.
60. Jay Silverheels role
61. Senator Hatch
62. Haggard heroine
63. Doctoral exams
64. Negatives

DOWN

1. Wilderness Road blazer
2. Korbut namesakes
3. Scout, for one
4. Two-wheeler
5. Blue hue
6. Crackerjack
7. Clever remark
8. Those against
9. Have a loud party
10. Celebrity chasers
11. Reading, to Wilde
12. Sanguinary Olympian
13. Modified organism
17. Mottos
21. Ice pinnacle
23. Tee off again
25. *Black Orpheus* setting
27. Author O'Casey
28. Blows it
29. Hebrew prophet
30. —— Raton
31. Softly spoken
33. Italian astronomer/ physicist
35. Arawakan language
37. Cattle call
40. In flagrante ——
42. Elsa's watcher
45. —— million
47. Divine blood
49. Film opener?
50. Accustom (to)
51. Roman nose
52. Elvis' middle name
53. Enrages
54. Benelux land: abbr.
55. Hit signs
58. E Coast sight

ACROSS

1. Gate hardware
6. Econ. indicator
9. Shah Jahan's Mumtaz
14. Menachem's co-Nobelist
15. Latin hail
16. Having wings
17. The "Choral"
20. Olive or Castor
21. Stoical
22. —— Na Na
23. Prism effect: abbr.
25. Scatter
26. Otto's ocean
27. Chinese pagoda
29. Sir McKellen
30. Kilmer of films
31. Composer Clara
34. Carpet cleaner
37. Where *Otello* premiered
38. Franco's party
39. Nobody special
40. Rimsky-Korsakov opera
41. Subj. of this puzzle
42. *Rosenkavalier* article
43. Broadloom cut
44. Sound boosters
46. Great, to Galba
48. Noted times
51. Yeah's opposite
52. Circus flooring
54. LAX info
55. Stern specials
58. Of the mind
59. Finale
60. Film segments
61. Philippine island
62. Antique auto
63. The tube, to Brits

DOWN

1. Toil
2. Keep —— on (watch)
3. Shostakovich's *To The Memory of Lenin-1917*
4. Jellicle pet
5. Palace abbrs.
6. Oratorio solo
7. Invaded
8. Of the time before Easter
9. Krull's creator
10. Ms. MacGraw
11. Opera starring a witch
12. "Casey —— Bat"
13. Operetta composer
18. Harvest deity
19. Toothed cutter
24. Squawky
26. Rhesus monkey
28. "The way to —— heart..."
30. Heroism
31. Hearst holders: abbr.
32. Slammer
33. Stein filler
34. Time off, in Bath
35. Actor Tognazzi
36. Simone's sea
38. Schubert opus
40. Fibula or tibia
42. Tap pro
44. "—— Chorus" (Verdi)
45. Acadia state
46. Hominid
47. Bowed line
49. Coral isle
50. Impudent
52. Wear out
53. *Company* costar Larry
56. Rent
57. *Lough* in Ireland

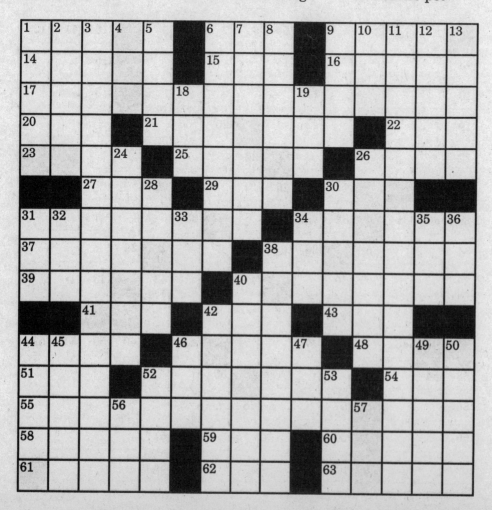

ACROSS

1. Extreme; utmost
4. Parisian copper
8. Ruminant's rehash
11. Column style
13. Spore case
15. *Dos ÷ dos*
16. Chinese pain treatment
18. Highway: abbr.
19. Salt Lake City player
20. Stage signals
21. Bird of prey
23. Dog treat
25. —— dozen (cheap)
26. GI factory?
27. Land unit
28. Short smokes
31. Wend
33. Fruit weevil
35. Italian bowling
36. Latin preposition
37. Fraud finisher
38. Gourd-shaped vessel
40. Relieves (of)
41. Blighted urban area
42. Boise–Cheyenne heading
43. In the style of
44. Moroccan city
46. Trunk armor
50. Blasphemer
52. Now, to Nero
53. Scroogy sound
54. Tell's canton
55. Adapt to society
58. Prohibit
59. Glove material
60. Alleviated
61. Math subj.
62. Fodder root
63. T-shirt size: abbr.

DOWN

1. Night: prefix
2. Makes balanced
3. With it
4. Lapidary's surface
5. Omaha Beach craft
6. Hospital area: abbr.
7. Lithographer Nathaniel
8. Shortened
9. Golden rule word
10. Type-A type
11. Smear
12. Coolness exemplar
14. Fabric worker's union?
17. Nantes night
22. Eccentric
24. Turmeric plants
25. Tympanic membrane
27. Sharp
29. Cotton cleaners
30. One in his cups
31. Moving spirit
32. Taking place
34. Fancy flourish
35. Ancient times: abbr.
36. Neolithic burial chamber
39. Little grizzly
43. Cousin's mom
45. Lillie and Arthur
46. Face of a gem
47. Degrade
48. Overfed
49. Storage place
50. Island country
51. Russian range
52. Oil subject
56. Fair mark
57. Cote pop

ACROSS

1. Bogs down
6. Record an old standard
11. Summer hrs.
14. Bipedal
15. Actress Jergens
16. Japanese statesman
17. Shelve
18. Reforms a loafer?
19. Bando of baseball
20. Quaffs, for Quintilian
21. Hard as ——
22. Heat measure: abbr.
23. With 48-Across, why Chanel shut up shop
26. Humdinger
27. Embroiders with gold
29. Of the mail service
33. French pronoun
35. Mother of Prometheus
36. Musty
38. Turns blue
40. *Bonnie and Clyde* director
41. Unknown John
43. Armstrong and Truman
44. Take —— at (try)
46. Paperboy's yell
48. See 23-Across
54. Mythic raptor
55. Love, Italian-style
56. Like some rumors
57. Wilder play opening
58. Frugal fellow
59. "Believe it" alternative
60. Columbus sch.
61. Motif
62. Casino request
63. Turkey topper?
64. Raced at Henley
65. Smoke detectors

DOWN

1. Riveting medium?
2. Basra citizen
3. Argue back
4. Showy effect
5. Superman can bend one
6. Melon variety
7. Aromatic
8. Cream sauces
9. Vote into office
10. Omit again
11. Pays out
12. VT-NY boundary, e.g.
13. Fragrant gum
24. Sniggled
25. College squares
28. Lip
29. Bug stage
30. Get —— in order (settle personal affairs)
31. California isle
32. Turner and Yothers
34. Curved blade
37. Repeats
39. Letter type
42. Drastic
45. Bud: prefix
47. Eric's epithet
49. Plains tribe
50. Objet d'art
51. Clues
52. "Behold, —— as a thief."
53. Cell suffixes
54. Annual runway

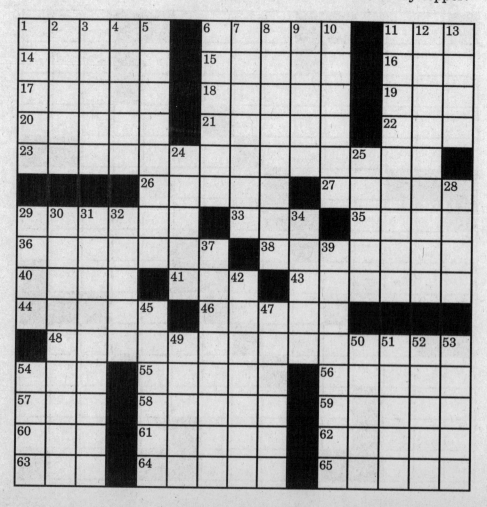

POINTS OF INTEREST

ACROSS

1. (Self-explanatory)
10. Actress Sullivan
15. Gourmand
16. "— bleach"
17. Prop for Vallee
18. Hatted, spatted pachyderm
19. Overwhelm
20. Lennon's mother
21. Invitee, in Innsbruck
22. Pack animal
23. Courtier in *Hamlet*
26. Old Testament book: abbr.
27. Calendar pp.
29. Bristles
31. Re a sleeve style
34. Art of jazz
36. "This — recording"
37. Neglects
38. Broadcast
39. Ms. Nin
41. Suo Sea port
42. Punctual, plus
44. Mr. Chips, on screen
45. Like Gaul, or so said Caesar
47. Jujube
48. *— soit qui mal y pense*
49. Buffed hide
52. Map abbrs.
55. Solomonic
56. 0
57. Queequeg's skipper
59. Dairy purchases
61. Fill with confidence
63. Psalm mystery word
64. Eases
65. Roman railway
66. (Self-explanatory)

DOWN

1. Arles appellations
2. Hobby of HEW
3. — Pat. Off.
4. Send
5. With it, once
6. Cowpokes' cries
7. Jackets and collars
8. Hombre's honorific
9. It's past *due*
10. Teacher for a day
11. Habits
12. King of Portugal (1557-78)
13. Oscar role for Ingrid
14. (Self-explanatory)
24. Pod attachment
25. Raw, in Rouen
28. "The light that never was, — or land"
30. "— It Through the Rain" (Manilow song)
31. (Self-explanatory)
32. Do appliqué
33. Bargain event
34. Estonian town
35. Need nursing
40. Field film
43. Latin skill
46. Tart maker
47. Wisconsin city
50. Scorer Morricone
51. Word after *mirabile*
53. "Is — fact?"
54. No fools, they
58. #1
60. Kyoto measure
61. Printers' spaces
62. Cry of disgust

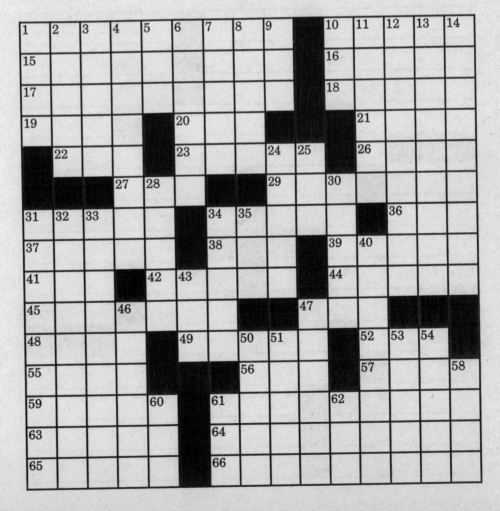

ACROSS

1. Squint; crumple
6. Ad-free TV
9. Come to an end
14. Kipling's Kim
15. Knock
16. Wing it
17. Men's clothing store
19. Card game authority
20. Crude cartel
21. Weather line
23. Scratch the surface of
24. Assumed
26. Army
27. Connecticut Bulldog
30. Miller's Paris pal
31. Loire Valley region
33. Udderance?
34. Alarming change?: abbr.
35. No longer pure
38. Calling the shots
40. Gandhi's pa
41. Minoan script
44. Ruth's forte
46. Army officer
47. Israeli statesman
48. Menlo Park monogram
49. Fashion initials
50. In-tents experience?
52. Penitence
55. Cleo's nonwitherer
56. Modern
57. Pilfers
61. Bluegrass instrument
63. Preside ceremonially
65. Playful paddler
66. Indian flour
67. *Carmen* creator
68. Irritable
69. Careless
70. Crowd cries

DOWN

1. NYC gallery district
2. Guy
3. *Streamers* playwright
4. Standing tall
5. Hawks' milieu
6. Introduce
7. Lowly peer
8. Scout vessel
9. He had the lion's lines
10. Bother
11. 1620 settlement
12. Weaver Marner
13. Critic who's all thumbs?
18. Bright robes
22. Leo's heroine
25. "Night ——"
26. Get to the point?
27. *Herr* Jannings
28. Burt's ex
29. Mosaic subject
32. Jonahs
36. "—— Tu" (1974 hit)
37. Yawn-provoking
39. Tide type
42. Blue-moonish
43. Full of tales
44. Neolithic tool
45. Lunar view
50. Explorer John
51. Semiprecious gem
53. Indian-born maestro
54. Banks of the Cubs
56. Actor Calhoun
58. Soft slime
59. Dixie kin
60. Fast fliers
62. Spurt
64. Sent. part

VOWEL PLAY

ACROSS

1. *Titanic* sinker
5. "Shut up!"
10. Ernest Rutherford's study
14. US
15. Private line?
16. Significant other
17. Costa chaser
18. Resolute
20. Chef's stock
22. "What's in ——?"
23. Poetic preposition
24. Vegan's bane
26. Slalom tracks
28. Recipe abbreviation
30. Government center
32. Vamp Bara
36. Blackjack necessity
37. Gabriela's game
40. Part of
41. Brown, heavy metal container
44. Otherwise
45. Bird dog
46. Legal ending
47. Shell out
49. Marc's mark
50. Reed the reviewer
51. Δ
54. Part of the process
56. Sternward
59. Bed on board
61. Matriculate
64. Kept up
67. Battle or Price

68. Best of Hollywood
69. Foam
70. Puts to work
71. Minimal high tide
72. Lakota
73. Shut (up)

DOWN

1. Pointed remark
2. Fujairah bigwig
3. Pay
4. Prepare Romano
5. Bounder
6. Lost
7. Insect catcher, rather than Cole fan
8. Glimmerings

9. Contract provisions
10. Poetic pug
11. Resiliency
12. Exceeding
13. Media man
19. Assemble
21. Wasteful trait
25. Prom attendees
27. Barking place?
28. *Soap* family
29. Take to the cleaners
31. Pot starter
33. Picard's pride
34. Extinguish
35. Wing
38. Division word

39. Galley commands
42. Work at the bar
43. Steamed
48. Bankruptcy factor
52. Slightest
53. Tommyrot
55. Reach, ultimately
56. Orison ending
57. Run out of gas
58. 1993 role for Angela
60. Blood: prefix
62. Hot spot
63. Go the distance
65. Saw wood
66. Secluded room

ACROSS

1. Bridal degree?: abbr.
4. Rise again
11. Well-informed
14. Euripidean drama
15. Sufferings
16. Athens eye-chart letter?
17. Imminent danger
20. Rainless
21. Facing a glacier
22. Small-scale philanthropy
23. Betel palm
25. Naples number
26. Prepare for winter
32. Shut-eye quickie
35. Intern's oath
38. Dudgeon
39. Up to the job
40. Strewn with soot
41. —— T. Morton (US Treasurer)
42. Author Santha Rama
43. Frugal fare
45. Miro's métier
46. Like a mortarboard
47. Jazz trombonist
49. Corpulent
53. Cantina nosh
55. Mold opening
60. Pout
61. Mighty efforts
64. Pvt. pension plan
65. Perform again
66. Helm heading
67. Tippler
68. Cooks up concepts
69. Sigma

DOWN

1. Beethoven's —— Solemnis
2. Shell crewman
3. Make zzz's
4. Super cool
5. Head swellers
6. Out of shape
7. Ruin
8. Creeks
9. Some muffins
10. Within: prefix
11. Turn Attic
12. News bit
13. Macho maneuver
18. Child's formula?
19. Jam ingredient
24. Tropical bird
25. Slang sleuth
27. —— Flow (Orkney basin)
28. Major and Minor star groups
29. Bert and his biographer
30. To head, to Henri
31. Of sea surges
33. Sills' ditty
34. Zest source
35. Tokyo tummy
36. T-beam associate
37. Capitalist
41. "I —— to tell the crooked rose" (Dylan Thomas)
43. Oinker's pad
44. Court splitter
48. Sinbad's bird
50. Daniel or Pat
51. Highland bard
52. Affirms
53. Este
54. Space launcher?
55. Husky's haul
56. Algiers role
57. —— avis
58. Component
59. More
62. Tell's canton
63. Roman bronze

SOOT-ABLE

ACROSS

1. Jest
6. English springs
10. Own (up)
14. Bathsheba's hubby
15. Lofty prefix
16. Jesus or Felipe
17. Sooty appliance?
19. Sully
20. Get it
21. Friend of Françoise
22. Vast wasteland
24. Fine silk
25. Half a vitamin deficiency
26. Saddle flaps
29. Wallis Simpson, e.g.
33. Double-curved moldings
34. XY, genetically
35. Trademark
36. Asian deer
37. Continued
38. Nice notice
39. Upcoming Olympic site
40. Loving god
41. White poplar
42. Affability
44. Job
45. O'Casey's land
46. Engender
47. Beams
50. Sorry sigh
51. TV's Arthur
54. Tuber's cousin
55. Falling soot effect?
58. African lily
59. Inclination
60. Cove
61. Dollars for quarters
62. Male principle
63. Base chaplain

DOWN

1. Foam
2. ——-dieu
3. River to the Seine
4. Fall yell
5. Contravenes
6. Tidal river harbor
7. Aerobics aftermath
8. Roman numeral
9. Apocalyptic riders
10. Well sooted?
11. Raines on film
12. Turned
13. Koran section
18. Author Kingsley
23. Wing's homologue
24. Sooty head protector?
25. Luzon knives
26. Cancel
27. Cultural heart of Honshu
28. "—— what I say!"
29. River craft
30. Birth mark?
31. Author Zola
32. Timer button
34. California county
37. Showing negligence
41. Dirigible
43. Mined-over matter
44. Diagonal
46. Unconventional speech
47. Duel reminder
48. Double agent
49. Strange stick?
50. Actor Mowbray
51. Shameless
52. Water holder
53. Feed the kitty
56. Green sphere
57. Gene letters

ACROSS

1. Pueblo dweller
5. Pancreas or liver
10. Coup d'état, e.g.
14. —— even keel
15. Dynamo part
16. Show spot
17. ONE
20. Sugary ending
21. Fusion candidate?
22. Removes
23. FBI worker
24. Touch on
26. TWO
33. Après-ski beverage
34. Between, in Bourges
35. Inlet
36. Limpid pools
37. Look at ledgers
38. He played Klinger
39. Beluga harvest
40. Bittern
41. Won à la Kasparov
42. THREE
45. He has his pride
46. Profit from pan handling
47. Scares off
50. Table grains
52. Tangled mass
55. FOUR
59. Warning sound
60. Worn away
61. Tibet, Laos, etc.
62. Supreme Supreme
63. Aged brew
64. Apothecary: abbr.

DOWN

1. Train hopper
2. Burden
3. Gait rate
4. Cuttlefish camouflage
5. Cave
6. Business symbol
7. "Up and —— !"
8. Negative joiner
9. GPs, e.g.
10. Tiling compounds
11. Rips off
12. Tons
13. Plays the perfecta
18. Rough
19. Provoke
23. Connective words
24. Pro tem
25. Parks of pageants
26. "Happy Birthday ——"
27. Revoke a legacy
28. Pain feeler
29. *The —— the Affair*
30. Choleric
31. Trunk items
32. Lateen support
33. A seabird
37. Of planes
38. Encounter
40. Stickup
41. Actress Toren
43. Matures
44. Long wave
47. Go a few rounds
48. Jolly sound
49. Juárez rahs
50. Air tainter
51. Church section
52. Filmy fabric
53. *La Bohème* highlight
54. Despot
56. Sinuous one
57. Pavo's neighbor
58. Shrill bark

ACROSS

1. Son of Alcmene
9. Plant partitions
14. Thespian Duse
15. Preachment
16. Going by kayak
17. Caught (trout)
18. Straightens up
19. Rubbed the wrong way
21. Dealing with
22. Order
23. Fuel for a duel
26. Part of the Sahara
27. Rauma native
28. Practical
29. Smart
31. Distaff seniors
32. Band gear
35. Binary digit
36. Peat's place
37. Court recovery
38. Yoked
40. With less loose screws
42. Had enough
43. Auto pioneer
44. Mass array
47. 1990 series champs
48. Orange or grapefruit
49. "___ Apart" (Frost)
51. Fletcher of films
53. *Rhapsody* ___
54. Rookie salmon
56. Steelmaking step
58. John or Bob
59. Friml piece
60. Pundits
61. Saintly honors

DOWN

1. Numerical prefix
2. Astolat lady
3. More florid
4. Product-price bar symbols
5. Vacant
6. Clark's colleague
7. Avian sea fisher
8. Droopy
9. "Move!"
10. Che's given name
11. Drummer's specialty
12. Pigskin holder
13. Throw in
15. Mattress support
20. Campaigned
22. Clarify
24. Out of the wind
25. Gnat, e.g.
27. Come upon
28. Push
30. Hammered slantingly
31. Attica residents
32. Flatterer, of a sort
33. Neck warmer?
34. Insignificant
36. Directed
39. Dieter's aid
40. Shelve until morning
41. Made a long story longer
43. Hosp. theaters
45. Nabokov novel
46. Largess
48. Shea level
49. Theater director Gregory
50. Artist Edgar
52. Manipulates
53. Footnote word
54. Point players: abbr.
55. Actor Stephen
57. "___ Lazy River"

ACROSS

1. Metrical stress
6. Lady lobster
9. R.U.R. author
14. President rumored to have authored quote
15. Atlanta torch lighter
16. Like some grandmas
17. Eldritch
18. Quote: Part 1
20. Quote: Part 2
21. Skeet target
23. Alibi and Turner
24. Make a choice
25. Platonic dialogue
27. Quote: Part 3
35. Gave an edge to
36. Liza's sister
37. *Cygni*-to-be
38. Role for Ingrid
39. Then, to Etienne
40. Jenny's cry
41. EPCOT state
42. Dress style
43. Pairs
44. Quote: Part 4
47. Setting for an eclogue
48. Quote: Part 5
49. Knucklehead
52. Amy and Jo's creator
56. Quote: Part 6
59. End of the quote
61. Test of faith
63. Draft horse
64. Make tracks
65. Takes in
66. Scornful yells
67. S&L device
68. Linnaeus, e.g.

DOWN

1. Porter song opening
2. Varsity eight, perhaps
3. Tahitian tuber
4. Cycle starter
5. Strode
6. Reagan cabinet member
7. Cinematic Sommer
8. Oaxaca tad
9. Corvine call
10. Consecrate, in a way
11. Paragon
12. She, in Maine
13. Linotype levers
19. Strong bulbs
22. Possessive pronoun
24. SSS rank
26. *A Tale —— Tub*
27. Pike fees
28. Retract
29. Rigid North
30. *Nemo*
31. Fluffed
32. Diurnal ÷ 24?
33. Skirt
34. Giant among Giants
35. Sound investment
39. Ash product
40. Fictional foretopman
42. Ayr pronoun
43. Kicks in
45. Victoria's love
46. New World gp.
49. "Poppycock!"
50. Emperor in 69 A.D.
51. Taft's home
53. Fed. factory watchdog
54. Regiment
55. Squib
56. Jade
57. Four inches
58. If not
60. Legal matter
62. Biting

ACROSS

1. Units of light cavalry
10. Radar blip
14. Sydney and Adelaide's home
15. Dollops
17. Alimentary science
18. Start suddenly
19. Provide (with)
20. Romantic adventures
22. Correlative word
23. *Foucault's Pendulum* author
24. Attendant to Dionysus
25. Edible Asian nut
26. Thrill greatly
28. Slip
29. Retired temporarily
31. Lenity
33. Fake gems
34. Treacherous temptress
37. Intoned
39. "—— man with seven wives…"
40. Blouse
41. Throw —— (revel)
43. Timely abbrs.
44. Large number
48. Jacob and Leah's third
49. Catchall phrases: abbr.
51. Article in *Le Monde*?
52. Before
53. Opening installment
54. Somewhat, slangily
56. Warning, down under
58. Objective
60. More veridical
61. Patience, to Yanks
62. Prow
63. *Catriona* author

DOWN

1. Actress Frost and others
2. Fruit for preserves
3. Applied to
4. A Near Island
5. Endure: Scot.
6. Turncoat
7. One of the ruling elite
8. Words of commiseration
9. Fresh
10. Weakens
11. Actor Gulager
12. Most calloused
13. Out
16. Like some toothpastes
21. Refrain start
24. Watery fluids
25. Delivers, as a kiss
27. A Karamazov
30. Take-off sites?
32. Gulf of Aqaba port
34. English, to West Germanic
35. Purple wearers
36. Skip
37. Cumbrian town
38. Sound of a slow leak
40. Etagère
42. Voice vote
45. Golfer Strange
46. Frontal: prefix
47. Soundproof
50. Bridge style
53. Hair wave
54. Overfill
55. —— even keel
57. Shoe width
59. Ms. Ullmann

ACROSS

1. Ember
5. Starchy dried tubers
10. San —— (Riviera resort)
14. About
15. Nonpareil
16. Radiate
17. Gubernatorial power
18. X-ray technician who's not all there?
20. Stopover site
21. Horseradish flavoring
22. "—— the Chief"
23. Age-mates
25. Mtg.
26. ——-poly
27. Speaks with little knowledge
31. Preference
33. Mil. schools
34. Royal sleep disturber
35. *Off the Court* author
36. Construction members
37. Fabricate
38. Southeast Asian
39. Atrium
40. *Twelfth Night* clown
41. It often comes in rounds
43. Actress Washbourne
44. Church feature
45. Took care of
48. Pollen holder
51. Decide
52. Loire holm
53. Briefly taking a whirl?
55. Principal pipe
56. ——*Alone* (Milland film)
57. Burn slightly
58. Mound builders
59. Arp's movement
60. More together
61. "Aha!"

DOWN

1. Town related
2. ——-trump (opening bid)
3. Leaderless joint venture?
4. Sign of summer
5. Sans incident
6. Berlin pronoun
7. Schmo
8. Rocker Brian
9. Headless pit vipers?
10. Strain against
11. Author Ludwig
12. Atomizer output
13. HRE bigwig
19. Hops kilns
21. Woe, in poetry
24. Plebiscite, e.g.
25. Tony
27. Give a start to
28. Shrinking Protestant group?
29. Schism
30. Glut
31. "Later!"
32. PDQ
33. Harsh invective
36. Plenty, almost?
37. Darn
39. *Roi* Hugh
40. Very tender
42. Thin plate
43. Horse trough
45. Depend (upon)
46. Flower
47. Tightly packed
48. Herring kin
49. Satie subject
50. "When I Was ——"
51. Lahti native
54. Shore inlet
55. *Printemps* time

LEAVING CAMP

ACROSS

1. Asian servant
5. Reputation
9. Wield the gavel
14. "Judging Amy" costar
15. Mild oath
16. Revenue, in Reims
17. Lorain's lake
18. Jejune
19. Clean thoroughly
20. "No new taxes," e.g.
23. Playwright Mosel
24. Hawaiian isle
25. Circus barkers
27. "Leave as is"
30. Pass through a membrane
34. High times
37. Carved trunk
40. Latin I word
41. Play about FDR
45. Sand, to Chopin
46. Courage
47. Strongly desire
48. Femme follower
51. Tar
53. Venetia city
56. Position
60. Expense bill
63. Sprain balm
66. Cottonwood
68. Acronym re PC data quality
69. Hammett dog
70. More tenuous
71. Dark, to Donne
72. Shadow
73. Tarsus
74. See 56-Across
75. Turgenev's birthplace

DOWN

1. Hall's offer
2. Baroness Von Trapp
3. True up
4. Spotted scavengers
5. Stingy
6. Earth: prefix
7. Disables
8. Carrie's dad
9. Catch holders
10. That ship
11. Gray's subj.
12. ―― *Pleasure* (Henie film)
13. Sax part
21. Famed Florentine palace
22. ―― Tomé
26. Hook's mate
28. Aurora, to Zeno
29. A crowd, in Cádiz?
31. De Gaulle alternative
32. Auction
33. Broad collar
34. Its acad. is in Colorado
35. Catamount
36. Fit of pique
38. Undermine
39. Lift man
42. Garner
43. Cape Horn native
44. ABA's Melvin
49. Pakistani metropolis
50. Tokyo, once
52. Love apple
54. Presses
55. Offer an excuse for
57. Composer Franck
58. Free
59. Fair counter
60. Scarlett's homestead
61. Actor Bates
62. Cork source
64. "―― Rhythm"
65. Prayer hour
67. Actress Harris

ACROSS

1. Guard word
5. Well-known northern highway
10. Puppy protests
14. Son of Isaac
15. Sierra ___
16. Comic McClurg
17. Betty finishes furniture?
19. Solo
20. Actor Beatty
21. Kline film
22. Rang
24. Cubes of chance
25. Advertising award
26. Put into words
28. The worse for work
32. Actor Tom from Lodi
33. Physical chemist Otto
34. MacNelly strip
35. News tidbit
36. Use dowels again
37. It does this
38. Claudius' stepson
39. Actress Gray
40. Reactor sites
41. George III, to George I
43. *Olympia* artist
44. Title
45. Deep mud
46. Allergic condition
49. Post-snow spread
50. German article
53. Chunk of ice
54. Rich's favorite music?
57. Ambience
58. Cheer up
59. Against
60. Split apart
61. Discourage
62. Snug retreat

DOWN

1. Axed
2. 1975 Wimbledon winner
3. Made eggs
4. "Piffle!"
5. Region of NE France
6. GI's vacation
7. Edible container
8. Furthermore
9. Little bird
10. Sallow Oliver?
11. Joss, for one
12. Yule aroma
13. Rank, for 2-Down
18. Public order
23. Squeak squelcher
24. Neil's noggin?
25. Comic Myron
26. Member of the electorate
27. Met medium
28. Short putt
29. Chicago touchdown?
30. Thesaurus chap
31. Cape
32. Buck's dancing partner?
33. King of Judea
36. Taped up again
40. Blanche leader
42. Rep.'s foe
43. Flour sacker
45. Photo finish
46. Way off
47. Pivot
48. ___ *Curtain*
49. RBI, for example
50. Through
51. Behaves
52. "SNL" staple
55. Holm on the Rhône
56. Tried for office

ACROSS

1. Heyday meal?
6. Pitfall
10. Toy marketer's targets
14. Winning margin
15. Tramp
16. Garfield's pal
17. Summer ermine
18. "We have met the enemy, and he ——" ("Pogo")
19. English county
20. Physician's curse?
23. Raises
24. Skye cap
25. Logician's sarcasm?
32. Forelimb features
33. Great review
34. Actor Bannen
36. Tallow source
37. Exchange
39. Israeli seaport
40. Distinguished time
41. Mute avian
42. Mix
43. Philosopher's age?
47. Turned on
48. Mauna ——
49. Poet's cheer?
58. Wild goat
59. Alhambra resident
60. Humble
61. Burt's former belle
62. Verge
63. Pension-law acronym
64. D'Urberville damsel
65. Have a loaf?
66. Author Françoise

DOWN

1. Waist material
2. Contra- cousin
3. El locale
4. PDQ kin
5. Bypasses
6. Intense craving
7. Revolutionary Luxemburg
8. Impinge (on)
9. On the plus side
10. Hoosier city
11. Think-tank output
12. Force
13. Time-honored Thomas
21. Number cruncher: abbr.
22. Anxiety
25. Imbibe audibly
26. See 57-Down
27. Grimalkin
28. Tabriz native
29. Rascal
30. More polite
31. Stories
32. Exploit
35. Novelist Buntline
37. Double-crosser
38. Kurosawa's *Lear*ish epic
39. In the style of
41. Arouse
42. Small hounds
44. Actress Smith
45. Red wine
46. *Sie*
49. Handle
50. Double reed
51. Department-store department
52. Cipher
53. Clears (trees)
54. Circle dance
55. Nest bit
56. Ms. Lanchester
57. With 26-Down, Barry Lyndon portrayer

ACROSS

1. Manhattan pick-ups?
5. Vow
10. Dade Co.'s locale
13. Henri's heartthrob
14. Legendary arts patron
15. Guitarist Paul
16. Immunity fluids
17. Lift sites
18. Delicacy for Dobbin
19. Frequent pass receiver
20. Highest pt. in 43-Across
21. Excellent
23. Scale tones
24. Theater trophies
25. Print-shop employee
26. Old Greek coins
28. Tango minimum
29. Requisites
30. Code letter
31. Count Tolstoy
32. Unexciting
33. Unhearing
34. Out of bread
36. Believe —— not
39. Trees with needles
41. Gene's designer?
42. Variable star
43. Minoan isle
45. Mil. address
46. Cubist painter
47. Takes the chill off
48. Paris tube
50. Pitcher's stat
51. Great civilization, until 1519
52. Has pain
53. Ditty syllable
54. Tokyo drama
55. Seeded
57. Penknife
58. Compass point
59. Zombiesque
60. Prefix for cure
61. Slangy pronoun
62. Front
63. Hostile deity

DOWN

1. Lawyer's list
2. Open to suggestion
3. With 10-Down, a description of 5-, 6- and 35-Down
4. Landlubber's eschewal
5. Niece of 6-Down
6. Cartoon rapper
7. Texas city
8. Heady potable
9. *Otello* composer
10. See 3-Down
11. Dripped
12. Mary and Nancy
14. On the issue of
20. Freight wgts.
22. Octave portion
27. Big name in piracy
31. Vital stat abbr.
32. Latin pronoun
35. Nephew of 6-Down
37. Pull rank on
38. Oner
40. Wash again
43. Lon of many faces
44. Divide anew, as a city
45. Williams heroine
46. Madrid article
49. Funny Foxx
56. Gas-pump suffix
57. Health club

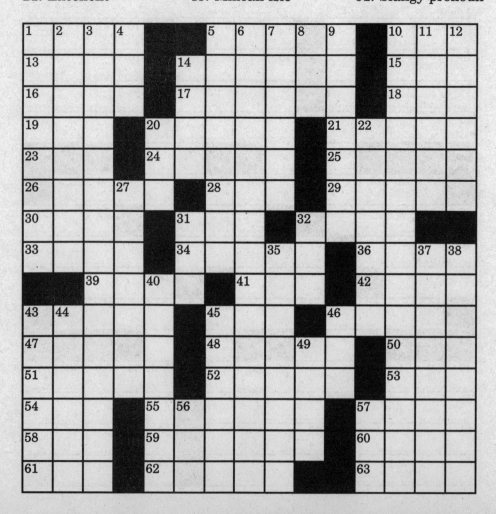

ACROSS

1. Be a fifth at bridge?
7. Wee folk
14. Cather title lass
15. Epithet for Ed Jones
16. Pay heed
17. Spanish mayor
18. *Doctor Faustus* author
19. Pastoral poem
21. London parish
22. Actor Byrnes
23. Barker, to Brutus
25. Coconut fibers
27. Main entry
28. Cow palace
29. Asian language
32. Part of Churchill's description of Russia
35. Foe of Captain Marvel
36. *My Fair Lady* setting
38. School known for its playing fields
39. Part of the cosmos
41. Song of lament
43. *Each Dawn ——* (Cagney film)
44. "Hello, —— Be Going"
45. Japanese immigrant
47. Parts of a bibliotheca
48. Where to be in a brawn study?
51. As
52. Auction closer
53. Blood chart
54. Made state-of-the-art
57. Blonde
60. Green isle
61. Green men?
62. In a palatable way
63. Sunday entrees

DOWN

1. Work on dough
2. Read —— weep
3. Native
4. Press paste
5. Stalemate
6. Premeditated lunacy
7. Spends the night
8. Straw vote
9. Fabulous flier
10. Call —— day
11. Reproof
12. Church officer
13. Oodles
14. Wistful sigh
20. Map datum
23. Pro's opposite
24. Small primate
25. Put up preserves
26. Acquaint
27. Storefront
28. Part of advice from Polonius
29. Dance for mid-March
30. Arab robe
31. Defensive fences
33. Chic
34. Vague amount
37. Resistance register
40. Nero's dozen
42. Close curve
45. Fed up phrase
46. Above: Lat.
47. Winter quaff
48. Play host
49. Parts of annals
50. Rx items
52. Top mil. man
53. *Esta*
55. Model Carol
56. Asian people
58. Lennon's widow
59. Charleston st.

ACROSS

1. Roz Russell role
5. High craggy hill
8. Benefit from will power?
14. Beach party
16. Bride's party
17. Unexpected party
18. Evening party
19. Mint material
20. Bouquet greenery
22. Cloth measures: abbr.
23. Montand of film
25. Manufactured
27. French party
30. Spirit, as at a party
34. Russian range
36. Pantheon goddess
37. Lakes lead-in
39. Coming-out party
41. Expert
43. Male parties
44. Flight necessity
45. Burmese VIP
47. Mrs. Chaplin
48. Fiancée's party
52. Remote
53. Adored one
54. Arthur on court
56. Long, on Lanai
59. Heavenly grizzly
61. Lectures
64. Workers' party
66. Grads' parties
69. Outdoor party
70. Drinking party
71. Hair holders
72. Invite
73. Catch sight of

DOWN

1. Announcers: abbr.
2. Astringent substance
3. Broody one
4. Inane
5. Concluding part
6. Approvals
7. Lagoon sight
8. Book of Ezra, to Catholics
9. Lavish parties
10. Heavy weight
11. Having bristles
12. Started, at golf
13. Makes a gaffe
15. Heroic
21. Aussie avian
24. Dance sequence
26. Keep an —— the ground
27. Would-be flowers
28. Lofty ridge
29. Leah's father
31. ——-scarum
32. —— Galilee
33. Grand, to Galba
35. Nobelist Pirandello
38. Autocrat
40. Betrayed
42. Draft rating
46. Separated
49. Bridge maven and family
50. Urban lines
51. Be grateful to
55. Upper crust
56. Hearth fuel
57. In the twinkling —— eye
58. '70s hairdo
60. Church chest
62. Hawaiian trees
63. Cut
65. June vow
67. Dawn goddess
68. Like a fox

ACROSS

1. Final notice abbrs.
5. Home sick
8. Taj town
12. Emanations
14. Part of 1-Across
15. Actress Teri
16. Collar
17. Start of a quote by Bert Leston Taylor
19. Quote, Part 2
21. "Be of good cheer; it ___" (Matthew)
22. Cry of triumph
23. Journalist Joseph
26. Venetian boat
29. 1993 Nobelist
31. *Ragged Dick* author
32. Tight
34. Bird's instrument
35. He said "Ignorance is never out of style"
39. Stand-in
42. Take it easy
43. Marine mammal
47. Stowe tow
50. Begin, e.g.
52. Lucky number
53. Viper
54. Tried for office
55. Quote, Part 3
60. End of the quote
62. Noted quints' name
63. Son of Leah
64. Print measures
65. Extract

66. North American Indian
67. Role for Field
68. "___ Tu"

DOWN

1. Folding sunshade
2. Actor Charles
3. Sketched
4. Window part
5. Hell's Canyon locale
6. Auto job
7. Nicaragua town
8. Ancient
9. Roman names
10. B&O, et al.
11. Southern constellation
13. Dairy seat
16. Hernando's honey
18. Nolan of mound note
20. Curio holder
24. Ending for pay
25. Peace, to 9-Down
27. ___ Leppard (rock group)
28. Great Bruin
29. Loach or bowfin
30. One ___ time
33. APB info
36. Pol Landon
37. Neither's mate
38. Greek letter
39. Letters from the draft board?

40. Prop for Tiny Tim
41. Clam, for one
44. Playwright Rattigan
45. May and Stritch
46. Salon solution
48. Actor Nielsen
49. Prepares the press
51. Potter Josiah
53. Entertain
56. Actress Martha
57. Scottish island
58. Broad
59. Short hand signal?
60. Rx for humankind
61. Auction closer

120

DOUBLE TALK

ACROSS

1. Tree trunk
5. Rodeo rope
10. Seed covering
14. City north of Provo
15. Mountain nymph
16. Ohio town
17. Fabulous fireplace
19. Zulu warriors
20. Joint below the belt
21. Citizen of Qom
23. Spicy stews
25. Grain beard
27. Roman plotter Beatrice
28. Causes loss
29. Correct ceremony
31. Wings
32. Duffer's dream
33. Dawn deity
34. Tibetan beast
35. File clerk, often
37. Beltway agent
40. Cliburn of the keys
41. Small amount
42. Show concern
43. Peeper on a pulley
47. Artifice
48. Byzantine empress
49. 54-Across employee
50. Blew it
51. Country divided in 1954
53. Arabic letter
54. KGB predecessor
55. Jaded directors
60. Prone one
61. Foolish
62. Egg on
63. Anent
64. Borders
65. Play backs?

DOWN

1. Peat place
2. Boston hockey great
3. Bulb ooze
4. Flow forth
5. Seat at *La Bohème*
6. JFK abbr.
7. Coral follower
8. Glut
9. Polish river
10. Wheel adjusters
11. Francesca da —— (Paolo's lover)
12. Collision
13. Actress Kazan
18. Tracy's Trueheart
22. Stage presence?
23. Anita of jazz
24. Actress Kedrova
25. Fine equine
26. Bug, sort of
30. Obey
32. Gasp
35. Burdened
36. Refined maid
37. Commuter's concern
38. Agatha's confrere
39. Legal paper
40. Risky business
42. Inquisitive
43. Lazio commune
44. Beginning
45. Niobe, e.g.
46. Donny or Marie
47. *The Berlin Wall* author
52. Irish Rose fancier
53. Fruit drinks
56. Tabloid
57. Compass point
58. Mil. unit
59. —— Moines

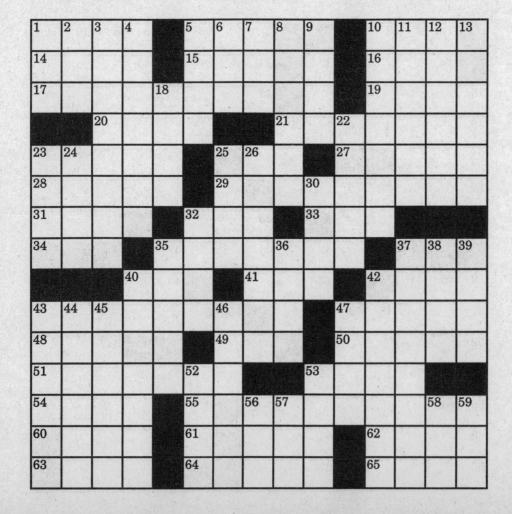

To solve Diagramless Crosswords, use both the definitions and the definition numbers as aids in supplying the words and the black squares that go into the diagrams. As in a regular crossword puzzle, the pattern of black squares in each Diagramless is symmetrical: When you have discovered the correct placement of a black square, its mate can be inserted in a corresponding position on the opposite side of the diagram. The following example illustrates the concept of diagonal symmetry within Diagramless Crosswords.

Insert the corresponding number from the definition list with each starting letter of an Across or Down word. In addition, be sure to insert a black square at the end of every word. Continue to plot the black squares in the mirror-opposite portion of the diagram as you complete the top; as you make your way through the puzzle, its emerging design will reveal the length and placement of other words.

If you need help getting started, the box in which each puzzle begins is listed on the last page.

ACROSS

1. Two, in Toledo
4. ___ the finish: 2 wds.
6. Sesame Street resident
7. Jaguarundi, for one
10. Dada's daddy
13. Offspring
16. Urban transport
17. Frost or Plath
19. Tenor's showpiece
20. Bestowed
21. Choir voices
23. Star-crossed: hyph. wd.
25. Answer
27. Life-preserving instincts
28. Spoil
29. According to
30. Alan or Diane
32. Municipal council member
37. Fence of stakes
39. Comb cotton
40. Beat at chess
41. Juicy fruit
43. Show off pecs
44. Summit
45. Result
47. Ingest
48. April expense
49. Dash
51. Lucy lover
52. Critic Reed

DOWN

1. Peter (out)
2. Sole
3. Margaret Mead field-study site
5. Pleasure traveler
7. Spelunkers' milieus
8. Canned
9. Pantry item
10. On ___ with (equal to)
11. Actor's quest
12. Favorites
14. Luxor's waterway
15. Unit of acceleration
16. Josip Broz
18. See 44-Across
20. Attic
22. Like many scandals
24. Nourish
26. Indicates agreement
29. Satisfied
30. Paint variety
31. Emcee Trebek
32. Gulf of the Arabian Sea
33. Ump's kin
34. Cob or hart
35. Cruising
36. Busy deli cry
37. Haydn moniker
38. Simian
40. Bath pad
42. King or queen
46. Breeziness
50. Put the kibosh on

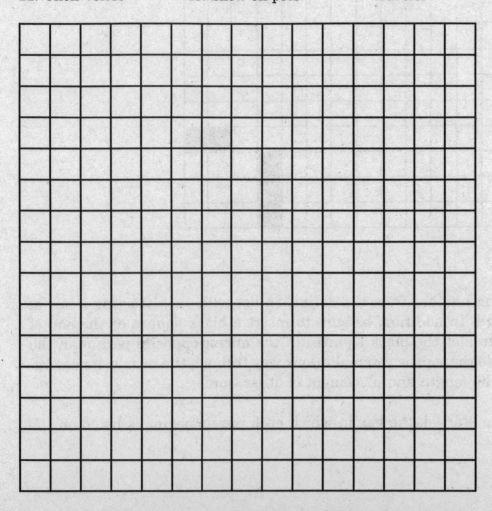

ACROSS

1. Be in arrears
4. Viand list
8. GI's mailing address
11. Practice with Tyson
12. Graph base
13. Tend the lawn
14. Simple Biblical weapon
15. Care for
16. Rec-room fun: hyph. wd.
18. The first Vicar of Rome
19. Gargantua's creator
21. In hot pursuit
24. Marine raptor
25. Abbreviation for items as yet unknown
28. Contents of a spy's closet?
30. Lincoln, to Whitman
33. Spill the beans
34. Yoked together
35. Pencil attachments
37. Stick
38. Singer Shannon
39. Brewery container
41. Underlings
42. Military group
45. Jewelry fossil
48. Cabalistic
52. Tee party?
53. Circus structures
54. In the past
55. Supported by evidence

56. Roman rage
57. Drops on the grass
58. Nostradamus, for one
59. Grate residue

DOWN

1. Put your two cents in
2. Procure by chicanery
3. North African wasteland
4. Stag-party attendees
5. Theater sign
6. Goddess of victory
7. ___-friendly

8. Heavy-metal gear
9. Luau staple
10. Have title to
11. Thorn in a neat-freak's side
14. Effervesce
17. Superior ones
18. Fiesta hanging
20. Bow
21. Behaved
22. Accident alert
23. Add up
25. Made compliant
26. *Vin* alternative
27. Aconcagua's location
29. Volleyball player, at times

31. Dull dons
32. *Bounty* pit stop
36. Droop
40. Race officials
42. Direct
43. Asian starling
44. Noble family of Ferrara
45. They take 10 pct.
46. Twist's plea
47. Union soldier
49. Bounder
50. Lifetime
51. Lea lament
53. Mother's *hermana*

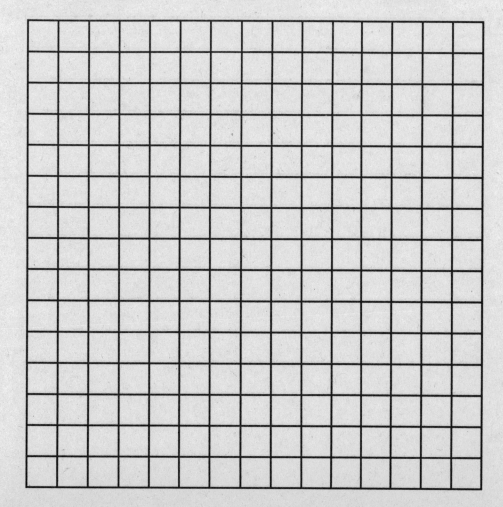

ACROSS

1. Lady in Spain: abbr.
4. Sigma lead-ins
5. ___ *Is Born*: 2 wds.
10. Olivier/Caine flick
12. Valerie Harper role
13. Rap session?
14. Mobs
15. Diplomatic trait
16. Mature: hyph. wd.
17. Zeus's sister
20. Like sashimi
21. One of Smiley's set
22. Made an impression
24. Pittsburgh player
27. Highfalutin hi-fi
29. Mini-albums, briefly
32. Dined
33. Montreal world's fair
35. Act the mail carrier
37. At any time
40. Gave a mark to
41. Hit town
43. Change
44. Lamented loudly
45. Bowling-alley button
46. Kitchen closer
47. Wedding-announcement word

DOWN

1. Diverted
2. College marching group: abbr.
3. Arthur of court fame
4. Get to
5. Cupid's shaft
6. Turn up
7. Hamlets' larger cousins
8. Total: 2 wds.
9. Hoarse
10. Fast plane, for short
11. Poet's field
14. Nursery purchase
16. One with a glad hand
18. Legal thing
19. Picnic gate-crasher
23. Put through one's paces
25. Before, to bards
26. A Harrison
28. Work in a hospital's theater
29. Mystery writer's prize
30. Hostess Mesta
31. Blind elements
32. Ward off
34. Sheeplike
36. Thought, in Tours
38. Holiday preceder
39. Carmine, e.g.
41. Last word
42. Sound of the surf

ACROSS

1. Tuscan waterway
5. More frilly
7. Beat treader
10. Yes man, usually
11. Poet Alighieri
13. "___ got a loverly bunch…"
14. Lend ___: 2 wds.
15. Motorcycle adjunct
20. Antinuke abbr.
21. Absolutely zero
23. Dry: prefix
24. Out of sorts
26. The latest
28. Wilson Phillips, e.g.
29. Moderate position: 4 wds.
34. Brainstorm
35. Commit a rink infraction
36. Galena or pyrite
37. Earth part: abbr.
38. Give one's all
40. Flat components: abbr.
42. Math branch
45. Expect
47. Hat
48. Velvety-petaled bloom
49. Root veggie
53. Banned insecticide
54. Getaway
55. Squad

DOWN

1. Expletive from Steffi
2. Carioca's hometown
3. Formerly named
4. Great Bruin
5. A son of Jacob
6. Served perfectly
7. Name on a slate
8. *Beyond the Horizon* author
9. School group: abbr.
11. German article
12. White-tailed eagle
13. Key of a sort
16. One far away from 29-Across
17. Large game fish
18. *Tosca* tune
19. Crucifix
22. Deduce
25. Hawaiian garland
27. Personnel query
29. Isinglass
30. Graven image
31. Xiaoping of China
32. Two quartets
33. Gofer's task
39. Kisser
41. Messy pad
43. Radar picture
44. Ready for picking
46. Clump
49. Asian lunar festival
50. Employ
51. Sarnoff's business: abbr.
52. Lake in Tibet

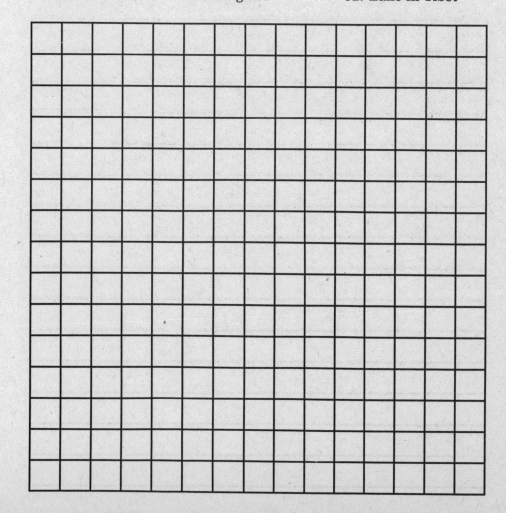

ACROSS

1. Computer terminal, initially
4. Follower of: suffix
7. Encourage
9. Bed backs
12. Glee
13. Thrice CCCLI
14. Prepare for war
15. Kyrgyzstan mountains
17. Revving sound
21. Princess detector of lore
22. Generic: hyph. wd.
24. Disorganized situation
25. Ignorant response: 2 wds.
26. Do nothing
27. Sugar source
29. Columbus school: abbr.
30. Bellicose god
31. Marmalade ingredient
32. Dec. visitor: 2 wds.
34. Shelley creation
35. Paul or George
36. Clever one, for short
39. Risk
41. Evil look
42. Three Dog Night hit
43. Distributed cards
45. Came to
47. Without limits
49. Kicked the bucket
50. Sweetie pie
51. Bradley and Marinaro

DOWN

1. Schmooze
2. In the act of wrongdoing: hyph. wd.
3. Typewriter key
4. Rocky's handle (with "The"): 2 wds.
5. Dustin's *Tootsie* costar
6. Salad veggie
8. Classical feature: 2 wds.
9. Take on
10. Author Bombeck
11. Kay's title
12. Former gas station freebie
16. A Costello
18. Southern mountains
19. Seep slowly
20. Howard et al.
23. Sicilian spewer: 2 wds.
25. Deeply felt
26. Torn
27. Riding accessory
28. Right-hand person
33. Seine holm
35. Turn white
36. Lamb coat
37. Black
38. Ultimate letter
40. A mean Amin
44. '70s hairdo
46. Gets hitched
48. Five-star nickname

ACROSS

1. Smidgen
4. ___ au rhum (dessert)
8. Start of Montana's motto
9. Premed course: abbr.
10. Evergreen tree
11. Democratic donkey deviser
12. Stolen-goods unloader
15. Social group
18. Pack away
19. Stone of *Intersection*
20. Laudatory lyric
21. Monte Cristo wrap
23. Energy unit
24. "Let ___" (Beatles hit): 2 wds.
26. Article
27. Nada
29. Title role for Omar
30. Gladiators' venue
31. Actress Claire
32. Chop
33. Grating
34. Wad fillers
35. Home for *un oiseau*
37. Habit wearers
38. "Gotcha!"

39. Light-colored cigars
41. Ceremony
43. Puts piping on
44. Prepped apples for baking
46. Swan variety
48. Actress Mary
49. Mother of Prometheus
50. Famed diarist
51. Quadrilateral figure: abbr.
52. Musical pitch

DOWN

1. Lift, as a hat
2. Stellar ram
3. Steppenwolf song: 4 wds.
4. Prohibition
5. Cursed one
6. Iraqi port
7. Togs
13. Body of laws
14. Palindromic sheep
16. Judy Garland song: 4 wds.
17. Motor
19. Lays out lucre
21. Slender appendage

22. Supped at home: 2 wds.
24. Prussian pronoun
25. From that place
28. Spanish article
30. Deity doubter
34. Glenn's state
36. *I Remember Mama* lass
38. Rainbow
40. Employ anew
42. Mysterious
45. Refuse
47. Munch lunch

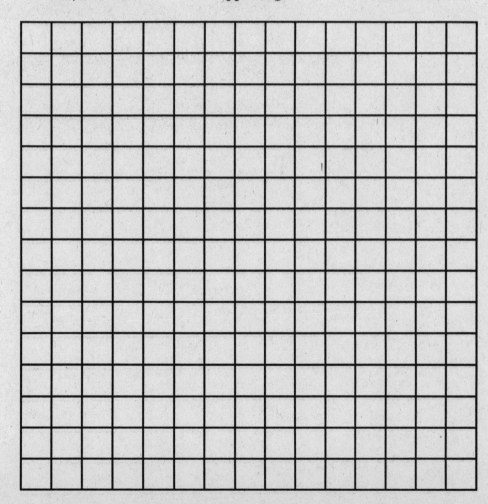

ACROSS

1. Not clerical
5. Lincoln copper
9. World hoister
11. *Otello*, for one
13. Seniors sitcom spin-off flop (with "The"): 2 wds.
16. Lodestone
17. Argot
19. Henri's head
20. Parakeet's place
22. Kettle and Joad
24. Nice season
25. Stalwart
26. Scatter (hay) for drying
27. Winglike feature
30. Constitute
31. Yucky place
32. According to
33. Mischievous maiden
34. Perón or Gabor
35. Dander
36. Showed again
38. Curved trajectories
42. CD reader
44. Emulate a top gun
46. Ritter sitcom's short-lived sequel: 3 wds.
49. Good hole for Els
50. Divided land
51. *Damn Yankees* vamp
52. Military meal

DOWN

1. Fall behind
2. Small particle
3. —— ease (edgy): 2 wds.
4. Scrounge
5. Egyptian Christian
6. Smog watchers: abbr.
7. Role for Jodie
8. Gallivant
10. Posted
12. Dermatologist's concern
14. Prenuptial name indicator
15. Leggy waders
18. Two bridge tables
21. Actress Lamarr
22. Seine tributary
23. Michael J. TV role
25. Classic rock opera
27. Copycat
28. Use a dozer on
29. Ark resting place
33. "Twenty Questions" category
37. *Days of Grace* author
38. An ex of Mickey's
39. James or Mears
40. Ricochet
41. Cached stuff
43. Conduct, to Caesar
44. Confused
45. Cote coddlers
47. House annex
48. Prosecutors: abbr.

DIAGRAMLESS NUMBER EIGHT

ACROSS

1. Prepare (wool) for spinning
5. Half note
10. English horn's kin
11. Battery terminal
12. Garden State cagers
13. Lauder of cosmetology
14. Dubious claims
17. Sole cleaner
18. Big lug
19. Kennedy and Merman
21. May Day march site: 2 wds.
25. Woman with will power?
26. Bran source
27. Had a spat
33. Clear
34. Gwen of *Damn Yankees*
37. Vogue, in Vichy
38. New Haven student
39. Straining a point
43. Mideast peninsula
45. Bank job
46. Puccini opera
47. Bumbling sort
48. Symbol of strength
49. Public-house potations

DOWN

1. Admit reluctantly
2. Assist in crime
3. Paper section, briefly
4. Lucie's brother
5. Solti and Stokowski
6. Office holders
7. Phrase of denial: 2 wds.
8. Perfect
9. Gets together
14. The cost of leaving
15. Lofty tip
16. Cherished
20. Practice witchcraft
22. Derisive feeling
23. *The ___ Fellow* (Behan play)
24. Out-and-out
27. Theorem-ending abbreviation
28. Wifely
29. Of prime quality: 2 wds.
30. Hispanic people
31. Princely prep school
32. Mao's successor
34. Waistcoats
35. *Daniel Deronda* author
36. Washer cycle
40. Provençal love song
41. Inscrutable
42. Cloud over
44. Wilander winner

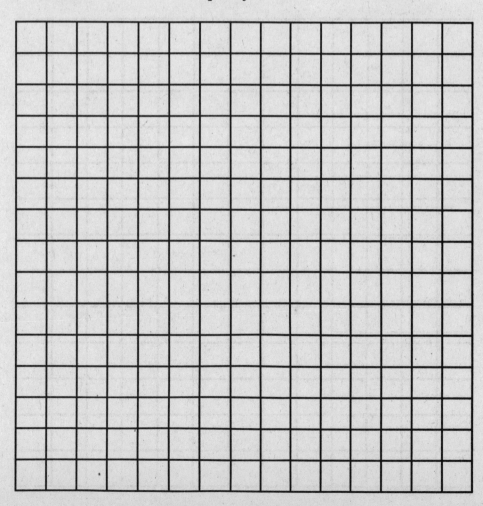

ACROSS

1. Buddies
5. Loll about
11. New York stage award
12. Plains dwelling
13. Chafe
15. Cleared the tape
16. Boy king, for short
17. CSA monogram
19. Heart test: abbr.
20. Numerical prefix
21. Actor Mineo
22. Opposite of NNW
23. O. Henry's specialty
26. Shankar improvisation
29. Intense focus
34. Colorful fish
35. Toss back and forth
36. —— Z (the gamut): 2 wds.
39. Monogram of Long John Silver's creator
41. *Répondez —— vous plaît*
42. Slangy sleuth
43. Ex follower
44. Arafat's group: abbr.
45. Lay down the law
48. Irish moonshine
51. Garden shrub
52. A Waugh
53. Lease arrangement
54. Shrove Tuesday follower

DOWN

1. Share
2. Loose desert wear
3. Topper
4. Sign readers
5. Outstanding
6. For each
7. Actor Stephen
8. Church parts
9. Calendar divisions
10. Shelf
13. Room at the top
14. Beast of burden
18. Terrestrial
24. Chevron wearer: abbr.
25. Laconic agreement
27. Verbal gift
28. —— loss (confused): 2 wds.
30. Horned cetacean
31. Check over
32. *Swan Lake* character
33. Hosiery stuff
36. Even, in golf: 2 wds.
37. Canonical hour
38. Vast expanse
40. Calyx part
46. Pretense
47. Spy group: abbr.
49. Corrida yell
50. Decade

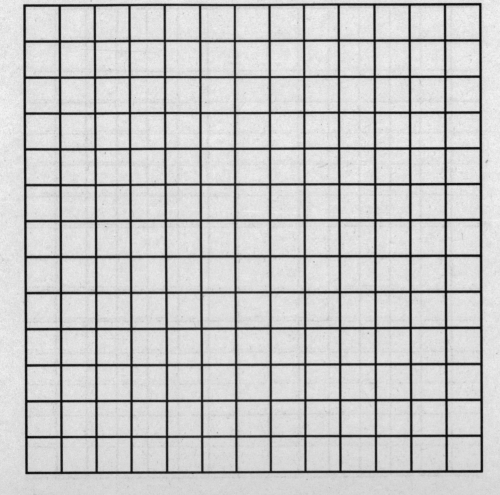

ACROSS

1. Every last one
4. Brown of renown
7. Good score for a duffer
10. Rue's costar
11. Architect's afterthought
12. Roman road
14. Singer Christie
15. Forest clearing
18. Buccaneer
20. Oner: 2 wds.
23. Bryn ——, PA
24. Indy entrant
25. Neighbor of Pavo
26. Withstand
28. Mystery writer Josephine
29. Mathers' costar
30. Author Zola
32. Swiss capital
33. Moderation ideal: 2 wds.
37. Diamond in the rough
39. Belle or Bart
40. Asian coin
41. Patsy
44. Model T starters
47. On in years
48. From Cork
50. Labor
51. "Good work!": 2 wds.
53. Noun gender
55. Domain
56. Nigerian native
58. High-schooler
59. Cha

60. Passionate fan
61. Bath, for one
62. McMahon, et al.
63. Hurricane center

DOWN

1. Competent
2. Summer sign
3. Tierney classic
4. Stowe villain
5. Queen of mystery
6. Thick slice
7. *Great Expectations* lad
8. "One Day at ——"
9. Showed a show again
13. Bad bargain: 2 wds.
16. Tiara
17. Glitch
19. Bridge maneuver
21. Play part or play parts
22. Break of day
24. Depend (on)
27. Thespian Torn
31. Emma Samms has four
32. Workaholic's risk
33. Mug feature
34. Engrave
35. —— es Salaam, Tanzania

36. Steamed
37. Gloat
38. Edmonton athlete
41. Moved edgewise
42. Fragrances
43. Get flat on the mat
45. Writes bad checks
46. Morpheus' milieu
49. Paris divider
52. Tardy
53. Eminence
54. Gene letters
57. Pay good money for

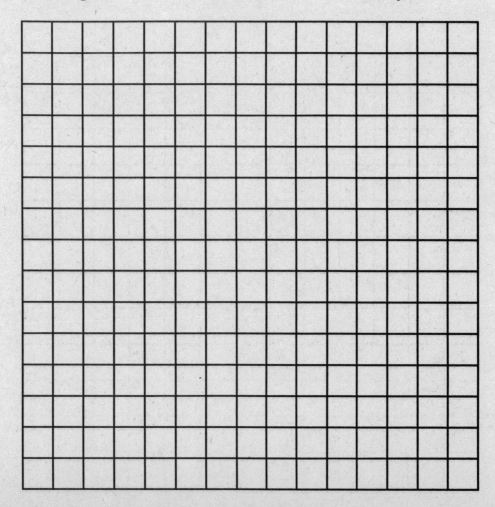

ACROSS

1. Special-interest group
5. Playwright Pirandello
6. Good-bye, on the Ginza
9. "— Tu" (1974 song)
10. Old-time auto
11. Michelangelo masterpiece
13. Draw to a close
16. Good-bye, in a groaner
21. I.M. the architect
22. Board VIP: abbr.
23. Grimm villain
24. Cry of dread: 2 wds.
26. Express disapproval
28. Farm tower
29. Old stairway sound
31. Count Tolstoy
33. The old college cry
34. Good-bye, to a guest: 2 wds.
36. Greek vowel
37. ?#@% and $#@%, in the comics
38. Chase game
41. To be, in Brest
42. Good-bye, in Grenoble: 2 wds.
44. Pester
45. Venus de Milo's lack

DOWN

1. Burger bread
2. Colorer of facts
3. See 23-Across
4. Good-bye, to Guido
5. Spanish article
6. Good-bye, for now: 3 wds.
7. Bachelor's specialty?
8. Matzo's lack
11. Larrigan
12. "Oh, sure!": 2 wds.
13. Important period
14. Indian leader
15. Beanery
17. 1040 people: abbr.
18. *Bête* — (bane)
19. — ease (edgy): 2 wds.
20. Good-bye, on Kauai
25. Water paddle
27. High chaser
30. Site of Nijo Castle
32. Approves
35. Adriatic port
38. Good-bye, in Gloucester: hyph. wd.
39. Actor Mischa
40. Unit of mass
41. Festive night before
43. Tight turn

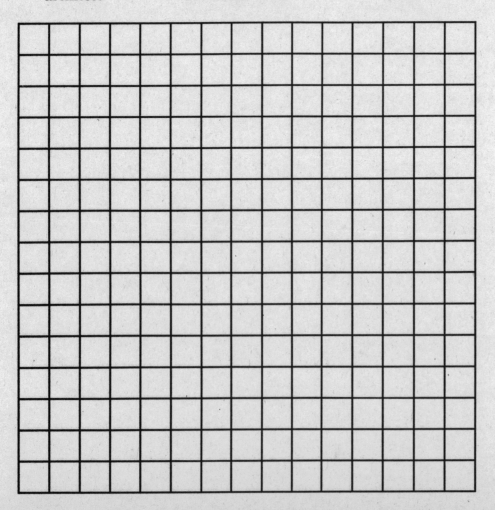

ACROSS

1. High peak
4. According to
7. Film terrier
11. Page
13. Way back when
14. Actor Delon
15. Imperfect circle
16. Sartorial slipup
17. Teed off ... way off
18. Unfortunate store event: 2 wds.
20. Motorists' org.
21. Approx.
23. Get hitched
24. Antiballistic item
27. Beatles' meter maid
30. Angled
33. Church projections
34. Coral isle
37. Kanga's kid
38. Yorkshire city
39. Goddesses of the seasons
40. Mythical hoarder
42. Surrounded by
43. —— Mill (gold rush site)
47. Guys in uniform
49. Common contraction
50. Old card game
51. Neighed contentedly
55. Dire
58. Coop resident
59. Garfield's pal
60. Son of Asia
61. A Gershwin
62. Bloody events
63. Change direction
64. Solidify
65. See 64-Across

DOWN

1. On high
2. Third son of Jacob
3. Jack of talk shows
4. Flawless place
5. Norse hero
6. 1948 Hitchcock thriller
7. Wanted-poster word
8. Pouch
9. Ascot, for one
10. "...baby, cradle ——": 2 wds.
12. Left the coop
14. Jai follower
17. "Cheers" barkeep
19. Eden spoilsport
22. Vandyke, e.g.
25. Third Crusade warrior
26. Land in the water
28. Lewis or Mack
29. Pompous type
31. Neither partner
32. Brown bread
33. Tons
34. Cry of triumph
35. Gobbler
36. Unplagiarized
41. Composer Mahler
44. "Pomp and Circumstance" man
45. *Reines* mates
46. Assn.
48. Skier's desire
49. That is: Lat.
51. Tory's foe
52. Roll call
53. Lupino and Tarbell
54. Emerald Isle
56. Map abbr.
57. Pub quaff

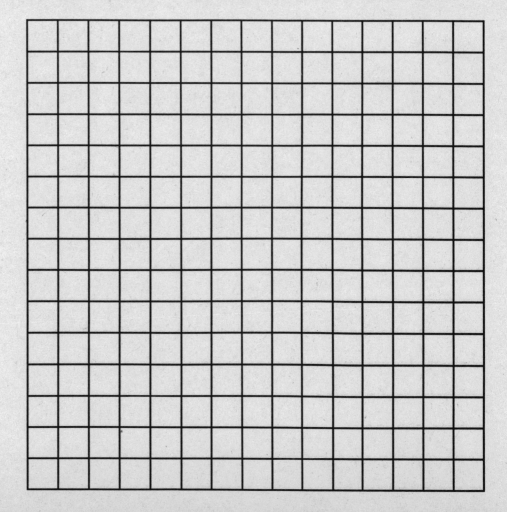

ACROSS

1. Egyptian ophidians
5. Bruce of Hollywood
9. Oscar —— Renta
10. Effortlessness
11. Fads
13. Sears
16. Big galoot
17. Realistic art school
20. Hankerings
22. Twelve in.: 2 wds.
24. Overseas destn.
25. Medical suffix
26. He loved Lucy
27. Create picots
28. Predicament
30. Nobody's fool: 2 wds.
33. They can't stay away from bars
34. Ice-cream flavor: hyph. wd.
35. Overshoot: 2 wds.
36. Mouth: prefix
37. Season
41. Wellsian race
42. Prosecutors, initially
43. Steve's mate
44. Blab
45. Framer's joints
47. Mess up
48. Granola ingredient
50. Annapolis force: 3 wds. (abbr.)
52. Chip off the old block?
53. Brit's brig
54. Actor Joel
55. Actress Sylvia

DOWN

1. Proverbs
2. "—— who?" (slangy reply)
3. Kilt feature
4. Fresh talk
5. Exclude
6. Have coming
7. Bee Gees' longtime record label
8. Gotham: 3 wds.
11. Oaf
12. Ancient alphabet character
14. Je —— quoi: 2 wds.
15. Take potshots (at)
18. Learn about: 2 wds.
19. Ruthless
21. Compass point
23. Skidding sideways
27. Unspoken
28. Maestro Georg
29. San Francisco's —— Tower
31. Clever remarks
32. Golf links
33. Dome kin
34. A film Chan
35. Buy
38. High principles
39. Mil. missile
40. Hair-raising
42. Two-bit
43. Prose composition
45. PC accessories
46. They may be underfoot
49. Guinness' title
51. Paris appellation

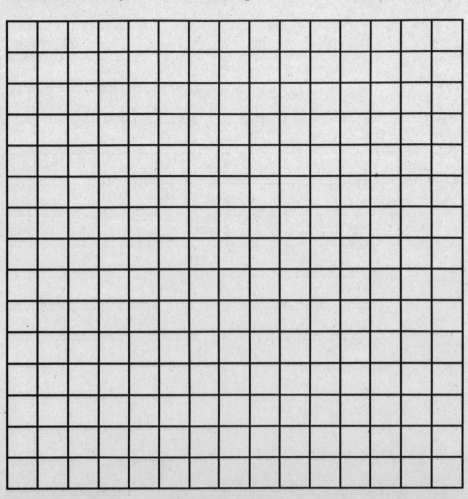

DIAGRAMLESS NUMBER FOURTEEN

ACROSS

1. G–K filler
4. Coffee
8. GI entertainment group
9. Eyelashes
10. Scientific wonders
12. Grimm creature
16. Hangs (over)
17. Star racing driver: 3 wds. (abbr.)
19. Messy place
21. Straighten
22. State of Brazil
23. Character actor Erwin
26. Motion pictures
27. Marsh growth
28. Spigot
29. Bar barrel
30. Give it a shot
31. Futuristic cartoon family
33. Target for Holyfield
36. Raven's cry
37. Yale alumnus
38. Revolting
39. Icelandic moolah
41. Gumshoe: slang
42. "Watch out, —— a roll": 2 wds.
43. Lowest point
44. Gymnast Olga
46. Casts out
48. Writer Horatio
49. Financial security
50. Dappled horse
54. Lash of oaters
55. Paraffin, for example
56. World War II alliance
57. Comedian Louis

DOWN

1. Drill sergeant's call
2. Vague suffix
3. *Cabaret* star: 2 wds.
4. *Rear Window* star: 2 wds.
5. Tavern tipples
6. *Ordinaire* quaff
7. Madison Ave. group
9. Eccentric oldster
11. Edged (out)
12. A pack —— (prevarications): 2 wds.
13. Operational
14. Infielder Sandberg
15. Summers, in Somme
18. Golf great: 2 wds.
19. Separate
20. Bubbly bucket
24. Create lace
25. Derangement
31. Actress Rule
32. Corrida cheer
33. Ex-Cleveland footballer: 2 wds.
34. Baseball's Matty
35. Split
36. Spy glyphs
38. Greenfinch bird
39. Patella site
40. Hindu bigwig
45. Leer at
47. Part of a *casa*
48. Fool's day: abbr.
51. Irenic goddess
52. Speak
53. Tree toppler

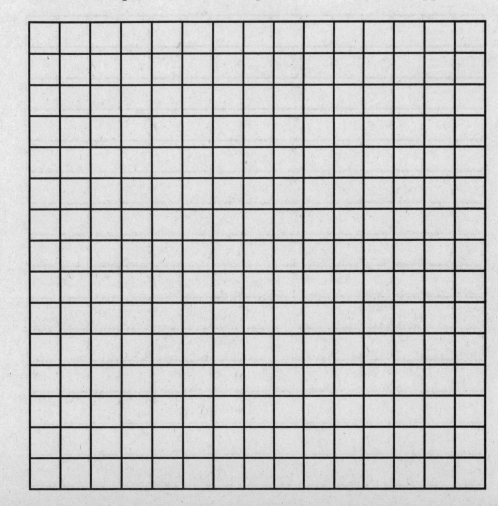

ACROSS

1. Pipe piece
5. Walter —— Mare: 2 wds.
6. Have a migraine
10. Storewide event
11. Talent; knack
12. French flower
13. Deviates from vertical
14. Protests for pay
16. New Deal monogram
19. Futhark characters
20. Verbal betrayer
21. *Jo's Boys* author
24. Cannes honorees
25. Go on the lam
26. Cleo's bane
28. Pizzeria fixture
29. Strange twist of fate
30. Portable abodes
32. Lease
33. Levitated
35. Dog-days quaff
36. "—— in two places…": 3 wds.
38. Writer Bret
39. Network in the UK
41. Curved moldings
42. Pastoral sites
44. Heave about
45. Acts human
46. Scorecard datum, e.g.

DOWN

1. 1960s radical group: abbr.
2. Freshwater duck
3. Emily's pseudonym
4. Baton wielder
6. Very similar
7. Docket listings
8. Triumphs for angels
9. Bitter vetch
11. Bedrock residents
15. Actress Lee
16. Rasps
17. Make anathema
18. Transit lines: abbr.
20. Not taped, on TV
21. Hermitic
22. Was generous for a while
23. Ron on third base
24. Opponent
25. One of 11-Down
27. Pismire, often
29. Tax-delayed fund
31. See 25-Down
33. Land units
34. London property taxes
36. Emilia's husband
37. Chicago critic
38. Like fenced stones
40. Singer Irene
43. Fast flier: abbr.

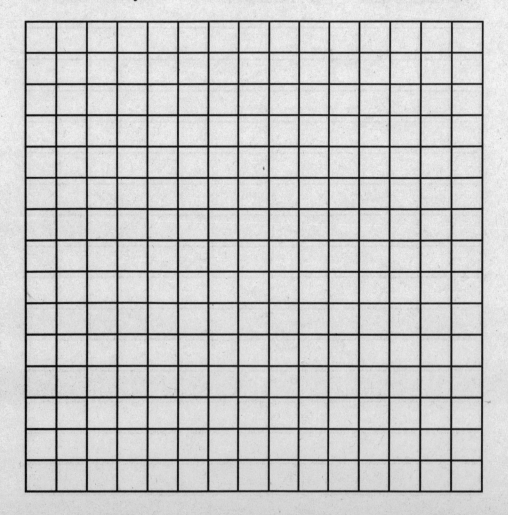

DIAGRAMLESS NUMBER SIXTEEN

ACROSS

1. Lacking body
5. Ness
9. Lollapalooza
10. Allege in pleading
11. Ming thing
12. Frosty equine hue
13. Definite article
15. Cupidity
17. Heavy drenching
19. Organic compounds
20. Bore the cost of
23. Nigerian tribesman
24. Shelters
25. Landers at Logan
30. Land unit
31. Most torrid
33. Beluga harvest
34. Essential
36. Charles' pup
37. Fruity quencher
38. Of the East
41. Playing marbles
44. Negates
45. Enduring composition
47. Sort
48. Saharan antelope
49. Shirt shaper
51. Drying chamber
52. Clinton's canal
53. Extreme liberals
54. Pricey

DOWN

1. Pews for paramours: 2 wds.
2. Actress Claire
3. Oater backdrop
4. Triumphs
5. Buzzard breakfast
6. Shun
7. State of concord
8. Sea raptors
13. Dartmoor outcropping
14. Newman film
16. Sphere of influence
17. *Uno* follower
18. Volume
20. Asian mountain range
21. Spore producer
22. Meter measures
26. One who looks for volunteers
27. Formerly, formerly
28. Tribunal of the papal curia
29. Circus performer
31. Skins
32. Partial: hyph. wd.
35. Gorp sweets
36. Response: abbr.
39. Adverse
40. Maned deer
41. Board strutter
42. Damsel's token
43. Stared open-mouthed
46. Devotion
50. Narrow ocean inlet

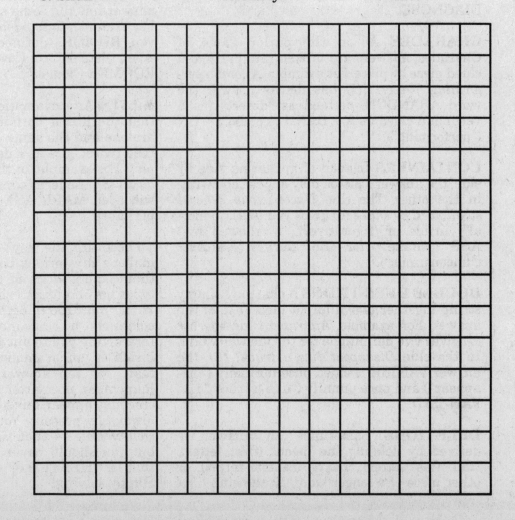

CRYPTIC CROSSWORDS

Cryptic crosswords are puzzles specially designed for lovers of wordplay. Each clue in a cryptic crossword is a miniature game of wits. To play, you need to know what's in the puzzlemaker's box of tricks. The keys to that box are given below, to get you started in the game.

The master key is knowing that every cryptic clue is like an equation with two parts: a normal definition of the answer, plus a second hint using wordplay. These two parts are strung together; figuring out where one part ends and the other begins is the challenge of the game. Seasoned solvers learn to look for the following types of wordplay:

ANAGRAMS The letters of the answer may be given in scrambled form in the clue, along with a figurative word or phrase to warn you. In the clue *Analyze San Diego wrongly (8)*, you are asked to find an 8-letter word meaning "analyze" that is an anagrammed (i.e., wrongly spelled) version of "San Diego." The answer? DIAGNOSE.

CHARADES As in the parlor game of Charades, answers are broken into parts and clued piece by piece. For example, *A combo performing "Desert" (7)* has for its answer the word ABANDON, defined as "desert" (as a verb) and clued as A + BAND ("combo") + ON ("performing").

CONTAINERS Instead of appearing side by side, the answer's pieces may appear one within the other. The clue *Unconscious general swallowed by snake (6)* gives you LEE ("general") inside of (figuratively, "swallowed by") ASP ("snake") for the answer ASLEEP ("unconscious").

DOUBLE DEFINITIONS A clue may simply string together two different meanings of the answer. For example, *Apartment lacking air (4)* gives two definitions for the answer FLAT. In the clue *Disappear like a truck? (6)*, the answer VANISH is clued once normally ("disappear") and once punnily ("like a truck," i.e., VAN-ISH).

DELETIONS Sometimes an answer is derived by deleting the "head" (first letter), "tail" (last letter), "heart" (central letter), or other piece of a longer word. In the clue *Bird dog loses its head (5)*, the answer EAGLE is derived when BEAGLE sheds its front letter.

HIDDEN WORDS On occasion, the answer may actually appear within the clue, camouflaged. In the clue *Santa's teddy bears sampled (6)*, the phrase "Santa's teddy" carries (i.e., "bears") the answer TASTED. Easy, when you know what to look for!

REVERSALS A clue may playfully hint that the answer spelled backward would create a new word. In the clue *Lucifer was returning (5)*, the answer DEVIL results when the word LIVED ("was") turns backward. In Down clues, which refer to vertical diagram entries, look for hints like "rising," "northward," "overturned," etc. For example, the Down clue *Jeans material is dug up (5)* gives the answer DENIM, which is MINED ("dug") when seen upside down.

HOMOPHONES A clue may tell you that the answer has the same sound as another word. For example, *Gossip lodger overheard (5)* gives you RUMOR (defined as "gossip"), which when listened to ("overheard") sounds like ROOMER ("lodger").

& LITS. An exclamation point will tip you off that the literal definition and the wordplay are one and the same. The entire clue can be read twice: once as a definition, once as wordplay. For example, in the clue *A grim era, perhaps! (8)*, the letters in AGRIMERA "perhaps" will spell MARRIAGE, which is "a grim era, perhaps!"

These are the keys that unlock the cluemaker's mysterious box. Be aware, however, that combinations of two or more wordplay types may occur in a single clue. For example, *Writer put $100 in battered portmanteau (6,6)* combines a container and an anagram, instructing you to put C (short for a $100 bill) inside an anagrammed version of "portmanteau" for the answer TRUMAN CAPOTE. Remember, no matter how weird or twisty a clue may appear, fair hints for its solution will always be present. You may get temporarily *sick of Dole* — that is, FOOLED (anagram), but you should never feel *Centigrade-hot* — that is, CHEATED (C + HEATED).
Happy solving!

ACROSS

1. Foot problem makes Taft feel awful (4, 4)

5. Rise of a perfume (6)

9. Wrongs in court groups (8)

10. A second-rate travel route overseas (6)

11. One has objections to neighbors (5)

12. Foul merinos I'm soaking (9)

14. East Street meandered, becoming distant (9)

16. TV I'm returning has bugs (5)

17. $100 fishing equipment in fisherman's basket (5)

18. Specialized with funny catch line (9)

20. A can's rich new sugar substitute (9)

22. Former President's money gift (5)

24. Flier who crashed one vehicle near America (6)

25. Someone lassoing the devil? Wrong (8)

26. Listen to Frost's poems (6)

27. Lantern I moved inside (8)

DOWN

1. Boat dress seen in *Kismet* (7)

2. One day in France, almost in a French region (5)

3. Cut off wood, everybody (9)

4. Strange vine twisting around light seen at dusk (7, 4)

6. True Confederate heading north on the wagon (5)

7. Stuck-up Stoic I get mad (9)

8. News time is interrupted by bell sound (7)

13. Doctor in Maine roaring about movie theater (8, 3)

15. Teach Cory all about Iran's system of government (9)

16. Me and an old horse at Great Lake zoo (9)

17. Fire makes first of coals grayer (7)

19. Some other time, Pacino to make a pass (7)

21. Garden tool keeps us home (5)

23. Quaker is like writer (5)

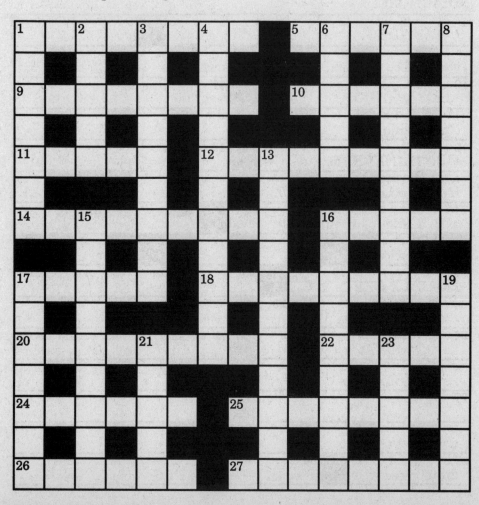

ACROSS

1. Turner ordered "Riot" series (10)

6. Double cord, almost (4)

10. Eruption in Florida pure madness (5-2)

11. Miserly one in season (7)

12. Governor catches small-town thief (7)

13. Needlework could become an eccentric habit with time (7)

14. Calms boyfriends? (8)

15. Didn't fail History, I hear (6)

18. "Charge" found in Latin dictionary (6)

20. Scold Republican pest (8)

24. Virus to give birth to monster (7)

26. Charms a stubborn person with last pair of tickets (7)

27. Backward section of Reno—it's a bettor's stronghold (7)

28. Work of art returned to ski area (7)

29. Feeling rejected? It's fate (4)

30. Church and Sunday school buttressing a teen's shaky virtue (10)

DOWN

1. Busted from getting into residence improvements (7)

2. Flaky nerds can't excel (9)

3. Raced around wing, relieved (7)

4. Former bellhop is international dealer? (8)

5. Bug in group (6)

7. Think on method aloud (5)

8. Canceled requirement involving gun (7)

9. Sire deity in front of a temple (6)

16. Draw old naval officer (9)

17. False start takes a long time, backing up races (8)

18. During climb I bedeviled drunk (7)

19. Praise Cincy player in town endlessly (6)

21. Playing a louder musical ornament (7)

22. Has less troublesome annoyances (7)

23. Second-rate farm outlet (6)

25. Soldiers standing on Medical Officer's thingamajig (5)

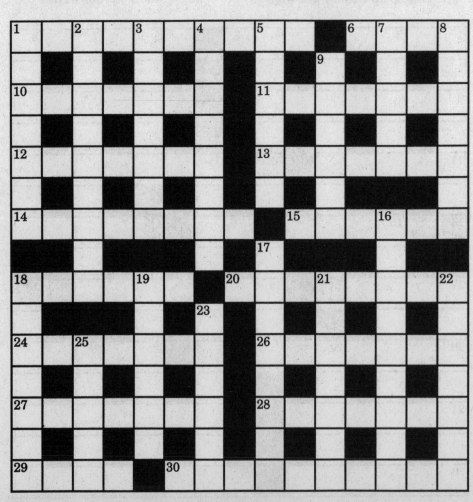

ACROSS

1. "Footwear in military boat," jock snarled (8)

5. Preserve piece of marine lab with Maine retrospective (6)

9. Sluggish, running light race... (9)

11. ...before crossing jauntily (5)

12. Pair of Europeans pitched rake — I've found it (6)

13. Not solvent there in Indiana (2, 3, 3)

15. Jerry, do I free dangerous driver? (8)

16. Fancy hotel read out legal documents (4)

19. Telephone gang (4)

20. Down east, surrounded by dads (8)

23. Declares no one recalled dislike (8)

24. Bill attractive individual at topless bar (6)

27. So there — it joined with island country (5)

28. English surgeon in bed, covered with sores (9)

29. Terribly ragged knife (6)

30. Complains against being stuck in boats (8)

DOWN

1. Romeo's love story is included in project (6)

2. Smash crate to provide food (5)

3. Servant absorbed by live schoolyard fight's outcome? (5, 3)

4. Bess' man doesn't start overindulgence (4)

6. Rude hum toy released (6)

7. Doctor adores its heavenly bodies (9)

8. Produce notes from soft colors, we hear (8)

10. Nunneries not in favor of escapes (8)

14. Bet mob I'm tossing explosive (4, 4)

15. Traveling free, spraying ink jet gun (9)

17. Article in bread was inspiring? (8)

18. Blood-clotter quite enveloped in warmth (8)

21. Seek Cleopatra's snake with anger (6)

22. Stared when changing lines of work (6)

25. Roll, curl tousled piece of hair (5)

26. City helps to make junkie violent (4)

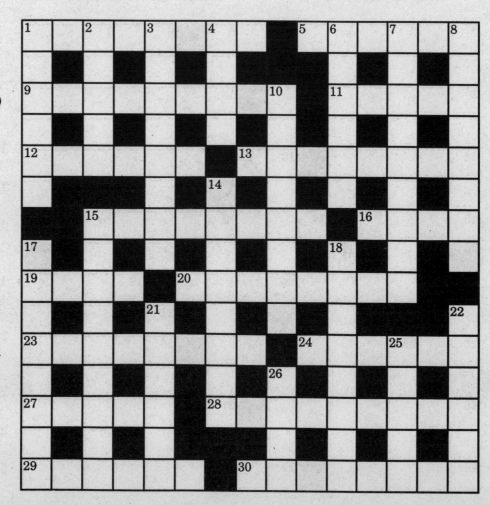

ACROSS

1. Acquisitive desire to own name car with working license (5, 4)

6. Abated or eliminated right out (5)

9. Wild boar introduced into act with circus performer (7)

10. Gem dealer worked around center of diamond (7)

11. Chicago train is boarded by the Kennedy spouse (5)

12. Broadway star is clumsy, mum? Not yet (5, 4)

13. "Johns Hopkins Stores" boutique (4)

14. Saint Laura goes wild for Crocodile Dundee, e.g. (10)

18. Creative muse holding 2,000 with bizarre rite in season (10)

19. On some potato pancakes (4)

22. "Exactly," holds Ms. Rand; "Stay clean" (4, 3, 2)

25. Engineer eager to come to terms (5)

26. Fantastic beast described in runic or Norse (7)

27. Ola made bananas with ice cream (1, 2, 4)

28. Component of engine Edsel can't do without (5)

29. Absorbing snippet of rumor, key stock exchanges soar rapidly (9)

DOWN

1. Said, "Go brush out beards" (7)

2. Burrowing creature chewed up the marrow (9)

3. Unable to go to seed cloud in space (6)

4. Start unit organized against monopolies (9)

5. Picture 500 papers (5)

6. The common fellow may never put out (8)

7. University supporters upset with foul-up (5)

8. Irish bomb failing to explode, gone astray (7)

15. Prorate my rent for a short time (9)

16. Weave or knit lace without a mesh (9)

17. Sent Sue out so endlessly voluptuous (8)

18. Thus, after the first of June, our night visit (7)

20. Avert public relations incident (7)

21. Indian tribe makes father flee (6)

23. Courage is almost upright (5)

24. Pulls for Northerners (5)

ACROSS

1. Admitted everyone was in debt (7)

5. One bridge club in disorder (7)

9. During trip, endeavor to become mature (5)

10. Feeling it's even is wrong (9)

11. Fabricated steel pads for foundations (9)

12. Notorious boss is head of toxic waste plant? (5)

13. Some sailors blanket east with counterfeit money (6)

15. Composer brought back part for single man (8)

17. Abnormal insect split by Yogi (8)

19. Ribald tossing of newlyweds (6)

22. Reportedly located and arraigned (5)

24. Condemned "Mr. Italy" to death (9)

26. Some, having undefined debts, left impatiently (9)

27. Broken toe constrains Connecticut eightsome (5)

28. Psychotic state doctor restraining a federal agent (7)

29. Spare tire eventually girds leisure person (7)

DOWN

1. An award for Wilt ? (7)

2. Before day's dawn, displaced Pole jogged (5)

3. Cast hires Dawn for *Fear of Flying*? (4,5)

4. Expel attorneys weaving braids (6)

5. Blackout in the east: men confused (7)

6. A fight with lances is crooked (5)

7. Small piece of egg found in cold cut (9)

8. "Poor deli rye," this one concedes (7)

14. Strained open cut (9)

16. The woman leads each fight in this area (9)

17. Hail current chlorine goal (7)

18. In *Ms.*, see exotic goddess (7)

20. Still wearing dilatory child's garments (7)

21. Singer Charles is in, according to Grace (6)

23. Motivated crowd (5)

25. Resident relinquishing last plant (5)

CRYPTIC CROSSWORD SIX

ACROSS

1. Places for storing a rare herb (8)

5. Badger spies trap's opening (6)

10. Seminole dances around chief of tribe for important event (9)

11. Parts of speech ought to divide sisters (5)

12. British philosopher heard to make gentle sounds (6)

13. Adhesives experiment with wall decoration (8)

14. Indoctrinate — bath's first; shower with what remains? (9)

17. Unacceptable bar bill — two rounds (5)

19. Dog losing bark initially — it's way below par (5)

20. Those vending franks outside home for couples? (9)

21. Dispute piece of research in story (8)

23. Hose problem lawn initially before summer (6)

26. Was sore head possibly catching cold? (5)

27. Dish from Mexico and Chile a bust (9)

28. Shoot holes in problem (6)

29. Suavest men trendily showing off fine garment (8)

DOWN

1. Fine officer, having penned book *End of Justice* (9)

2. Reportedly hawks more than one unit (5)

3. No license? Resorted to back talk (9)

4. School's reputation on the rise (4)

6. Pound's part is "Uncle" in opening of fairy tale? (5)

7. Honest error — forsake expert (9)

8. Impatient for tryout with club (5)

9. Harp to me about figure of speech (8)

15. A knight enthused about one in distress (9)

16. Clothing entrances tailor — he's normal except for name (8)

17. Doctor, the sentence is true (9)

18. Keen-eyed old British butler? (9)

21. Blonde gets front of limousine bent (5)

22. Boy! It returned with ebb and flow (5)

24. Rising journalist getting standard cover (5)

25. Top came off (4)

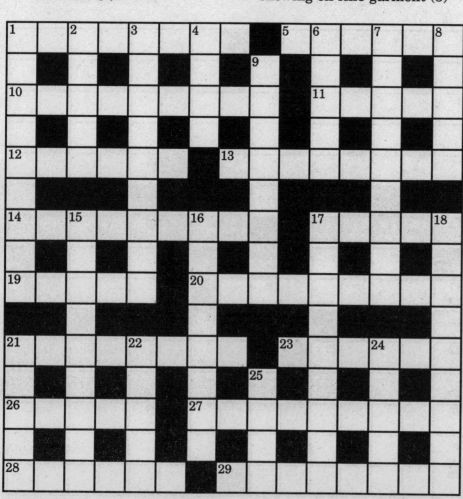

ACROSS

1. Bury damaged gem (4)

3. Republican assistant inside supports giving details (5, 5)

10. Jail Capone, holed up in last car (9)

11. Harvest includes bit of rice seed (5)

12. Disorder, of a type, equals religious feelings (7)

13. Mom gets one that's more insect-ridden (7)

14. Horse farm near Anchorage is unfenced (6)

16. Not quite intoxicated from dessert (5)

19. Subject of story gets halfway through (5)

20. Be an informer or be a carrier (6)

23. Launder slips in a British town (7)

25. A comedian may do this for a place to sleep (7)

26. Little maintained by Spanish soot cleaner (5)

27. Long story to begin with a pivotal point (9)

28. Pee-wee Herman's opening with rough rehearsal (3-7)

29. Large and light (4)

DOWN

1. Doctor Pierce giving prescription (6)

2. Prove otherwise false notion (6)

4. Chambers for new husbands without leadership (5)

5. Met with crew near bow of vessel (9)

6. Drunk little bird has mercury rising (5)

7. Is a charm, maybe! (8)

8. Guards southern gates (8)

9. Poor GI able to get into debt (8)

15. *Cowboy Plot* role in adaptation (9)

16. That is among product names for drinks (8)

17. "Carlene's Mystical Soap"... (8)

18. ...turned Laurence blue (8)

21. Female lawyer left at one A.M., without a bit of money (6)

22. Half-upset, Hitchcock got angry (6)

24. Department head's initial profundity (5)

25. Deliver above-average item from the jeweler's (5)

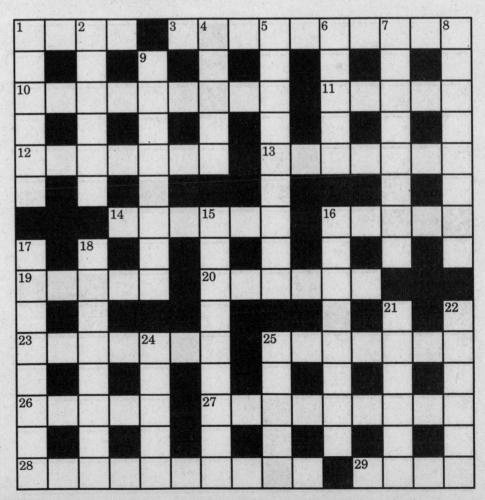

ACROSS

1. Worry about a political lobby getting back protection (8)

5. Experiment involving second character of family (6)

9. Cruise feature following transit with railroad worker (8)

10. Associate difficulty upon returning material (6)

12. Bit of lime put in for one's plants (5)

13. Tender women hurry back around 1 (9)

14. Actress with no room while member of an audience (5, 7)

18. Grumpy might circle America with ship (12)

21. Notes doctor made about Holmes' foe (9)

23. Something belonging to a seer's apprentice (5)

24. Wrong fish beheaded (6)

25. Titmouse, after flying, rests (8)

26. Wet turf to study (6)

27. Damned song about one American (8)

DOWN

1. Trouser part having to separate (3, 3)

2. Think about a kid (6)

3. Does some writing on a pop city of the South (9)

4. Sick man is gripped by stifling addictive habit (5-7)

6. Stir halfway up in wine (5)

7. Good time without alcohol requires a writing of songs (8)

8. Model rapidly absorbing a stone-cutting art (8)

11. Keeping peace at first with native American region (12)

15. Gear alien set outside jokers? (9)

16. Runs south with some vacationers (8)

17. In love letter #4, has Latin written up (8)

19. Run into small purple tree (6)

20. State question in a musical tone (6)

22. Some Wild West land called "empty" (5)

CROSSWORD 1

```
BRAISE  HARK   KOL
LUMMOX  ADEN   ERE
STOPBELIEVINGIN
   REMIT    TELEG
ALAI  PRIAM   RENT
PULSATE  REBIRTH
BIGOT     FINE
 SANTACLAUSAND
    ILLY   OLEAN
TREACLE  FATLADY
HUNG  YODEL  EPEE
ENDOR    UNIFY
YOUGETUNDERWEAR
RUE   NARC  NEATER
ETD   DONE  SAYERS
```

CROSSWORD 2

```
CHAMP  OMIT   CRAB
HAGUE  MADE   HAIR
ALITTLENONSENSE
PONT   ALE   TRILL
    ARE    SERENE
NOWANDTHEN
EVADE    ORDAINS
TENDS  EVE   TRIPE
RESTORE    RIGEL
    ISRELISHED
 PAROLE   PEA
ARDOR   NON   DESK
BYMOSTGENTLEMEN
LOAF   LIVY  AMIGO
ERNS   CLAM  COROT
```

CROSSWORD 3

```
LIMA   HASTA    SAP
OMIT   ELMAN   LEDA
GETTYSBURG   AVON
STEAMS    PEERAGE
    ICE   WORLDS
AMANA   BAN   LETIN
CARS   GER   FEDORA
ARM  BATTLES   PAP
DIANAS   IAN   COTE
SAGES   AMP   ARLES
   EMIGRE   OFA
RIDESIT    BASTES
ALDA  BUNKERHILL
IKON   ERIES   EDIE
DAN   DONNE   SEED
```

CROSSWORD 4

```
SPUR   MADAM   TIOS
MENU   ALANA   URDU
ODIN   TARAS   RAIN
GETSITINTHENECK
    ORE    IRS
SPANISH   BERTHAS
CORES   ALL   SHONE
ALES   YOU   UVEA
MANET   EAR   SMELL
PRAYERS   BAUBLES
   ERE    DES
PUTONESFOOTDOWN
SLAV   SOLAR   OLEO
SERE   ELATE   WISP
TSAR   SETHS   NOTE
```

CROSSWORD 5

```
TOW   POPES   STAR
ERAS   INLAY   AHME
MILE   PEARL   REIN
POTATION   LAGGED
END   ANNE   ABEL
   IDIG  TUBE   OPT
EDSEL   BONUS   BAR
DUNE   TAFTS   HERE
NEE   ERATO   PATSY
ALY   GISH   BOTH
   WAAC   EBAN   ETS
APOLLO   AARDVARK
CARL   LAPSE   ATEE
MILO   ODETS   GREW
EDDY   RESET   ESS
```

CROSSWORD 6

```
MAE   SCAB   BRAC
ELF   PUCE   LASH
ALF   IRAQ   OKIE
   USEITUPWEAR
INSIDE    IAN
BAIT   ICC   SID
ITOUTMAKEITDO
DEN   HAM   GOIN
   WAX  ALLUDE
ORDOWITHOUT
ROAR   LOOT   ILL
BURT   LULU   SEA
SETH   ARES   HEX
```

CROSSWORD 7

```
BASH   ALUG   CALL
ILIAD   TOTE   ALAE
RALLY   LOAN   NINA
DIK  LEATHERNECK
  PEALS   ROONEY
CHURNS   SPAWN
AURA   AWHILE   SIB
VESTA   HAP   DRACO
EYE   MOONED   ATOR
   PIPPA   ROVING
INSANE    MATIN
COTTONMOUTH   DIT
HOAR   EARS   ERODE
OSLO   NYET   RILLE
REEL   DOMS   GLEN
```

CROSSWORD 8

```
SEER   MEAT   LAB
ELLE   PESTO   WAVE
WOODYALLENMOVIE
  INSETS    ERAS
   ANT   TACIT
 BRITISHCARHOOD
AROLL   PECS   PLO
VOUS   FIDOS   ATIP
ETS   ONOR   OGIVE
CHEATINGDEVICE
   LILYS   SET
 FOOT   ATRACE
METHODOFBATTING
ARIA   ARABS   ONCE
ENS   METE   REEL
```

CROSSWORD 9

```
APE   SHA   JAM
PAL   IAN   EXISTS
FOGY   CHAPTERTWO
OLES   AMAHL   RID
ALBERT   ERR   BAND
MOO   EEL   ORANGE
   YEAROF   OLDEN
   SPINELESS
SPATE   ZODIAC
TAVERN   TIE   OPT
OMAR   OOF   TRIVIA
REL   WORLD   RENI
CLOSEDBOOK   ORAL
HANSEL   ADA   NUT
EKE   TOY   SPA
```

CROSSWORD 10

```
RAMP   SCROD   DARN
OBOE   MOORE   IDEA
PEOPLEWHOLIVEIN
YEN   YALE   SELMA
   ERRS   POSSESS
REPLAY   CLOUT
ARAM   GAUZE   CEE
GLASSHOUSESSHAVE
SER   HARSH   USER
   TRIKE   BARELY
LATHERY   LOLL
AHEAD   GOTO   BOK
TOANSWERTHEBELL
IMRE   ELITE   ELIE
NESS   DINER   DANE
```

CROSSWORD 11

```
STAR   MAIL   AGUA
ARNE   ARNO   DUNCE
MINDONESPSANDQS
   OSLO   TEEN   OUT
PAT   ERR   CONNIE
DRAM   EDGE   AET
QATAR   GRADED
  BEHAVEONESELF
  LEANON   PRIES
ETE   STLO   SCAT
CLARET   NAP   ORR
ATT   VETO   NEAR
DOTHERIGHTTHING
SPEAR   FLEE   ACES
ODDS   FENS   BETA
```

CROSSWORD 12

```
ASCAP   TSE   OMAR
STARE   MIEN   LALA
TAROT   ALEC   IRAN
IFYOUAREDRIVING
RFS   LIT   LONE
  CANADIAN   GEE
ASIAN   ENC   ALLY
HOMETONIGHTMAKE
ORAN   NUS   EIDER
YEN   GERMFREE
  MUTT   LET   ABC
SUREYOUHAVEACAR
ASIS   ORIG   RIATA
REST   NESS   ERGOT
AREA   EDS   DEERE
```

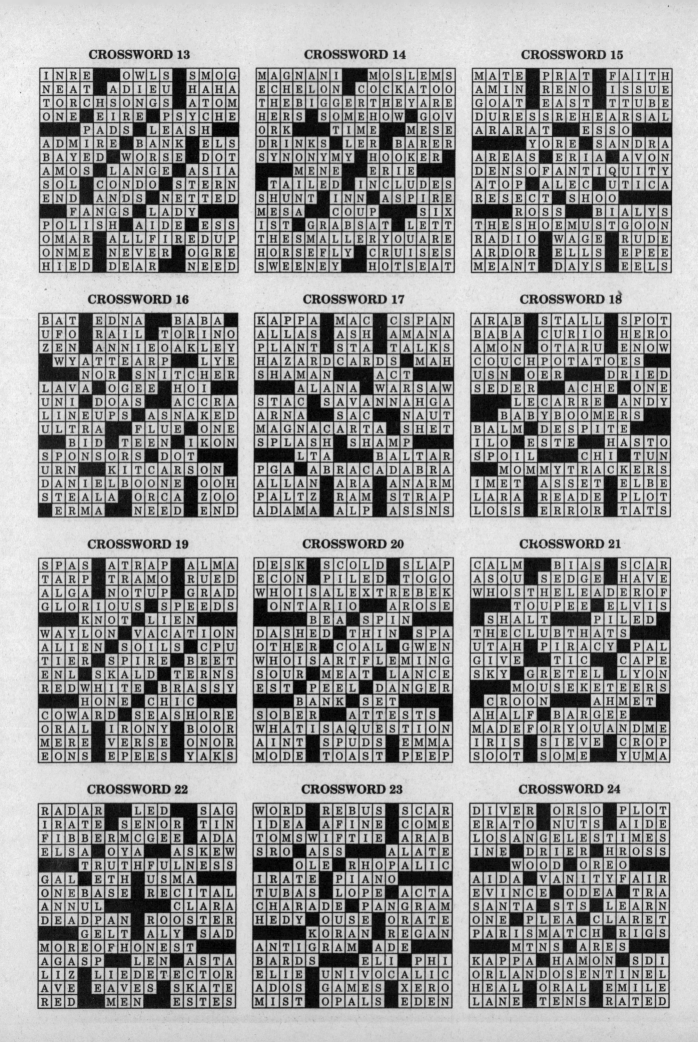

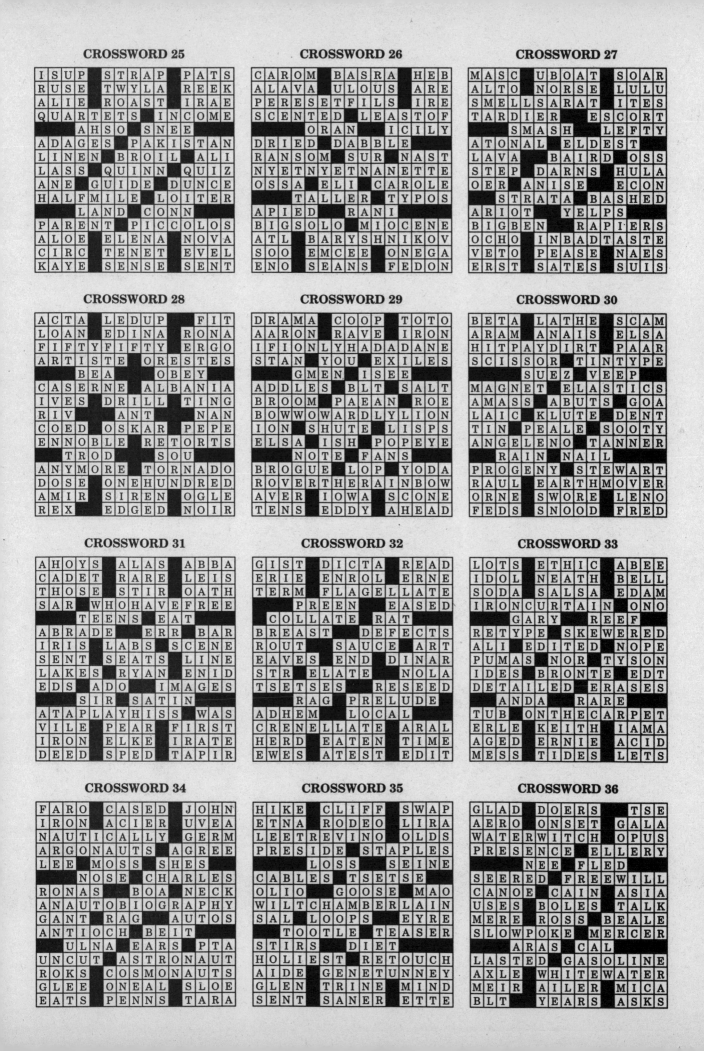

CROSSWORD 37

```
BAIL  SCAMP   GOB
AGRA  COLOR  CLUE
BUMBLERBEE   LINT
YEA ONES   SCOTCH
      SLID CURATE
ZODIAC  REMAKE
EARNS  MODEM   RUG
SHAG  PAWED   EBRO
TUG  GOLDS  ROUGE
   OVERLY  GANGES
  JOINTS   TORS
SUNTEA  AIDE   INK
ALFA  BOWLWEEVIL
WELL  LANDI  LACE
SPY   ESSEN  KNEE
```

CROSSWORD 38

```
RAHS  DINAR   EDGE
ALOE  ENOLA   ERIN
FERRICCLADALIBI
TUNICS   TRIO   BED
  TYNE  DEMAND
   MAR  SNEAKER
SEAFARER    INTO
ARGENTICBULLETS
PIER    ALLEYWAY
SEDATES   AES
   LAMEST   SLOP
MAT  LEVI   PEEDEE
AURICRETRIEVERS
STAR  GREAT   ETON
TOPE  ESSES   LONE
```

CROSSWORD 39

```
PALM  SALEM   BOBS
ABOU  PLAYA   ELLA
SELF  LINER   LION
TRAFFICGRIDLOCK
     LANE     ADO
BAREST  RACECARS
ALERT  BACH    LIT
BAAS  DELHI   RISE
AMT   IRES   REBEL
ROADHOGS  MARINE
    AAM   FARO
OVERHEATEDAUTOS
VIEW  DARED   TYKE
ATRI  ERODE   ERAT
LOON  SEDAN   SOYA
```

CROSSWORD 40

```
PALS  LIMAS   BASS
EDIT  ALONE   RILL
TOTO  BLOND   ARIA
    PLEASEGIVEMY
SAL  ALTE  ERODES
CLOTHE    BSA
REGARDSTO    GIFT
ATOMS  ION  FLOOR
PASS   GENEAUTRY
   HEN    STEAMS
SCHOOL  DATA   SST
YOURWIFEDALE
ROMA  DIVOT   DOLE
UTIL  ELOPE   EROS
PEDS  DENTS   NEWT
```

CROSSWORD 41

```
CABS  SAMOS   LOFT
OLLA  TRAMP   ARLO
MIEN  OILER   TEAM
MEN  AUSTRALIANS
ANDANTE    WENDS
   UTE  SALTS
BOSTONIANS    DAB
UNION  ARI  UTICA
TEX   ENGLISHMEN
    FALSE   NEE
  CLARA   STREAKS
FLORENTINES   PIP
ROOM  EATEN   DATA
APSE  TREES   ICER
YSER  SARRE   DESK
```

CROSSWORD 42

```
TANG  SALAMI   FLA
ABOU  LIONIN   LAR
BLUNDERBUSS   ISM
SENSED    STUNTS
    HAST   AINT
RADON  HOW  LILAC
ABET  CEREAL   OER
SERS  HIRED   ACRE
EAR  DERIDE   SKIP
SMILE  SSE  ASSET
   NEAR    RAGE
PAGODA    PIRATE
ICE  SIXSHOOTERS
SIR  ELITES   ERAT
ADS  ASSUME   DOPE
```

CROSSWORD 43

```
STEP  SEAT   RAZOR
MARL  APSO   EBONY
UCLA  VEIL   CANOE
THEINVETERATE
    DOI    DEL
PUNSTERFOLLOWSA
ANY  ASEA   SLIER
NILS  TOUGH   ALEE
IDOOD   NEAT   LMN
CONVERSATIONASA
    SUI    RIO
   SHARKFOLLOWSA
DECAL  KATE   SHIP
ALOFT  IRIS   EERO
MITTS  MESS   SEED
```

CROSSWORD 44

```
WEST  AVAS   TAMS
ECTO  POLKA   EMIL
THEWORLDIS   MOSE
   ERAS  TARS  PERE
ALERT  ASTAGEBUT
GOODEN    MORALE
ENS   EASY   BASED
   THEPLAYIS
CANOE  TYKE    UGH
AVOIDS    SARTRE
BADLYCAST   RURAL
BIDE  REAR   ODIN
ALIT  OSCARWILDE
GENT  DORIS   SLED
EDGE  PELT   HORS
```

CROSSWORD 45

```
TALE  CIGS   ALMA
EMIL  ARETE   LEAP
DALI  RERAN   ONTO
  TIMEONMYHANDS
   IDLE     ALE
BERNIE  EDNA   APE
UBOAT  ODIC   GRID
FORTHETIMEBEING
FLEE  MILE   ENATE
SIM  LESE   AGENAS
    SIR    TRET
  TIMEAFTERTIME
RENO  LIANA   CAKE
BACK  DAMON   AMEN
IRAE  TART   LADE
```

CROSSWORD 46

```
VOID  KABOB   GARP
EASE  ICAME   OTOE
STENTORIAN   STUN
THESIS   THEFLEET
   INKY   ATEIN
EMPTY  ALS  ANDBE
RORY  FRI  ASGARD
INE  CONTENT   NAG
CATCHY  ETA   ECCE
ADELE  ARC  STEED
   NARAS   HALE
WASRIGHT   FORAGE
ABIE  ACONTENDER
SLOT  PAREE   AUTO
HENS  ENTER   LEAS
```

CROSSWORD 47

```
ROMA  CUSSO   TABS
IDOL  OREAD   RTEI
DIMINUENDO   ERGO
INSTEP   ARABIAN
    ALOFT   FLAT
MISERERE    ITE
ANAI   ARPA   CEIL
RING  ELMAN   LADE
UTAH  BEAT   ERIN
  THO  TRUFFLES
SOHO   PAINE
CHARTER   TEAPOT
HAKE  PIANISSIMO
IRIS  OSSIE   CLEO
SPET  SEPTS   HANK
```

CROSSWORD 48

```
LUST  IMPS   GREAT
ENTO  MOIL   LUMPS
ADEN  POGO   USURP
PELICANSTATE
RACER    HIT   LED
    STAG   MORALE
ABED  ERIE   NOMAN
SEVENDEADLYSINS
SLIME  ANNA   SADE
ALLOUT   TAWA
YES  ROW    FLAME
   COVETOUSNESS
ATLAS  DOLL   GATA
PRIDE  GOAL   EDOM
TIDES  ENVY   REPP
```

CROSSWORD 49

```
SCAM  VERSE  UPTO
NODE  ELOPE  SHOW
ICED  EMBER  ALOE
POPLARSENIC   OLD
EATER      TELEX
   YEAST   RETYPE
AJA   HEAD   FAGIN
CANADATHISTLEAD
ADELE  SOAK    NFS
DEMURS  ELITE
   OMAHA    AMASS
BAN  TOBACCOBALT
ACES  COBRA  ARIA
WHOA  KILOS  ROCK
LYNX  SLEPT  KNEE
```

CROSSWORD 50

```
SLAP  BOHR  [ack]PINE
PARR  ELIE   HONER
ONEEYED[ack]S AORTA
RANCOR    TEMPEST
ESTER   ALARMS
   PERVERSE  [ack]AL
[ack]POT  SENT  RELEE
DECOCT    ASNERS
ASTRO  BALL   EGOS
WOO  MILLIBAR
[ack]FRUIT   DVINA
VERBOSE   REASON
ADOOR  [ack]OLANTERN
IDIOT  EDEN   ERSE
LASTS  TEST   SEES
```

CROSSWORD 51

```
FISH  PRIME  SEER
IOTA  RETAG  EDDY
TWELVECARGARAGE
SAM  UPON   SPUME
   FLAN    AHEM
PAPACY  AXES   HOT
ELIZA  TALL   TARA
SEVENTHHELPINGS
TROD  ORES   STOAT
OTT  ABED   BYLINE
   SLEW    RACE
TRIOS   BETH   OFF
QUINTUPLEHEADER
URDU  ROUSE  DOTE
ONES  EPEES  DRAT
```

CROSSWORD 52

```
LIES  FIBER   HIS
ARROW  ADELE  ANT
WONDERNICKS   LYE
SNEAKING  HOLLOW
   ICY    SOUTH
AMBUSH  BOUNDARY
DYERS  MRAND   NEO
ACRE  LAIRD   GNAW
MUM  BILES   LEAVE
SPACEBAR  BATHED
   NICER    PEU
SCHOOL   BRANCHED
PIA  MILLERCLOSE
ETC  ESSAY  HAUTE
EEK  STUBS   WRAP
```

CROSSWORD 53

```
AVEC  SWIT  SCROD
LIMA  URDU  AHARD
ODIE  NYET  PAGES
UARSOBEAUTIFUL
   AJAR    HEE
MARAT   OPENDOOR
RUM  IHAVENTACLU
ALIT  IAN    TEES
ITSUSSRTHEM   AOK
DISCLOSE  PAWNS
   KOP    VISE
SEETHELIGHTFDA
ALERT  POOR   BOOP
PUREE  ELLA   AXLE
ORODD  ELAM   RYES
```

CROSSWORD 54

```
ELAL  CHASM  TASS
REGO  HATLO  OTOE
MERV  ISMAN  BLAT
ARIELPHOTOGRAPH
   BAS    COUSYS
POLONIUSMONK
SPEAK  PLATE   ADD
ARAT  POURS   TRIO
TYS  ARNEL   AHEAD
   STEADYASIAGO
STAIRS    NEG
CASSIUSCATCHCAN
AHIT  MARSH  PULE
LODE  EROSE  AJAX
PEER  SICEM  DONT
```

CROSSWORD 55

```
WART  CHAS   CHAP
AMOR  LALLA  HARE
ALAI  UHLAN  ERNE
CIRCUMNAVIGATOR
   YRS    MIT
BISCAY  BOAS   ABA
AWILL  PORTHOLES
TOME  SORTE   UTAH
CROSSINGS  STALE
HEN  ANTE  SPORES
   TIU    OAF
WHEELSOFFORTUNE
EARN  ELIOT  OVER
AILS  SELAH  WEAR
KLEE  SEME   NAPS
```

CROSSWORD 56

```
CREEP  IBID  DAFT
OATER  NANA  INRE
LYNLEYKINGBAKER
ASA  FEELS  ALLAN
   WELD   CREEKS
AWHIRL   BEARD
BEAR  SERIO   MIA
LANECANNONWIEST
ERG  OMITS   OLEO
   BRATS  TANDEM
ASCEND   LALA
SHORE  SHARE   YEP
KAHNRHUECARROLL
EREI  ACRE  TORSO
DINE  SHOD  SWEET
```

CROSSWORD 57

```
ACED  LAPPS  PACK
PATE  ARRET  ORAL
ACHE  SMILE  TULE
CHERCHEZLAFEMME
EER  REDE    TON
   RED    SIXTEEN
STEAD  FEET   ARE
TOUJOURSPERDRIX
DIR  NEST   ISLET
STEELIE    DAM
   REV  LAIT  STA
ATORTETATRAVERS
DIDO  RAMON  IRAN
ONER  STAND  NUDE
GARS  EASEL  OMER
```

CROSSWORD 58

```
SOS    AVGS   BEAK
TLC  ABOUTA  EERO
ALY  NULLANULLAS
SILENTSPRING
HELMET   SMU   DEE
  SAP  ELM  ASSIST
   INDIANSUMMER
LOIRE  TRE   AISLE
AFTERTHEFALL
INASIA  EFT   EAR
COL  TRA   HOOTED
  LIONINWINTER
DIRECTIONAL   IFA
ETON  SOWERS  REP
REBA   NAST   ERE
```

CROSSWORD 59

```
MAMA   IRA   SIAM
IRON   NIX   OONA
LEAD  ⑩DERFOOT
KANSAS    ATONE
   OREGON
PER④M  ANGULAR
ALIT  TIE   NONO
HIGHHAT   DITTY
   AUSTEN
HAGAR   IN④MAL
OMNIPO⑩T  MAUI
OMAR  REL   EYES
POTS  ATE   DOLT
```

CROSSWORD 60

```
RAJA   AMPS   NOVA
AGER  SNEAK  ONCE
DISC  LEGWARMERS
IFTHEYWANTED
ITSALL    ENEMY
   NAYS  ODE   OOH
ALIGN  METOWALKI
SOME  TENON  SLED
WOULDHAVE  STYLE
ENS  ORR    SPAR
   STAVE   SKOALS
BEENAMAILMAN
FLOORMODEL  ABBA
LAWN  ATEAM  BEER
AXLE  NEST   ERLE
```

CROSSWORD 61

```
ATOM SPOOL GONG
LIRA PAULA LION
LACKLUSTER ALVA
  HOARSE DANCER
POI STERN ICALL
UNDRESS ALDENTE
NOSE ABIE SYD
  SEAMYSIDE
ORA ANON GILD
BUSSTOP SWAGGER
SNIPE STEAD NAY
CANINE ONTAPE
EMIT ABSTEMIOUS
NONE RECUR CUSP
EKES LEAPS ASEA
```

CROSSWORD 62

```
SABOT BLUSH
MYSORE SLOSHY
SIMPSON HOWARD
CAPS BAKE IRA
RST SALOME IVAN
AMO EMILE CRETE
GAMALIEL BAINES
NETS POTS
QUINCY BIRCHARD
UPSET MICAH BEA
OARS GALAXY STR
DNA MENE BOAT
DELANO RUDOLPH
ULSTER INLOVE
PITTS MOIRE
```

CROSSWORD 63

```
FLAG STOAT DOGE
IAGO CABLE OREL
STUN ONION LENA
THEFRUITEDPLAIN
AIRS ERODED
CALLAS STRIP
OLEO CHILL ATE
DAWNSEARLYLIGHT
END PANEL NEON
TIRED CETERA
ASWARM MAGI
THEBOUNDINGMAIN
TAIL FEINT ACRO
IDLE FARCE TEAR
CELT STEER EDNA
```

CROSSWORD 64

```
ACED BESET ADAM
COLE RANGE PICO
DISCOURAGE ISTO
CLEAVING YACHT
DENS SEENO
RADER INCH UKR
AMIND ODOR SNEE
DISCOMBOBULATED
ONCE EONS EMEND
NEO REET SPRAY
VOLTS PAIL
GLESS REVOICES
RARA DISCONNECT
OLEG ALTAI GITA
WADE MOUND SLOG
```

CROSSWORD 65

```
RASH SLING OLES
OHIO TONAL SOYA
ZASU ARISE COED
BIRDINTHEHAND
GERE CAR
SPALLS ABLY AHA
ALLAH ACLU BLOB
BATSINTHEBELFRY
ONES ANEW RAINS
TER PROS MONEYS
FOR SASK
AFLEAINTHEEAR
SILO TRAIL TROT
IDEA EMILE EMMA
BEET SAFER DYED
```

CROSSWORD 66

```
BOWS GOTT PETS
ALIT ALLAH ARIA
HERUBBEDMEWRONG
SOYBEANS ROASTS
ELD POND
GOTOBLAZES EURO
OPINE OSE NAP
NEMO SORTS ETTE
ERE ORR ALIEN
RASP MYOILBILLS
IBEX NAB
LANCET PAPOOSES
ITAKEITINSTRIDE
EMIL MELEE CLAW
DOLE EDER ALMS
```

CROSSWORD 67

```
DOIN MAT ATME
GOLDA CEDE LEAD
INSET ORME TAPS
THEACTIVITYOF
SON OWN THE OAT
SLOSH TARSI
INTELLECTISTHE
OREO BOLLA AWED
KEENESTPASSION
INDEX SITAR
EES ONE MEL SOB
CANEXPERIENCE
CZAR STAR ELATE
HARM TRIS NIGER
APES SAX TEST
```

CROSSWORD 68

```
SAGS TWERP GRUB
CIAO ARLES LURE
ARBORMISGIVINGS
MSS HITES ANTES
PIN AID
MAKINGTHEGLADE
ELITE RENI IAL
SANS SUSAN FARE
ART ARAT AORTA
MOREBOWERTOYOU
AAU ATL
SPENT CACTI SAW
ILLCALLTHECOPSE
LOKI LAMED KEIR
OPED BRONX DEFT
```

CROSSWORD 69

```
RAGSTO WEST SON
ABOARD ACHY AVE
BELLYDANCER LAW
BEDS SWEEP FELT
ITA GOES HORS
BOND TENABLE
STAIN FORENOON
POTBELLIEDSTOVE
ANTERIOR HIKES
REELING BLOC
NOLO SUET DAM
BUTT LIARS SOLO
ERI BELLYBUTTON
ADO OUST ORIENT
NUN XMAS SURREY
```

CROSSWORD 70

```
NIPS ROWER BATH
OGRE ETHEL ASEA
LOIN PAILS SPAR
ARM EARPS STARK
EATSUP PIER
LARIAT EGAD ALS
EMIRS ADORE GOA
REBS AMPLE MUTT
ONS STOOD TASTY
ISO PORT CENSOR
FARM ASLEEP
NOBLY ETHAN EST
ALEE PROAS JAPE
PEER ALECS ORAL
SOFT PESKY ESTE
```

CROSSWORD 71

```
SOHO ARIOSE MIX
ETON NEURON ALY
THREEZOMBIS ROZ
SENORA RUST
ICANSEETHAT
WAFTS SAKE SAGA
IDIOT ATEST RAM
LEROI BUT ELATE
LAS CLERC NOYES
OTTO ELAH QUEST
WHATWILLYOU
ITAL DIODES
ADD HAVETODRINK
SUE ONECAR ANDI
HER OILERS LEST
```

CROSSWORD 72

```
PROW SCATS DAFT
EASE ELIOT ALOE
AILS CIDER MARX
DOTSONESISAND
BANK DIG
ATTEND THEPEARL
ROUND DOOR DOI
MINDYOURPSANDQS
ELI VATS GOOUT
DECIBELS CANNES
FUR FATE
CROSSESONESTS
IRON ERICA URAL
DILL LITUP CARE
OBEY LEASE HYDE
```

CROSSWORD 73

```
BOLL BOCA BABAR
ASIA RAYE ABACA
SCABBARDS CREEK
IAN ICES ECARTE
CRABBED DRAC
ALS SUITABLE
APACE BACKEDOUT
BANC VOLES AONE
ONTHEOUTS ABBAS
STEADILY ERR
NILE BREADED
BERATE CAEN IBO
ITALO MACCABEES
TAPIR ARCT OGRE
ETTAS BAYS BOTS
```

CROSSWORD 74

```
FEM STAG RAJAH
LIAO POLA ILONA
AGON ONAN FLUNG
THREEKINGS SEA
STIFLE EASTER
IBN KEENE
MANNA SUBDIVIDE
OBOE EDO EVIL
PERDITION SNAIL
AFUSS REV
LAWYER ATEASE
ARI FOURSAINTS
DOZED LEAH LIES
EMERY ALTE SMEE
RANGE VEER ERN
```

CROSSWORD 75

```
ACRE PROBE ITCH
CLAN LEVEL 5000
TEST AVERS PROM
20PERCENT SENSE
ROIL SEER
LEA ADES RECANT
ELSINORE ANEMIA
ALTO SAM NOTI
PIEPAN TACITURN
SERENA SLAT ROT
RANI ARES
EJECT 51PERCENT
DANE AMORE OLEO
AVON LETON PLAY
MAST SNAPS EARS
```

CROSSWORD 76

```
SATAT SALAD MOB
SLOTH ANITA ALE
WALTERMITTY NEE
SEDITION ASKFOR
TRAS ACTORS
SEQUEL ALKALI
ETUDE TUBER DEW
IRAE FIRED BARA
RES SRTAS MAYOR
INHAUL BABSON
AMIENS CURB
TROPIC FORCIBLE
ROD LILLIPUTIAN
USO ASIAN STEVE
EES HINTS ESNES
```

CROSSWORD 77

```
CRAM ORFF COPSE
HOLE PELE AVOWS
ABELLEFORADONIS
RECOURSE BRIDGE
DNA SLED
ABRAS COOS DSC
STOAT LOBO RATE
THYMEREMEMBERED
LOLA HOAR AGILE
OSE TONS BRINE
AHME EDS
ATHROB BESOTTED
THEGRIPESOFROTH
TIMON REAM ANTA
UNITY OPUS REEL
```

CROSSWORD 78

```
BASQUES DIJON
COQAUVIN HONORE
LAUREATE ARCHED
ASIDE HEADMAN
STEIN EZRAS RUN
HST SPREAD AERO
VISOR RECESS
FREEZER NEXTDAY
INLIEU SOAPS
SWAN DOTOME CBC
TYS POBOX DARER
THENAVY IGOTA
APIARY EGOTISTS
VICTIM REVERSES
ANSEL SNARLER
```

CROSSWORD 79

```
ZXCVBNM BAFFIN
ORRERIES UGLILY
LAURENCE GRAVES
AYEAR CAS AMEX
LEBLANC NET
ASCLEAN OLD ITT
BURLAP SRA IMRE
BLUEREDANDGREEN
ALEN LAX DROWSE
SYL ASC PIANIST
WIZ CRIEDIN
OOLA ATL USNAS
APRILS WASAHERO
VELVET ORATORIO
ENDEAR STETSON
```

CROSSWORD 80

```
ORAL ROMAN A◇IN
FORA AVILA BITE
□KILOMETER ONTO
PORT CARTON
ICINESS FORTH
CANINE MITE EBB
IVAN CANIS RUR
CEVA DORIC SOLI
LAI MINIS TULE
ETC EATS STAGER
IMAGE WEIGHTY
ILOILO AHIT
NOUN NOTINOUR☆S
ROSE ABELE ADOS
INOS LINED RAFT
```

CROSSWORD 81

```
JAG ARISTA BERT
APO NORTON ASEA
CRUCIVERBALISTS
KITH ESAU ALERT
SLYER DYER SOY
WOOF TAP
ACE MULISH ACME
THEMATICENTRIES
MIKE STYMIE ALE
MME ICAN
TAM ETCH ROSIE
ONAIR LEST ROSS
DOUBLEENTENDRES
ATRI PAROLE ERE
YEAS ANYWAY SEX
```

CROSSWORD 82

```
CABALS ITTY BRA
AMALIE SHOO AID
SONORA AEQUALSZ
BEQUALSY UNMAKE
ABU SET REGAN
HAEC IVE SCAR
UNSLOPED ERA
EVIBTLLWHLOERMT
LIC HOMEROOM
LEEJ ALA EGAD
PAGAN SSS INE
TEAPOT CEQUALSX
ETCETERA UPBEAT
ARK TAIL AERATE
RES AMOK TRADER
```

CROSSWORD 83

```
GRIP TDS ADDUP
IOLE ORK BREESE
STINGRAY ONABAT
THEANSWERWONTFIT
LOOS ALLS
MAIMS JED COB
GONZO CRAG PEAL
NOTENOUGHSQUARES
ASIS NATS UPSET
TEC SEN CAPED
SAND SORE
MUCHTOOSHORT
OVERIT TENYEARS
DELUNE ALE EMMA
SATBY BLY ROSY
```

CROSSWORD 84

```
PST PAGODA MESA
AAR OPENUP IVAN
SHESGOTTAHAVEIT
TABOO NIN ALL
ORLY LAREDO RBI
RAE AONE DADOO
JUBILEE LEAN
SPIKELEEJOINT
AHAB SEALERS
ROLES SECT PAR
MOM ASSERT BAMA
ATE MAP SATAN
DOTHERIGHTTHING
AUTO ATEASE ODE
STOW HELMET SAD
```

Cryptogram: Very good solving

CROSSWORD 85

```
HAUL  SCHELL  SAM
URSA  CRUSOE  IDA
MOUNTAINTOP   DAY
BURGERS    PETERS
USE  NEEDS   WEB
GERMS  SITS  DUCK
   AIM  DYED  RUE
MIDDLESEXCOUNTY
ECO  EWER   TON
LEWD  LAOS  RIDER
   NAN STEAM ANI
SASHAY   ALASKAN
ALI BELLBOTTOMS
NED  OLIVER  ATEE
DEE  BLENDS  BALD
```

CROSSWORD 86

```
CHEF  PAMPA  WADS
HARA  EMILS  OLIO
ABAT  RESET  ROOD
DISCOUNTBROKER
STEAM    SOAR
    TEENS  STOKER
OFF  GLOAT  ONTO
BARGAINBASEMENT
IDIO  ELIOT  WAS
ESTOPS   ELIHU
   STOA  ILLAT
 CHEAPDETECTIVE
OBOE  HEMEN  IVOR
DENG  ILIAD  MEIR
DREG  EARLS  ANDY
```

CROSSWORD 87

```
ZETA  EDOM  TACT
ALOP  ARENA  UTAH
PUMP  DINER  ROVE
SLEEPINGSINGLE
   NEE   MAILS
INADOUBLEBED
ROBIN  LARAS  WHO
APEX  PEPOS  VAIN
QED  TREES  HALVE
  TRIPLEDECKER
ODEUM   IRA
HOMERANDJETHRO
LAMP  ORONO  IYAR
OREL  SARAN  OPIE
WADE  ELMS  NODS
```

CROSSWORD 88

```
CAMP  SCAB  BEGIN
ALAI  POSE  OVINE
LAME  ANTE  DIRGE
FEATUREARTICLE
   ANT    WET
DLI  CASTLED  ALI
AORTA  WEAR  ONIT
CROSSWORDPUZZLE
CANE  ROSE  PSALM
ANY  FINESSE  CES
   ERN    END
 MANAGINGEDITOR
LILAC  SORT  VOTE
ERICA  LEAH  ANTI
SEATS  ELBE  NEON
```

CROSSWORD 89

```
ALTO  JAFFE  GHAT
LAIR  OBOES  RUNE
INTERIORDESIGNS
 KOLANUT  UPSET
   BET  GALE
AFFAIR  SALT  NOD
VIAL  STELA  OSU
EXTERIORLINEMAN
RIT  ARLES  GAGE
STY  COOP  RHODES
   FINN  GEE
SPIRE   FANATIC
ULTERIORMOTIVES
NEER  SWAMI  NADA
KAME  ALTAR  ANEW
```

CROSSWORD 90

```
SDAK  RIA  PALEO
STOREROOM  EMEND
TRUMPEDUP  TEASE
LAB  TEE   BIND
OWLS  DOTHETRICK
  EIN  SROS  ANOA
FORUM  IRS   GAY
BAR  BIDFAIR  QTO
ANN    MAL  ENNUI
LOOT  IDEA   DEE
INTHECARDS  ASSE
   HENS  AHA  TED
CLINT  NOPASSING
SONAR  ONTHENOSE
ANGRY  DAS  SYNE
```

CROSSWORD 91

```
RUDE  RAJAH  CROP
ARIL  ADORE  AIDE
SAVANNAHGEORGIA
PLANE  NODS  ANT
   ETAS  TELL
 BATTLED  ROADS
ARC  EARED  IRIS
BOULDERCOLORADO
OTTO  AARON  WET
 HEROD  LISTENS
  DAIS  CEIL
ADO  STOW  MISER
DULUTHMINNESOTA
ADES  EMDEN  HUNT
MESA  REEVE  ALAS
```

CROSSWORD 92

```
PIAF  SWAP  ADAPT
ARGO  CHER  FELLA
POURBOIRE  GLOOM
ANATIONOFSHEEP
   SPY  IHAD
FEINTS  OXEN  SEL
ATWAR  ANIL  SUMO
THEGOLDENFLEECE
HERS  ADOG  AEDES
ARE  FIRN  AGREES
   RARE  MSG
 CLOUDSLIKEWOOL
DRAWL  SATIRICAL
BENET  EVEN  LORD
LEERY  SARG  LASS
```

CROSSWORD 93

```
BRUT  DARNS  EDAM
ROTO  ELIOT  RENO
EVERYGOODPARENT
RESTORES  EVADES
   UKES  STAN
ENTREE  QUESTING
NARES  QUIRT  NER
ADES  QUITS  SUVA
RIN  FUELS  LYRES
MATERIEL  COMERS
   VEER  BOOB
FINEST  CONNOTES
ISANHEIRSTYLIST
JIVE  SLICE  ITTY
ITER  TETHS  COAX
```

CROSSWORD 94

```
CHAP  ACRE  SNAPS
HOLE  BRAT  HABIT
INON  BAIT  OILER
MONTHOFSUNDAYS
PRE  ETTE  ODD
   EXT  DRY  CAV
PHONE  ALUM  TOLE
HUNDREDYEARSWAR
ELLS  GEES  HALEY
WAY  AYN   FOR
   ASP  BLED  MCS
 EIGHTDAYSAWEEK
MASAI  ISNT  HARE
ASTIN  SIDE  IDEE
LEONE  HEAR  ZEST
```

CROSSWORD 95

```
SALA  BAKE  ACTOR
AMES  EMIT  LOOSE
COOPERATE  MUTES
RUN  RAZE  HONEST
EREMITE   PEST
   ACE  PRETENSE
OPALS  CLAD  RATA
DAME  CHEWS  SPAR
ALEF  LOAN  PIERS
SENATORS   LAG
  CEDE  CORNEAL
PASTES  BOAS  NRA
ONTOP  CONVERSES
STARE  URGE  AUNT
HANSE  PEAS  JETS
```

CROSSWORD 96

```
PRONE  ABO  CHAR
RAVEL  SENS  REMO
ABETS  PLOP  ARIA
MER  ACEDRUMMOND
    ERA  RIP
JACKSONMISS  SSR
AVAIL   NOS  ETE
CONTEST  SNIPPED
OWN  ETO  NOTED
BSA  KINGOFGLORY
   PEG  OTE
QUEENMOTHER  MID
URNS  ACHE  ORATE
IGOT  STAR  TAKEN
PEWS  OMS  EMORY
```

CROSSWORD 97

```
R F D   H A L O   P A W
A L A   I C E R   I T A L I A
C A N T A C T C A N T S I N G
E X C I T E   A N T I   G E E
    I N U S E   N O T C H E S
V A N E S S A S   S U E T
E G G S   E R N S   D E F E R
T E L   A S T A I R E   A S H
S E E M S   H I R E   O N C E
    S A P S   L E M O N T E A
R E S P I T E   S A N D A
I G O   R O T H   I T I S E S
C A N D A N C E A L I T T L E
A N S A T E   I T E M   I M P
    Y E S   R O D E   C O T
```

CROSSWORD 98

```
F L A T   S A M P   S P A S M
L O C O   I L I E   E R N I E
O V I D   D I S S I P A T E D
W E D D I N G S O N T V
S A Y   M E N   F I D D L E
    S P Y   W H O C A R E S
S M E E   E E L   E N T
C H A R L E S A N D D I A N A
A E C   U A R   E M M Y
G E R M F R E E   M V P
E T O I L E   I O I   J A W
    L U K E A N D L A U R A
Q U A D R A N G L E   D I D Y
O S I E R   V E A L   I C O N
M E R R Y   Y E W S   T Y R E
```

CROSSWORD 99

```
  B O P S   B A B A R   P G A
E O L I C   I C O N O   A A R
C O G N O S C E N T I   P O E
A N A T O L E   M I S S A L S
D E S O T O   R O S T E R
    E G R E T   E R A S E
A B S   R A I D   G R A Z E R
M O O T   N O R M A   C Z A R
O C T A D S   I O L A   I N S
S A T I E   O V O I D
  O N L I N E   L A M I N A
I N V O I C E   S E M I N A R
R E O   C H I A R O S C U R O
E T C   T O N T O   O R R I N
S H E   O R A L S   N O E S
```

CROSSWORD 100

```
L A T C H   C O L   M A H A L
A N W A R   A V E   A L A T E
B E E T H O V E N S N I N T H
O Y L   S P A R T A N   S H A
R E F R   S T R E W   M E E R
    T A A   I A N   V A L
S C H U M A N N   V A C U U M
L A S C A L A   F A L A N G E
A N Y O N E   L E C O Q D O R
    M U S   D E R   R U G
A M P S   M A G N A   E R A S
N A H   T A N B A R K   E T A
V I O L I N C O N C E R T O S
I N N E R   E N D   R E E L S
L E Y T E   R E O   T E L L Y
```

CROSSWORD 101

```
N T H   F L I C   C U D
D O R I C   A S C U S   U N O
A C U P U N C T U R E   R T E
U T E   C U E S   R A P T O R
B I S C U I T   D I M E A
    U M T   A R E   C I G S
S O R B   C U R C U L I O
B O C C E   C U M   U L E N T
C U C U R B I T   R I D S
S L U M   E S E   A L A
    R A B A T   C U I R A S S
C U R S E R   N U N C   B A H
U R I   A C C U L T U R A T E
B A N   S U E D E   E A S E D
A L G   B E E T   M E D
```

CROSSWORD 102

```
M I R E S   C O V E R   D S T
E R E C T   A D E L E   I T O
T A B L E   S O L E S   S A L
A Q U A E   A R O C K   B T U
L I T T L E B O U T I Q U E
      B E A U T   P U R L S
P O S T A L   S E S   A S I A
U N A I R E D   S A D D E N S
P E N N   D O E   B E S S E S
A S T A B   E X T R A
H A S L O S T H E R C H I C
R O C   A M O R E   J U I C Y
O U R   S A V E R   O R N O T
O S U   T H E M E   H I T M E
F E Z   O A R E D   N O S E S
```

CROSSWORD 103

```
N O R T H W E S T   S U S A N
O V E R E A T E R   U S E N O
M E G A P H O N E   B A B A R
S T U N   O N O   G A S T
A S S   O S R I C   E S T H
    M O S   A R I S T A E
S E T I N   T A T U M   I S A
O M I T S   A I R   A N A I S
U B E   E A R L Y   D O N A T
T R I P A R T   B E R
H O N I   S U E D E   M T S
W I S E   N I L   A H A B
E D A M S   E N C O U R A G E
S E L A H   M I T I G A T E S
T R E N O   S O U T H E A S T
```

CROSSWORD 104

```
S C R E W   P B S   L A P S E
O H A R A   R A P   A D L I B
H A B E R - E R Y   H O Y L E
O P E C   I S O B A R   M A R
    T A K E N O N   H O S T
E L I   N I N   A N J O U
M O O   D S T   T A I N T E D
I N , N D   N E H R U
L I N E A R A   S E X   : E L
    D A Y A N   T A E   Y S L
C A M P   R E M O R S E
A G E   R E C E N T   R O B S
B A N J O   • H E H O N O R S
O T T E R   A T A   B I Z E T
T E S T Y   L A X   J E E R S
```

CROSSWORD 105

```
B E R G   C A N I T   A T O M
A M E R   A S I D E   L O V E
R I C A   D E T E R M I N E D
B R O T H   A N A M E   E R E
    M E A T   E S S E S
T S P   S E A T   T H E D A
A C E   T E N N I S   I N O N
T A N T E N T O N T I N T U N
E L S E   S E T T E R   E S E
S P E N D   N O T A   R E X
    D E L T A   S T E P
A F T   B E R T H   E N R O L
M A I N T A I N E D   D I V A
E D N A   S P U M E   U S E S
N E A P   T E T O N   P E N T
```

CROSSWORD 106

```
M R S   R E S U R G E   H I P
I O N   A G O N I E S   E T A
S W O R D O F D A M O C L E S
S E R E   S T O S S   A L M S
A R E C A       T R E
    I N S U L A T E   N A P
H I P P O C R A T I C   I R E
A B L E   A S H E D   A Z I E
R A U   S P A R T A N M E A L
A R T   T A S S E L E D
    O R Y       T U B B Y
T A C O   S P R U E   M O U E
H E R C U L E A N L A B O R S
I R A   R E P R I S E   N N E
S O T   I D E A T E S   E S S
```

CROSSWORD 107

```
S P O R T   B A T H   F E S S
U R I A H   A C R O   A L O U
D I S H W A S H E R   S L U R
S E E   A M I E   S A H A R A
    C R I N   B E R I
S K I R T S   C O M M O N E R
C Y M A S   M A L E   N A M E
R O E S   R A N O N   A V I S
U T A H   E R O S   A B E L E
B O N H O M I E   B I L L E T
    E R I N   S I R E
S M I L E S   A L A S   B E A
C O R M   S P L A S H D O W N
A L O E   L E A N   I N L E T
R E N T   Y A N G   P A D R E
```

CROSSWORD 108

```
H O P I   G L A N D   G R A B
O N A N   R O T O R   R O L E
B U C K R O G E R S R O B O T
O S E   A T O M   O U S T S
      A G T   A B U T
T A N G O N E C E S S I T Y
T O D D Y   E N T R E   R I A
E Y E S   A U D I T   F A R R
R O E   H E R O N   M A T E D
N U M B E R O F G R A C E S
    L I O N       O R E
S H O O S   S A L T   M A T
P O L O T E A M P L A Y E R S
A H E M   E R O S E   A S I A
R O S S   L A G E R   P H A R
```

CROSSWORD 109

```
HERCULES   SEPTA
ELEONORA  SCREED
PADDLING  LANDED
TIDIES    GRATED
ANENT  FIAT  SLAP
 ERG  FINN  UTILE
   STING  CRONES
AMP  ONE  BOG  GET
PAIRED    SANER
ENDED  OLDS   ALB
REDS  TREE  AMOOD
  LOUISE  INBLUE
GRILSE  PUDDLING
DENVER  OPERETTA
SAGES   NAMEDAYS
```

CROSSWORD 110

```
ICTUS  HEN  CAPEK
GRANT  ALI  ANILE
EERIE  IKNOWONLY
TWO  PIGEON  IKES
   OPT    ION
 TUNESONEOFTHEM
HONED  LORNA  OVA
ILSA  ALORS  BRAY
FLA  ALINE  DUADS
 ISYANKEEDOODLE
  LEA     AND
BOOB  LOUISA  THE
OTHERISNT  TRIAL
SHIRE  HIE  EARNS
HOOTS  ATM  SWEDE
```

CROSSWORD 111

```
SQUADRONS  ECHO
AUSTRALIA  BLOBS
DIETETICS  BURST
INDUE  GESTS  NOR
ECO   SATYR  PILI
SEND  ERR  ASLEEP
   MERCY   PASTE
DELILAH  CHANTED
IMETA     WAIST
APARTY  HRS  SCAD
LEVI  ETALS   UNE
ERE  PARTI  SORTA
COOEE  UNSLANTED
TRUER  SOLITAIRE
 STEM  STEVENSON
```

CROSSWORD 112

```
COAL  SALEP  REMO
INRE  ALONE  EMIT
VETO  FLUOROSIST
INN  BEET  HAILTO
COEVALS   SESS
 ROLY  SMATTERS
TASTE  ACADS  PEA
ASHE  IBARS  MINT
TAI  COURT  FESTE
APPLAUSE  MONA
  APSE  HANDLED
STAMEN  FIND  ILE
HELITERING  MAIN
AMAN  SINGE  ANTS
DADA  SANER  ISEE
```

CROSSWORD 113

```
AMAH  NAME  CHAIR
DALY  EGAD  RENTE
ERIE  ARID  ERASE
AIGNPROMISE  TAD
LANAI    SEALS
  STET   OSMOSE
UPS  TORSO  ERAT
SUNRISEATOBELLO
AMIE  SPINE  YEN
FATALE   SALT
  PADUA  LOCUS
TAB  HORLINIMENT
ALAMO  GIGO  ASTA
RARER  EBON  TAIL
ANKLE  SITE  OREL
```

CROSSWORD 114

```
HALT  ALCAN  YIPS
ESAU  LEONE  EDIE
WHITESANDS  LONE
NED  DAVE  TOLLED
     DICE  CLIO
VOICE  TOILWORN
WOPAT  HAHN  SHOE
ITEM  REPEG  TAGS
NERO  ERIN  CORES
GRANDSON  MANET
   DEED  MIRE
ASTHMA  SALT  DAS
FLOE  LITTLEROCK
AURA  ELATE  ANTI
REND  DETER  NEST
```

CROSSWORD 115

```
SALAD  TRAP  KIDS
ANOSE  HOBO  ODIE
STOAT  ISUS  KENT
HIPPOCRATICOATH
  UPS    TAM
 SOCRATICIRONY
ULNAS  RAVE  IAN
SUET  TRADE  ACRE
ERA  SWAN  BLEND
 PLATONICYEARS
  LIT    LOA
HOMERICLAUGHTER
IBEX  MOOR  LOWLY
LONI  EDGE  ERISA
TESS  REST  SAGAN
```

CROSSWORD 116

```
CABS  SWEAR  FLA
AMIE  APOLLO  LES
SERA  SLOPES  OAT
END  MTIDA  SOCKO
LAS  TONYS  INKER
OBOLS  TWO  NEEDS
ALFA  LEO  MILD
DEAF  BROKE  ITOR
 FIRS  DNA  NOVA
CRETE  APO  LEGER
HEATS  METRO  ERA
AZTEC  ACHES  TRA
NOH  RANKED  SHIV
ENE  UNDEAD  PEDI
YER  BEARD  ARES
```

CROSSWORD 117

```
 KIBITZ  SPRITES
ANTONIA  TOOTALL
HEARKEN  ALCALDE
MANN   IDYL   KEW
EDD  CANIS  COIRS
  FOYER   BARN
JAPANESE  ENIGMA
IBAC  ASCOT  ETON
GALAXY  THRENODY
  IDIE  IMUST
ISSEI  TOMES  GYM
QUA   GONE   TREE
UPDATED  TOWHEAD
IRELAND  ENVIERS
TASTILY  ROASTS
```

CROSSWORD 118

```
MAME  TOR  ESTATE
CLAMBAKE  SHOWER
SURPRISE  DINNER
 METAL  FERN  YDS
  YVES  MADE
BAL  ENTHUSIASM
URAL  DEA  GREAT
DEBUT  PRO  STAGS
STAIR  UNU  OONA
 ENGAGEMENT  FAR
  IDOL  ASHE
LOA  URSA  TALKS
OFFICE  REUNIONS
GARDEN  COCKTAIL
SNOODS  ASK  ESPY
```

CROSSWORD 119

```
PDDS   ILL  AGRA
AURAS  DUE  GARR
ARREST  ABOREISA
MANWHOWHENYOU
ISI  OHO  ALSOP
GONDOLA  MANDELA
ALGER  TAUT  SAX
  FRANKDANE
SUB  LOAF  OTTER
SKILIFT  ISRAELI
SEVEN  ASP  RAN
 ASKHIMHOWHEIS
TELLSYOU  DIONNE
LEVI  ENS  EDUCE
CREE  RAE  ERES
```

CROSSWORD 120

```
BOLE  LASSO  ARIL
OREM  OREAD  LIMA
GREATGRATE  IMPI
  KNEE   IRANIAN
OLLAS  AWN  CENCI
DIETS  RIGHTRITE
ALAE  PAR  EOS
YAK  LABELER  FED
 VAN  TAD  CARE
TOWEDTOAD  GUILE
IRENE  SPY  ERRED
VIETNAM   ALIF
OGPU  BOREDBOARD
LIER  INANE  URGE
INRE  EDGES  SETS
```

DIAGRAMLESS 1

DIAGRAMLESS 2

DIAGRAMLESS 3

DIAGRAMLESS 4

DIAGRAMLESS 5

DIAGRAMLESS 6

DIAGRAMLESS 7

DIAGRAMLESS 8

DIAGRAMLESS 9

DIAGRAMLESS 10

DIAGRAMLESS 11

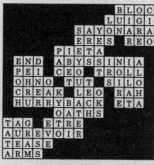

DIAGRAMLESS 12

DIAGRAMLESS 13

DIAGRAMLESS 14

DIAGRAMLESS 15

DIAGRAMLESS 16

CRYPTIC CROSSWORD 1

ACROSS
1. FLAT FEET (anag.)
5. A + SCENT
9. IN + JURIES
10. A + B + ROAD
11. A + BUTS
12. IMMERSION (anag.)
14. E + ST + RANGED
16. MI + TES (rev.)
17. C + REEL
18. TECHNICAL (anag.)
20. SACCHARIN (anag.)
22. GRANT (2 defs.)
24. I + CAR + US
25. IMP + ROPER
26. RHYMES (hom.)
27. INTERNAL (anag.)

DOWN
1. F(RIG)ATE
2. AN + JOUr
3. FOREST + ALL
4. EVENING STAR (anag.)
6. SO + BER (*Reb* rev.)
7. EGOTISTIC (anag.)
8. T + I(DING)S
13. ME + DI(CINEMA)N
15. THEOCRACY (anag.)
16. ME + NAG + ERIE
17. C + ASHIER
19. LATER + AL
21. HO(US)E
23. AS + PEN

CRYPTIC CROSSWORD 2

ACROSS
1. ROTISSERIE (anag.)
6. TWINe
10. FLA + REUP (*pure* anag.)
11. SP(A)RING
12. RU(S + T)LER
13. CROtCHET
14. STEADIES (2 defs.)
15. PASSED (hom.)
18. INDICT (hid.)
20. REP + ROACH
24. BUG + BEAR
26. A + MULE + TS
27. BASTION (hid. rev.)
28. TRA + VAIL (*art* rev.)
29. DOOM (rev.)
30. CH(ASTENE) + SS (*a teen's* anag.)

DOWN
1. RE(FORM)S (*from* anag.)
2. TRANSCEND (anag.)
3. SP(ELL)ED
4. EX + PORTER
5. IN + SECT
7. WEIGH (hom.)
8. NE(GAT)ED
9. PA + GOD + A
16. STALE + MATE
17. R(EGA)TTAS (*start* anag. + *age* rev.)
18. IMBIBED (hid.)
19. C(RED)ITy
21. ROULADE (anag.)
22. HAS + SLES (*less* anag.)
23. B + RANCH
25. GIS + MO

CRYPTIC CROSSWORD 3

ACROSS
1. JACKBOOT (anag.)
5. EM + BAL + M (rev.)
9. LETHARGIC (anag.)
11. UNTIL (hid.)
12. EU + REKA (*rake* anag.)
13. IN(THERE)D
15. JOYRIDER (anag.)
16. RITZ (*writs* hom.)
19. RING (2 defs.)
20. F(E)ATHERS
23. AVER S + I + ON (*no I* rev.)
24. DOLL + bAR
27. HA + IT + I
28. B(LISTER)ED
29. DAGGER (anag.)
30. K(V)ETCHES

DOWN
1. JU(LIE)T
2. CATER (anag.)
3. B(LACKEY)E
4. pORGY
6. MOUTHY (anag.)
7. ASTEROIDS (anag.)
8. MELODIZE (*mellow dyes* hom.)
10. CON + VENTS
14. TIME BOMB (anag.)
15. JUNKETING (anag.)
17. BREA(THE)D
18. HE(MOST)AT
21. ASP + IRE
22. TRADES (anag.)
25. LURC + H (*curl* anag.)
26. KIEV (hid.)

CRYPTIC CROSSWORD 4

ACROSS
1. GREE(N + CAR)D
6. ErASED
9. AC(ROBA)T (*boar* anag.)
10. E(M)ERALD (*dealer* anag.)
11. E(THE)L
12. TOMMY TUNE (anag.)
13. SHOP (hid.)
14. AUSTRALIAN (anag.)
18. SU(MM + ERTI)ME (*muse* anag. + *rite* anag.)
19. ATOP (hid.)
22. JUST S(AYN)O
25. AGREE (anag.)
26. UNICORN (hid.)
27. A LA MODE (anag.)
28. NEEDS (hid.)
29. SKY(R)OCKET (*key stock* anag.)

DOWN
1. GOATEES (*go tease* hom.)
2. EARTHWORM (anag.)
3. NEBULA (anag.)
4. ANTITRUST (anag.)
5. D + REAM
6. EVERYMAN (anag.)
7. SNAF + U (rev.)
8. DUD + GEON (*gone* anag.)
15. TEMPORARY (anag.)
16. INTERLOCK (anag. minus *a*)
17. SENt + SUe + OUt + So
18. SO + J + OUR + N
20. PR + EVENT
21. PAPA + GO
23. SPINEt
24. YANKS (2 defs.)

CRYPTIC CROSSWORD 5

ACROSS
1. ALL + OWED
5. AN + ARCH + Y
9. RIPEN (hid.)
10. SENSITIVE (anag.)
11. PEDESTALS (anag.)
12. T + WEED
13. Y(E)OMEN (*money* anag.)
15. BACH + ELOR (*role* rev.)
17. A(BERRA)NT
19. BRIDAL (anag.)
22. CITED (hom.)
24. MORTALITY (anag.)
26. AN(X + IOUS + L)Y
27. O(CT)ET (*toe* anag.)
28. M(A)D + NESS
29. RETIREE (hid.)

DOWN
1. A + TROPHY
2. LOPE + D (*Pole* anag.)
3. WIND SHEAR (anag.)
4. DISBAR (anag.)
5. A(MNE)SIA (*men* anag.)
6. A + TILT
7. CHI(S + E)LLED
8. YIELDER (anag.)
14. OVERT + AXED
16. HER + EA + BOUT
17. AC + CL + AIM
18. NEMESIS (anag.)
20. LA(YET)TE
21. P(RAY)ER
23. DROVE (2 defs.)
25. INTERn

CRYPTIC CROSSWORD 6

ACROSS
1. A + R + CHIVES
5. MOLES + T
10. MILES(T)ONE (*Seminole* anag.)
11. N(O)UNS
12. RUSTLE (hom.)
13. TAPES + TRY
14. B + RAIN + W + ASH
17. TAB + O + O
19. bEAGLE
20. M(ARK)ETERS
21. F(R)ICTION
23. L + ADDER
26. A(C)HED (*head* anag.)
27. ENCHILADA (anag.)
28. RIDDLE (2 defs.)
29. VESTMENT (hid.)

DOWN
1. ADMIRA(B)L + E
2. CELLS (hom.)
3. INSOLENCE (anag.)
4. ETON (rev.)
6. O(U)NCE
7. E + QUIT + ABLE
8. TEST + Y
9. METAPHOR (anag.)
15. A + N + GU(I)SHED
16. ARMHOLES (anag. minus *n*)
17. THE + RAP + IS + T
18. O + B + SERVANT
21. F(L)AIR
22. TI + DAL (rev.)
24. D(RAP)E (rev.)
25. ACME (anag.)

CRYPTIC CROSSWORD 7

ACROSS
1. RUBY (anag.)
3. B(R + ASST)ACKS
10. C(AL)ABOOSE
11. G(R)AIN
12. PIE + TIES
13. MOTH(I)ER
14. RANCHO (hid.)
16. BOMBEd
19. LIE + GEts
20. BE + TRAY
23. ARUNDEL (anag.)
25. BE + DROLL
26. S(WEE)P
27. EPIC + ENTER
28. RUNT + H + ROUGH
29. L + AND

DOWN
1. RECIPE (anag.)
2. BELIE + F
4. gROOMS
5. S(TEAM + BOw)AT
6. TI(GH)T (*Hg* rev.)
7. CHARISMA (anag.)
8. S + ENTRIES
9. OBLIGATE (anag.)
15. CABAL + LERO (*role* anag.)
16. BRAND(IE)S
17. CLEANSER (anag.)
18. CERULEAN (anag.)
21. PORT + I + A
22. FLA + RED (*Alfred* with *Alf* rev.)
24. DEPT + H
25. B + RING

CRYPTIC CROSSWORD 8

ACROSS
1. CAR(A + PAC)E
5. TRI(B)AL
9. T + RAIN MAN
10. BUR + LAP
12. F(L)OR + A
13. NUR + SEMA(I)D (rev.)
14. NO + RM + AS + HEAR-ER
18. CAN(TANKER) + O + US
21. ME(MORAN)DA (*made* anag.)
23. PUPIL (2 defs.)
24. hERRING
25. TIMEOUTS (anag.)
26. SOD + DEN
27. AN(A)THEM + A

DOWN
1. CU(TO)FF
2. RE + A + SON
3. PENS + A + COLA
4. CH(AINSM)OKING (*man is* anag.)
6. RO(U)SE
7. BALL(A) + DRY
8. L(A)PIDARY (*rapidly* anag.)
11. P + RESERVATION
15. E(QUIP MEN)T
16. S + CAMPERS
17. E(NAMOR)ED (rev.)
19. S + P(R)UCE
20. A + L(ASK)A
22. RANG + E

DIAGRAMLESS STARTING BOXES

Diagramless 1: box 4
Diagramless 2: box 7
Diagramless 3: box 4
Diagramless 4: box 12
Diagramless 5: box 4
Diagramless 6: box 1
Diagramless 7: box 1
Diagramless 8: box 6
Diagramless 9: box 3
Diagramless 10: box 6
Diagramless 11: box 12
Diagramless 12: box 8
Diagramless 13: box 3
Diagramless 14: box 1
Diagramless 15: box 3
Diagramless 16: box 7